THE COMPLETE GUIDE TO COMMERCIAL VEGETABLE GROWING

THE COMPLETE GUIDE TO COMMERCIAL VEGETABLE GROWING

Frank S.Hardy and
Graham D. Watson

FREDERICK MULLER LONDON

First published in Great Britain in 1982 by
Frederick Muller Limited, London SW19 7JZ.

British Library Cataloguing in Publication Data

Hardy, Frank S.
    Complete guide to commercial vegetable growing
    1. Vegetable gardening
    I. Title   II. Watson, Graham D.
    635   SB322

ISBN 0–584–11016–2

Printed in Great Britain by The Anchor Press Ltd., Essex

We are deeply grateful to The West of Scotland Agricutural College for their permission, help and encouragement for this book. Nor could we have completed this book without the invaluable assistance of Fiona Newton, who helped prepare and draw the art work as well as edit the copy.

Our thanks go also to Wendy (my long suffering wife) who put up with a multitude of papers and disorder in the house whilst Graham and I were writing into the long hours of the night.

Special thanks are due to Ian Walls, who both stimulated and encouraged us to undertake this book when we might have felt daunted by the task.

Frank S. Hardy
Graham D. Watson

Contents

THE COMPLETE GUIDE TO COMMERCIAL VEGETABLE GROWING

Chapter One

Vegetables – An Introduction to Cropping

Choosing a site

New growers with bright hopes set up in business almost every day. Some fail and a few succeed. But success is illusive and it is the initial choice of a site for a new holding that is critical. The perfect site probably doesn't exist and prime sites are much sought after in traditional growing areas. Also, vegetable growing is increasingly becoming a matter of large scale field production. Nevertheless, a vegetable growing book without a small section on choosing the perfect site would be like buying a house without going the rounds of the local estate agents.

Climate

The weather requirements of different crops vary tremendously. Rainfall is by far the most important factor. The majority of vegetables are grown on the east side of the UK, not in the wetter west. But some crops require high summer rainfall and these include swedes, early potatoes and cabbage. So many problems are created by high rainfall: diseases spread rapidly (halo blight on beans, blight on potatoes); slugs are more prevalent; access with heavy harvesting machinery is more difficult; and lifting/harvesting of crops in wet autumns and winters becomes impossible. The map showing the distribution of vegetable cropping in the UK is an indicator as to where different crops can be grown best (see Student summary map Figure 6).

Temperature becomes important at the extremes. High temperature and sunshine are required to ripen crops outside, notably sweet corn. Winter cold, particularly the incidence of heavy frosts, jeopardizes winter/spring brassica production. Hence, Devon and Cornwall are the major winter cauliflower producers. On the other hand, rhubarb needs winter cold before it will break dormancy. So rhubarb forcing is largely confined to areas like Yorkshire and Glasgow which are colder than other parts of the UK.

Equally important is the average time of last frost in spring and the first frost in winter. Check with the local meteorological office – it is an indicator of the length of the growing season. A long growing season means greater crop throughput (see Figure 1).

Climate and aspect

Traditionally, textbooks refer to the advantages of a south facing slope for earliness of cropping. On intensively run holdings of small size this may have credence, but it is much overrated. Handling of machinery on sloping sites becomes more difficult and soils are more subject to water erosion. Also, frost pockets tend to occur on lower slopes. Far more important is to find a sheltered aspect away from the wind. Higher land, especially above 91.4 m (300 ft), should not be contemplated since this is prone to wind. Likewise coastal areas are subject to high winds and cropping there should only be contemplated where there is good provision of shelter.

The availability of shelter

Young vegetable plants need protection from winds. The recent trend towards large field sizes to increase the scale of production has not helped. In East Anglia and in East Lothian the removal of hedges has led to considerable soil erosion on the lighter soil areas. Apart from physical crop damage the value of shelter belts should not be under-estimated, especially as yields can be greatly increased. At Luddington Experimental Horticulture Station work is being carried out to assess the extent to which crop yields can be increased by use of windbreaks and shelter material.

Special care with choice of windbreak is vital to avoid loss by shade, excessive loss of space and the material becoming a harbour for crop pests and diseases, (for shelter belts see page 17). Remember, if shelter does not exist on the chosen site, then you will have to provide it and this will cost money and time. Even hawthorn hedging costs about £30 per 100 m (328 ft) run for the plants, excluding labour.

Soils

Most crops will grow reasonably well on a wide range of soils. But the successful grower produces those crops which suit the soil type of the area, which in turn offers the greatest yield advantage. The soil type most suited to growing each crop is shown in table 1 on page 4:

Figure 1 Length of growing season in England and Wales

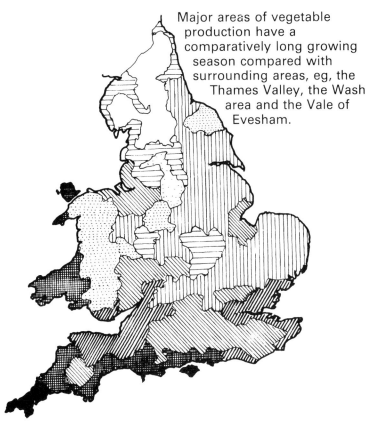

Major areas of vegetable production have a comparatively long growing season compared with surrounding areas, eg, the Thames Valley, the Wash area and the Vale of Evesham.

Average length of growing season (time when grass grows above a soil temperature of 6°C)

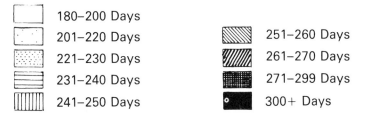

180–200 Days			
201–220 Days		251–260 Days	
221–230 Days		261–270 Days	
231–240 Days		271–299 Days	
241–250 Days		300+ Days	

Note: This does not take into account aspect, shelter or light. A south facing slope might have 20 days longer growing season. Height above sea level will decrease the growing season by an average of about six days for every 30 m (100 ft) above sea level (except in Devon and Cornwall where it is 10 days for every 30 m or 100 ft).

Table 1: Soil types for different crops

Brussels sprouts, cabbages, rhubarb	Heavy loams
Broad beans, beetroot, summer/ autumn cauliflower, leeks, peas, swedes, turnips	Medium moisture retaining loams
Beans (French and runner)	Fertile loams
Onions	Brick earths/silts
Early summer cabbage, lettuce, calabrese	Medium to light loams
Carrots, parsnips, radish	Sandy soils
Celery, courgettes, marrows	Peats, moisture retaining soils

The various advantages of differing soil types (texture) are summarized below:

SANDY
: Easily worked all year round, early cropping land, but low in fertility and consequently low yielding without heavy nutrition. These soils dry out quickly.

LOAMS
: Mid-way between sands and clays in their properties. Ideally suited to herbicide treatment.

CLAYS
: Naturally high in nutrients, heavy yielding soils, but difficult to work and are late cropping. These soils hold a high reserve of moisture.

SILTS
: Not easy to work, high moisture holding capacity, warm up quickly. But cap easily and need annual application of organic matter to maintain a good structure.

PEATS
: Warm, easily worked soils, highly humic, capable of holding up to eight times their own weight of water. But these soils are difficult to treat with residual herbicides.

If one soil had to be selected for best overall performance for vegetable growing, then a deep, fertile, well-drained light loam would be preferred. (For further details on soils, see pages 6–10).

The availability of irrigation

There are no major areas of vegetable production in the UK which do not suffer drought at some stage or another. The financial gains to be obtained from irrigation, particularly during dry seasons are well documented in Chapter 3. It is the provision of a source of water which is difficult. The problems associated with the various sources of water are discussed in Chapter 3.

Nearness to local markets

Until recently large growers tended to scorn local outlets in preference for the large wholesale markets. However, with the dramatic rise in transport costs more and more growers are looking towards nearby retail outlets or ways of marketing locally. Without nearby centres of population, local marketing and the recent innovation of self-pick and direct farm sales can be a disaster.

It is difficult to put a figure on the maximum distance goods should be transported to wholesale markets as this depends on the value of the crops. But certainly carriage above 50 miles at rates of ½p per mile for a lettuce crate is prohibitive for all but the highest value crops.

A supply of horticultural labour

Sometimes the remoteness of a site appeals to the more insular minded. But business sense should prevail since few crops can be grown without skill and seasonal peaks in labour demand. For example, labour demand at harvest time for spring onion crops constitutes about 80 per cent of the total production costs.

In choosing your site, remember that by going to an established growing area you are in a position to tap an existing pool of skilled labour. On the other hand, if you go to a new area you can train your own staff to your techniques.

Freedom from pernicious weeds, pests and diseases

No grower wishes to inherit weeds, pests or diseases. Of course, they may be difficult to detect if you arrive at your chosen site in winter. But here are some pointers which might help:

With weeds, watch out for really difficult-to-remove weeds – these include Japanese knotgrass, mares tails, giant hogweed and ground elder. Others might be considered difficult, like couch grass, perennial thistle, docks and bindweed, but these are relatively easy targets with good cultivation and modern herbicides. Buttercups, rushes and crowfoot indicate badly drained land. Chickweed and annual nettle suggest hearty land.

On the pest side few are considered to be real crop stoppers except eelworm. But ask around to find out whether there is a history of any specific pest on a local scale. The real trouble-shooters are soil-borne diseases – Fusarium wilt can wipe out pea crops in dry areas, white rot on onions and violet root rot on root crops are just as devastating. And club root in any soil spells doom for brassica growers. So check carefully, before acquiring any land, as to its past use and history.

Access and services

Modern transport services use large lorries so good road access to the vegetable packing shed is vital to bring in supplies and to take goods to market. Wide gateways and understanding of lorry turning circles should not be forgotten in the designing of road layouts and entrances. The cost of farm roads should not be overlooked if you are contemplating siting a new packhouse on the unit. At £6 a sq m for 'tarmac' surfacing it becomes costly to establish buildings too far from public roads.

Local advice services

An advisory service organization will be of considerable advantage, particularly if it is near. In England and Wales the Agricultural Advisory and Development Service (ADAS) gives free advice to the grower and in Scotland the Agricultural Colleges carry out the same function. (See Chapter 13.)

Cost of land

Good agricultural land costs £3,482/ha (December 1980 figure). Cheaper land can be obtained in remoter areas but this may be a false economy.

Soils and Their Fertility – The Key to Success

A key factor in vegetable growing is a thorough understanding of the makeup of soils, manuring and their management. This is only learnt by experience but some of the basic information is detailed in the next few pages. But no two soils are alike so each holding will present its own peculiarities, especially to someone starting a new venture.

Soils contribute to plant growth by providing: a storehouse for water; an oxygen supply for roots; mechanical support for plants; and essential elements. There can be little doubt that the ability of the soil to carry out these functions is highly dependent on the texture and the structure of that soil. A detailed understanding of soil texture and structure is a necessity when becoming a comprehensive grower.

Soil texture and structure

Students often confuse soil texture with soil structure. Briefly defined: *texture* is the feel of different soil particles. This is simply categorized into soil particle size groups, eg, fine sand particles are 0.02–0.2 mm diameter, clay particles are less than 0.002 mm diameter. *Structure* is the arrangement of the various particles within the soil, eg, crumb structure is the aggregation of soil particles into crumbs which is aided by the colloidal properties of soil. So when growers say: 'My soils are heavy clays' they are referring to the texture of the soil, having fine clay particles.

Tracking down a soil's texture

Field assessment of texture can be rapidly carried out by taking a small sample of soil in the palm of the hand and wetting it to its maximum water holding capacity. Break down the crumbs, then, simply rub the sample between the finger and thumb in an attempt to roll out a thread of soil. The feel of the soil will vary from the grittiness of sands through to the stickiness of clays and the silkiness of silts. For a detailed check list see Appendix 1.

Soil structure and how to improve it

It is rare for the soil to consist of just one particle size. This is often the cause of many soil problems since it is the arrangement of the various sized particles that determines the soil structure. Ideally we require a crumb structure with 52 per cent crumbs (particles aggregated together into groups) and 48 per cent pore space. The problem created by different particle sizes is that the finer silts run in between the sand particles blocking up the pore space. Silts do not aggregate together into crumbs easily because unlike clays they have no colloidal properties. Good structure is determined by the following factors.

SOIL TEXTURE   Sandy soils have plenty of pore space but are structureless because the grains act as individuals. Structure is improved by adding organic matter. Clay soils consist of fine particles which can be brought to crumbs if worked correctly and by adding lime and organic matter. They can only be cultivated at correct soil moisture content. Silts, on the other hand, cap or crust easily with heavy rain. Soils with more than 12 per cent silt particles are difficult to work and need masses of organic matter to encourage structured crumbs to be formed.

ORGANIC MATTER CONTENT   Organic matter helps bring soil particles into crumbs, increases moisture retention, especially on sands, opens up the soil pore space on clays and stops the finer particles running together. The choice of organic matter may depend on what is available locally but horse manure and bullock manure are said to be the best. However, with manure shortages any type is better than none at all.

Beware of chicken manure with its excessively high nitrogen content which can encourage a high nettle population.

LIMING   This is particularly useful on clay soils to help open up sticky, heavy land. Calcium, the major ingredient of lime, is also an essential mineral element for vegetable growth. Gypsum may also be used to add calcium, and condition the soil, without increasing the pH.

PREVIOUS CROPS GROWN   Some crops help with soil structure, their roots penetrating even the heaviest clays. Leeks are surprisingly effective as they grow well on a wide range of soils. Green manure crops (those turned in after growth) offer a valuble source of organic matter. Mustard sown at 16.5 kg/ha (15 lb/acre) will mature in eight weeks. Lupins are also grown for their deep penetrating roots and their nitrifying action to be turned in after one season. Rotation is a valuable part of cropping – maintaining soil structure and soil mineral balance.

DRAINAGE   Waterlogging of soils causes the pore space to fill up with water and encourages the re-arrangement of soil particles, bringing silts to the surface. Structure is destroyed and platey structures (horizontal layers in the soil) appear. By far the worst are clay soils which show typical red and grey mottling of iron and manganese oxides.

By improving drainage, incorporating organic matter, regular liming and careful choice of crop rotation the grower can ensure that good soil structure is maintained, provided cultivations are carried out at the correct time.

Cultivating soils

PLOUGHING, CULTIVATING AND TINING   The use of various ploughs, particularly the reversible plough, is common practice on market gardens. Autumn and early winter ploughing, if carried out correctly, should incorporate trash, weeds and crop residues as well as organic matter. It loosens the soil, introduces air into the matrix and exposes difficult soils to overwinter weathering. The temptation to deep plough and bring up more than a centimeter of unworked subsoil should be avoided. There is a wide array of equipment now available for working down the soil. Discs will certainly cut up lumpy soil clods, whereas various tines and harrows work the soil down to seedbed level. (For further details see Chapter 10.)

ROTAVATION   The rotavator does all the jobs of ploughing and cultivating in one pass. So why not use a rotavator all the time? It certainly produces a fluffy seedbed which may be suitable for spring cultivation work. Its action is quick and ideal for small strips of land between crops. But over-use of the rotavator leads to a very fine tilth which can run into a structureless quagmire with heavy rain. Continual rotavation to the same depth also tends to cause a soil pan at blade depth which discourages drainage and may cause various problems in crop growth. Certainly never use the rotavator for winter work where rain will inevitably destroy the soil structure.

ROLLING   Rolling of land is usually carried out to break up the soil particles at the surface prior to seed sowing/planting. The ideal roller is the ring roller since it cuts as well as compresses soil clods. Flat rollers are just as valuable on light soils. Firming the soil also helps maintain surface moisture in the seedbed.

BED SYSTEMS OF CULTIVATION (THE FERNHURST SYSTEM)   The bed system follows the principle that crops can be grown between the wide tracks of a modern tractor. Having planned to grow crops on these intensive lines, all cultivation, planting and harvesting are carried out by tractor mounted machinery spanning the bed and the wheels of the tractor run perpetually up and down the same tracks. The maximum wheel width is 1,830 mm (82 in) and the spacing for crops grown under this system has to be specifically designed to ensure economic plant densities. These are given in Appendix 2, page 279.

NON-CULTIVATION SYSTEMS   Non-cultivation systems are now being considered on a farm scale where vegetables are being grown after grain in the crop rotation. After the grain crop has been combined, the trash is burnt off leaving stubble and burnt debris. The next crop is then direct drilled into the land without carrying out normal cultivations. The reduction in labour requirement is as much as 25 per cent of the total for the crop. This is normally carried out with autumn sown onions and possibly brassicas. Soil structure is more stable and winter machinery carrying capacity of the land is far easier. To counteract nitrogen deficiency higher levels of nitrogen have to be applied but this must be divided between the autumn base dressing and the spring top dressing. Obviously direct drilling into the burnt stubble needs specially adapted drilling equipment. A small fluted disc just in front of the drill cuts the trash to help penetration of the drill. While yields are said to be equally high, a lot of work has yet to be carried out to perfect this technique for vegetable cropping.

CROP ROTATION   The idea of crop rotation has long been practised by gardeners and horticulturists. It implies that the ground on which a certain crop is to be grown will be planted or sown in rotation by another crop . . . usually in the order of legumes, brassicas and then roots. But the system falls down because few growers can economically grow a range of crops as wide and diverse as those mentioned above. Apart from which the soil requirements and climate needed varies so greatly. Most growers rotate as far as is possible within the limits of their crops. They mitigate the lack of rotation by manuring heavily wherever possible but not before Brussels sprouts or root crops. With limited rotation, disease and pest build-up may be rapid and the same foods are continually being drained from the soil, which may lead to nutrient deficiencies.

A simple two-year rotation for a strip of land might include early summer cauliflowers/leeks/early lettuce/late drilled beet.

Plant Nutrition – A Balanced Diet is Required

If soils are said to be the 'key', then perfect feeding opens the door to potentially high yields. A brief survey of the value of the nutrients is required and the soil's role in supplying these needs is given below.

The soil as a storehouse for essential nutrients

Soil contains essential elements, 13 of which are required for plant growth. They can be divided into major nutrients (nitrogen, potassium, phosphate, magnesium and calcium) which are required in relatively large quantities and minor or trace elements. The latter (manganese, boron, molybdenum, copper, cobalt, zinc, iodine and sulphur) are required only in the minutest quantities but without them problems in crop growth may arise. The value of each of the major nutrients is shown in table 2.

MINOR NUTRIENTS   Most soils are endowed with sufficient minute quantities of these, so that there is no need to add them for vegetable crops, except in special circumstances. Peas may have to be sprayed with a 2 per cent manganese sulphate solution to cure marsh spot (manganese deficiency). Cauliflowers with molybdenum deficiency show 'whiptail' symptoms. Preventative treatment with sodium molybdate at 300 g/ha (4½ oz/acre) is common practice. For heart rot of swedes (boron deficiency) borax is applied at 22 kg/ha (20 lb/acre) or boronated fertilizers are used as the base dressing.

Organic versus inorganic feeding techniques

The arguments about the value of organic and inorganic plant foods will continue until doomsday. Fortunately, vegetables are unable to

Table 2: Major nutrients

Nutrient	Chemical symbol	Value to crop	Crops on which nutrient of major importance
NITROGEN eg Sulphate of Ammonia Nitro-chalk Nitrate of soda (16%) Ammonium nitrate	N (21%) (25%) (36%)	Encourages leaf growth and greenness to plant. Deficiency shows as yellowing of leaves, stunted growth and smaller foliage. Excess causes lush oversoft dark green growth, prone to frost damage and disease attack. Overdosing can cause scorch. Nitrogen: Potash ratios are important.	Brassicas Rhubarb
PHOSPHATE eg Superphosphate	P_2O_5 (18%)	Encourages root growth. Rarely deficient on British soils. 'Locked up' at extreme levels of pH. However, steady replenishment essential. Deficient plants have poor root systems – become stunted, leaves blue. Important nutrient for root crops.	Potatoes Carrots Beetroot
POTASH eg Sulphate of potash Muriate of potash	K_2O (50%) (60%)	Encourages ripening of fruit, wood and plant tissue. Also discourages disease attack. Potash levels must be related to nitrogen to counteract oversoft growth. Potash deficiency affects fruit and flowering capacity. Leaf edges yellow and brown on deficient plants. Important on legumes.	Beans Peas Root crops
MAGNESIUM eg Epsom salts	Mg	Plays an important part in the chlorophyl molecule, so vital in photosynthesis. Few vegetables show deficiencies. Normally seen as interveinal yellowing of the leaves. Deficiency occurs where high applications of potash are applied.	required by most vegetables
CALCIUM eg Ground Limestone	Ca	Nutritional deficiency rare – symptoms only seen in nutrient cultures or container systems using composts. Calcium is applied merely to cure acidity problems – at low pH *many* nutrients, especially phosphorus and molybdenum, become unavailable.	required by all vegetables to maintain soil at a suitable pH.

distinguish the difference in the plant foods obtained from either source! Realistically most plant foods are applied as inorganic fertilizers, either as base dressings a few days before planting or sowing, or both before and during growth (as base and top dressings). Organic plant foods are mainly applied as bulky manure, and from a practical standpoint their special value lies in the physical action to soil structure – aeration and waterholding capacity. Nevertheless, the nutritional value of farmyard manure has to be taken into account and this is shown under 'The amount of fertilizer' detailed below.

FERTILIZER APPLICATION METHODS   Traditionally these are applied broadcast by tractor mounted fertilizer spreaders, but more recent sophistications include side band placement of fertilizer either side of the seeded row (potatoes) and nutrients incorporated in the row with the seed by fluid drilling.

TYPE OF FERTILIZERS   Compound fertilizers, those where the major nutrients (NPK) are combined into one material, are generally preferred to straight fertilizers. Apart from the difficulty of home mixing different 'straights', there is also the problem of chemical reaction between different materials. The recommended ratios for NPK for each vegetable are given in the appropriate chapter for each crop. One merely has to obtain a commercial near equivalent, eg, transplanted Brussels sprouts require a base dressing of 300 kg N, 75 kg P_2O_5 and 180 kg K_2O per ha. Using a commercial compound fertilizer 20 : 6 : 12 ratio, 30 × 50 kg bags would provide 300 : 90 : 180 kg applied over 1 ha. (Two 50 kg bags contain what is printed on the bags, ie, 20 kg N, 6 kg P_2O_5 and 12 kg K_2O). (see table 3)

Table 3: From soil analysis to fertilizer application

THE AMOUNT OF FERTILIZER The amount of fertilizer to use as given under each of the crop recommendations may be modified in light of the amount of manure applied, the type of soil, the previous cropping history, weather, soil pH and existing nutrition of the soil. Fertilizer dressings can be reduced by 15 kg N, 20 kg P_2O_5, 40 kg K_2O and 8 kg Mg for every 10 tonnes of farmyard manure applied (for imperial quantities see Appendix 5). The higher the organic content of soils the better nutrient retention soils will have. Legumes grown on land before early market gardens crops increase nitrogen content of soils so the N content of fertilizer base dressing is reduced. (Also see Appendix 3 for nitrogen assessment.) Soil type particularly affects nitrogen and magnesium levels. Nitrogen potassium and magnesium are leached out more rapidly on sandy soils. Magnesium may not need to be applied on an annual basis on very heavy soils where levels of the nutrient tend to be high. Wetter climes prevailing in the west encourage greater leaching of nutrients, so higher application of fertilizer is required. Plant species differ in their ability to take up nutrients at various levels of soil acidity. Shown below is a range of pH values within which different vegetables grow successfully.

Notes on Table 3: The numbers on the bags of fertilizer are the percentages of fertilizer nutrients contained. Bags usually hold 50 kg hence the figure 2 above the line in the second to last column. Straight or compound fertilizers may be used. With compound fertilizers the bags carry three numbers – the first is the N percentage in the bag, the second is the P_2O_5 percentage in the bag and the third is the K_2O percentage. For conversion to Imperial quantities see Appendix 5.

Table 4: Soil pH values preferred by vegetables

pH 5.0–6.0	pH 5.5–7.0		pH 6.5–7.0	
Rhubarb	Broad beans	Radishes	Asparagus	Cauliflowers
	French beans	Runner beans	Beetroots	Celery
	Marrows	Swedes	Brussels	Leeks
	Parsnips	Sweet corn	sprouts	Lettuces
	Peas	Turnips	Cabbages	Onions
			Calabrese	
			Carrots	

Soil analysis can be carried out on samples obtained from specific fields to determine the existing nutrition of the soil. Accurate figures for phosphate and potash and soil pH can be given but nitrogen will vary with time of year. Use these to help decide fertilizer requirement.

Using the fertilizer recommendations in this book

For each crop a recommendation is given for each nutrient index. When soil analysis is carried out the phosphate (P_2O_5) and potash (K_2O) index should be given to you. Use the index figures in conjunction with the tables, eg, with a phosphate analysis of index 2 and a potash analysis of index 3 for Brussels sprouts you require to apply 60 kg/ha P_2O_5 and 50 kg/ha K_2O (see table on page 61). If manure has been applied before the crop then for every 10 tonnes of manure reduce the application of phosphate by 20 kg/ha and potash by 40 kg/ha. If no soil analysis is available for phosphate and potash, then use the index values under-lined in the table. The nitrogen index is assessed by previous cropping on the land chosen (see the table with Appendix 3 page 282). Where, for instance, Brussels sprouts are to follow potatoes then a nutrient index of 1 would be recommended – 250 kg N.

Fertilizer ratios

The detailed amount of fertilizer to be applied is given in each crop. As a general quick guide the following ratios are required by different crops:

	N		P_2O_5		K_2O
Leafy crops	2	:	1	:	1
Root crops	1	:	2	:	1
General crops	1	:	1	:	1
Legumes	0	:	1	:	2

Liming and liming materials

Other than manuring and cultivation, nothing is more important than the incorporation of lime, particularly as so many areas are deficient. Thus, the pH of the soil should be checked on an annual basis, using simple BDH or Sudbury test indicators or obtaining an official soil analysis through local Ministry offices in England and Wales or the Colleges in Scotland. If the pH drops below levels stated earlier, then liming is a necessity. It is best carried out in autumn, usually as a split dressing to help incorporation – half before ploughing and half after ploughing.

Four types of lime are readily available – calcium oxide (quick lime), calcium hydroxide (slaked lime), calcium carbonate (ground limestone), and magnesian limestone (Dolomitic limestone). Most vegetable liming is carried out with the latter two materials which are safe to use and will not damage plants. Quick lime is unsafe to handle and slaked lime may be harmful to plants but can be applied to open land.

The table below gives a rough guide to applications of ground limestone necessary to bring various soil types up to a suitable level of pH to make vegetables grow well.

Table 5: Approximate liming requirement to bring soil to neutral from acid status assuming average humus content

| SOIL pH | Estimated calcium carbonate requirement | | | | | |
	LIGHT SOILS kg/ha	(cwt/ acre)	MEDIUM SOILS kg/ha	(cwt/ acre)	HEAVY SOILS kg/ha	(cwt/ acre)
4.5 & below	10,000	(80)	Not usually encountered			
4.6 – 5.0	7,500	(60)	9,375	(75)	11,250	(90)
5.1 – 5.5	5,000	(40)	6,250	(50)	7,500	(60)
5.6 – 6.0	3,125	(25)	4,375	(35)	5,625	(45)
6.1 –6.5	1,250	(10)	2,500	(20)	3,750	(30)
6.6 & above	Rotational dressings advisable to maintain pH					

Shelter – A Valuable Aid to Increase Yields

Wind damage is a major problem with large scale production of vegetable crops. In preventing damage one has to weigh up the probable cost of damage caused against the cost of providing protection. The sort of damage will depend on area, site and crops grown. But contact your local meteorological office. They can give the grower information like the commonest direction of wind and incidence of gale force winds which is invaluable, especially if you are to protect against the sort of damage detailed below.

The effect of wind damage
SEED BEDS DRY OUT RAPIDLY   Germination percentages are consequently lower than required, thus affecting crop densities.

DIRECT DAMAGE TO VEGETABLE CROPS   Vegetable plants suffer by being twisted and broken and yields are much reduced by heavy winds. Young lettuce, marrows and cauliflowers are particularly susceptible. Runner and French bean pods become twisted in high winds making them unmarketable.

STRUCTURAL DAMAGE TO GLASS/POLYTHENE STRUCTURES These are always very prone to wind damage. Apart from repairs, crops below can be ruined and the interference with cropping progammes in itself causes worry and delays. Some types of polythene structures are more prone to wind damage.

HEAT LOSS TO SOIL Cold drying winds in spring rapidly reduce soil temperatures as well as drying out the soil. This can be very damaging to newly seeded crops and to carrots and beetroot which 'bolt' easily, apart from delaying final harvesting.

POLLINATION Bees are less likely to pollinate flowers of beans during windy weather, which reduces set and consequent crop levels.

SOIL EROSION Soil erosion, a great problem in sandy soils, is obviously worst in highly windy sites. Wind breaks are valuable in protecting against soil erosion.

WORRY The worry involved with crops at risk during heavy gales and winds cannot be measured, both for horticultural managers and owners.

The Effectiveness of Windbreaks (see Figures 2 and 3)

DISTANCE OF EFFECT The effect of a windbreak can be directly related to the height of that windbreak. There is a reduction of wind speed (up to 50 per cent) found over a distance of 10 times the height of the windbreak.

POROSITY OF WINDBREAK Windbreaks should have a porosity of about 50 per cent to filter the wind. Solid barriers merely cause turbulence behind the windbreak.

ORIENTATION OF WINDBREAK All round shelter is ideal and this can only be given on an extensive scale with plant material. However, for glasshouses/polythene structures immediate materials (artificial) may be an expensive necessity. The most effective windbreak is one which is at right angles to the oncoming winds. So if only one windbreak is to be used put it at right angles to prevailing winds (see Figure 4).

Design and layout of windbreaks
Design of windbreaks to fit in with cropping areas on a market garden is critical to success. Permeable barriers, rather than solid barriers, should be used (see Figure 3). For most vegetable units this means

using hedgelines or tree shelter belts. At a lower level straw can be ploughed in so that the stubble stands up between lines of crops to give just enough protection to help germination of seedlings in spring.

Use of artificial materials (plastics, hessian etc) can only be considered on very high value crops or intensive situations of specific needs because of their cost. Propagating areas/structures may well be worth maintaining sheltered. Young seedlings or newly-planted out crops on a smallscale may be protected by mobile artificial windbreaks knowing that at this critical stage of growth protection will ensure quick establishment. Artificial materials available are shown in Table 6.

In the positioning of windbreaks, attention should be given to prevailing winds on the first count (usually from the west or south west). It is also advantageous to protect from the north or east. In conclusion all round protection is best but may not be feasible. A series of breaks across large fields might be considered basically at right angles to the prevailing winds (see Figure 5).

Table 6: Artificial Windbreaks

Name of material	Manufacturer	Type of substance
Intermesh	Wm. Jones & Co. Ltd., The Court, Bridport.	Heavy duty black plastic round hole mesh.
Lobrene KX 15/34 Lobrene NK 3	Low Bros. & Co. Ltd., PO Box 54, S. Ward Rd., Dundee.	Green knitted mesh of UV stabilized polythene
Nicofence 41 Nicofence 57	Clovis Lande Assoc. Ltd., Gaza Trading Estate, Hildenborough, Kent.	Black UV stabilized polythene (41–55% porosity) (57–60% porosity)
Netlon Tensar Cladding	Netlon Ltd., Mill Hill, Blackburn, Lancs.	Heavy duty black plastic round mesh (Netlon) elongated Mesh (Tensar).
Papronet HS 24	Papropack Ltd., Wedgnock Industrial Est., Warwick.	High density polythene + polypropalene. Available, blue, green, black or natural.
Paraweb	Environmental & Beach Control Ltd., 5 Pierrpoint St., Bath.	80 mm wide black plastic strips spaced 50 mm (2 in) apart. Vertical bands at 1 m intervals.
Rokolene 1728	Roko Containers Ltd., Shella House, 34 Storey St., Nottingham.	Green UV stabilized 100% high density polythene of knitted construction 50% porosity.

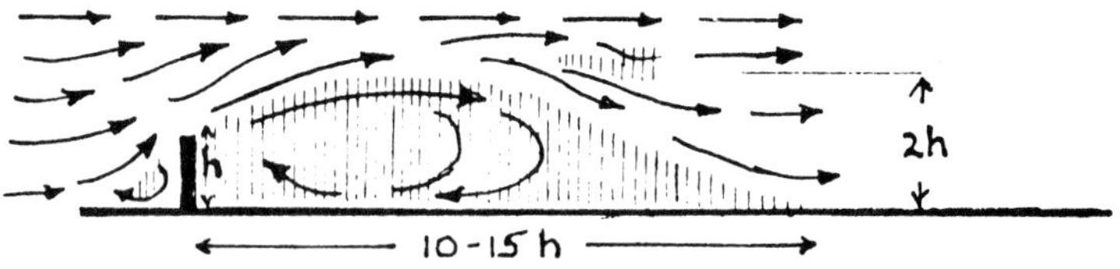

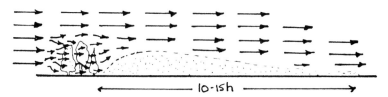

Figure 2   Impermeable barriers cause wind turbulence

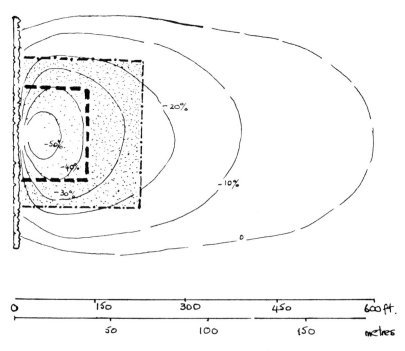

Figure 3   Permeable barriers filter the wind

Figure 4   Reduction of wind behind a 4.5 m (15 ft) high permeable barrier at right angles to the prevailing wind (Plan view)

Area of economic effectiveness of windbreak – 30–40% reduction in wind speed. (Shown by dotted area.)

Maximum area of effect of windbreak – 40–50% reduction in wind speed. (Shown by dotted area enclosed in heavy broken line.)

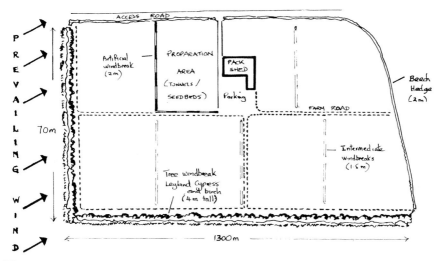

Figure 5   Plan of windbreaks for an intensive market garden unit of about 1 ha.

Note: Roadways are north of windbreaks so space is only lost in very shaded areas.

Plant materials

A wide range of plants is available – but this is not a cheap option. And they take some years to make the size required. Best of the trees for single lines are Leyland cypress (expensive), alders (*Alnus incana*) and poplars. But poplars harbour lettuce root aphid and break leaf late (except *P. tacamahoca* × *trichocarpa 37*). Of the small hedgelines, hawthorn is cheap but bare in winter. Beech is good, but rather slow and intolerant of wet soils. Whereas hornbeam is fast growing and tolerates most soils and a wide range of pH.

The willows, notably *Salix viminalis* and *S. daphnoides*, make good thick hedgelines but need cutting back hard each year to encourage new thick growth. But carrot growers beware, willows harbour carrot willow aphid.

For shelter belts on a large scale particularly in coastal areas *Pinus contorta*, *Picea sitchensis* and *Alnus glutinosa* make a good mix. These can be planted as young two year seedlings at 1 m intervals in three lines to give a fast growing belt at relatively low cost. Another good mix for less windy areas is the over-thick Leyland cypress and birch. The two complement each other to give the ideal density and porosity.

Student Summary Map

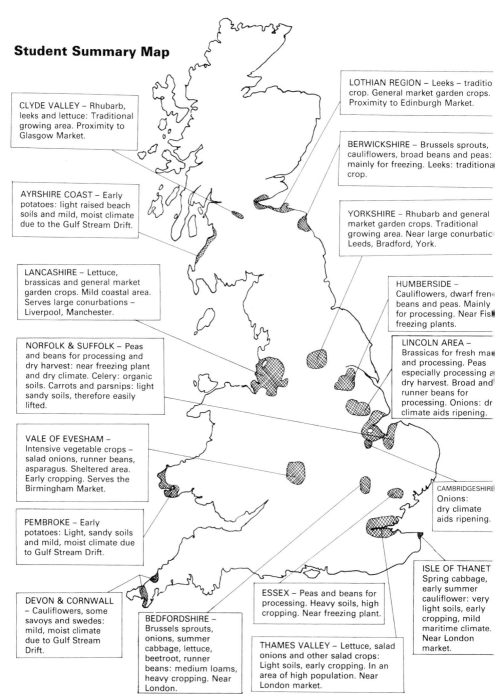

CLYDE VALLEY – Rhubarb, leeks and lettuce: Traditional growing area. Proximity to Glasgow Market.

AYRSHIRE COAST – Early potatoes: light raised beach soils and mild, moist climate due to the Gulf Stream Drift.

LANCASHIRE – Lettuce, brassicas and general market garden crops. Mild coastal area. Serves large conurbations – Liverpool, Manchester.

NORFOLK & SUFFOLK – Peas and beans for processing and dry harvest: near freezing plant and dry climate. Celery: organic soils. Carrots and parsnips: light sandy soils, therefore easily lifted.

VALE OF EVESHAM – Intensive vegetable crops – salad onions, runner beans, asparagus. Sheltered area. Early cropping. Serves the Birmingham Market.

PEMBROKE – Early potatoes: Light, sandy soils and mild, moist climate due to Gulf Stream Drift.

DEVON & CORNWALL – Cauliflowers, some savoys and swedes: mild, moist climate due to Gulf Stream Drift.

LOTHIAN REGION – Leeks – traditio crop. General market garden crops. Proximity to Edinburgh Market.

BERWICKSHIRE – Brussels sprouts, cauliflowers, broad beans and peas: mainly for freezing. Leeks: traditiona crop.

YORKSHIRE – Rhubarb and general market garden crops. Traditional growing area. Near large conurbatio Leeds, Bradford, York.

HUMBERSIDE – Cauliflowers, dwarf fren beans and peas. Mainly for processing. Near Fis freezing plants.

LINCOLN AREA – Brassicas for fresh ma and processing. Peas especially processing a dry harvest. Broad and runner beans for processing. Onions: dr climate aids ripening.

CAMBRIDGESHIRE Onions: dry climate aids ripening.

ISLE OF THANET Spring cabbage, early summer cauliflower: very light soils, early cropping, mild maritime climate. Near London market.

ESSEX – Peas and beans for processing. Heavy soils, high cropping. Near freezing plant.

BEDFORDSHIRE – Brussels sprouts, onions, summer cabbage, lettuce, beetroot, runner beans: medium loams, heavy cropping. Near London.

THAMES VALLEY – Lettuce, salad onions and other salad crops: Light soils, early cropping. In an area of high population. Near London market.

Figure 6 The map above shows major vegetable producing areas – the ideal summary to this introductory chapter, for it shows where specific crops are grown and why. It illustrates many of the points mentioned in this first chapter.

Chapter Two

Propagation Techniques Used in Vegetable Growing

Since most vegetables, with the exception of the perennials, (rhubarb and asparagus) are treated as annuals or biennials the seed raising of plants becomes the single most important factor in growing those crops. Seed and labour costs have risen so dramatically in recent years that plant raising is no longer the haphazard process of years gone by when one merely sowed far more seeds than were really required.

Recent developments by plant breeders in producing F_1 hybrid seed help to ensure uniform plant stands. Pest and disease resistance is being bred into new cultivars. Vigour testing of seed is another aid to help achieve correct crop densities. The development of improved cultural techniques has led to changes in machinery and consequently plant raising has become more of a mathematical science than before.

Efficiency at seed propagation is the basis of the entire crop and many growers now leave plant raising of certain vegetables to the specialists, notably for lettuce, celery, cauliflowers, leeks and brassicas. The grower must ask himself whether to produce plants himself or buy in – but the survey of techniques below might help with this decision.

Seed Propagation

Natural seed

The minimum germination percentage and percentage purity of this seed has been fixed by legislation for a number of years but natural seed is still a variable product in terms of physical size (and shape). For seed sown by hand, natural seed offers no special disadvantage. On the other hand, with drilling by machine, seed size variation means that only approximate densities can be achieved with many vegetables (see Chapter 11).

Natural seed is seed in its cheapest form and is always readily available. Its most common uses are for sowing into seed trays or seed beds for later transplanting. Direct seeding with natural seed has the disadvantage of requiring large quantities of seed per hectare. Also, accurate plant densities are much more difficult to achieve than with other forms of seed.

Developments in engineering have provided equipment capable of accurate sowing of natural seed into peat blocks. But this new technology is relatively expensive consequently restricting its use to the larger grower or specialist plant raiser. Further developments may soon make precision sowing of natural seed possible on a field scale.

Graded seed

To overcome the variation in seed size, those seeds which are naturally regular in shape, such as brassicas, can be graded into a range of known size grades. This enables the grower to have a uniform product which can be space sown by machine. With graded seed, a lower seed weight per hectare can be used but against this must be set the higher cost of graded seed (one-and-a-half to two times dearer). Sizes of graded seed are coded with letters from A–Z as shown below. This is used by the seed trade in their catalogues and by seed drill manufacturers in their specifications.

Table 7: Graded seed size coding

Code letter	mm	64ths of an inch	Code letter	mm	64ths of an inch	Code letter	mm	64ths of an inch
A	0–0.25	0–¾	J	2.00–2.25	5¼–5¾	S	4.00–4.25	10¼–10¾
B	0.25–0.50	¾–1¼	K	2.25–2.50	5¾–6¼	T	4.25–4.50	10¾–11¼
C	0.50–0.75	1¼–1¾	L	2.50–2.75	6¼–6¾	U	4.50–4.75	11¼–11¾
D	0.75–1.00	1¾–2¾	M	2.75–3.00	6¾–7¾	V	4.75–5.00	11¾–12¾
E	1.00–1.25	2¾–3¼	N	3.00–3.25	7¾–8¼	W	5.00–5.25	12¾–13¼
F	1.25–1.50	3¼–3¾	P	3.25–3.50	8¼–8¾	X	5.25–5.50	13¼–13¾
G	1.50–1.75	3¾–4¼	Q	3.50–3.75	8¾–9¼	Y	5.50–5.75	13¾–14¼
H	1.75–2.00	4¼–5¼	R	3.75–4.00	9¼–10¼	Z	5.75–6.00	14¼–15¼

Graded seed is available for most major crops which have approximately spherical seeds. Also some flat or irregular seeds are available in graded form for semi-precision drilling, eg, parsnip and leek. Beet seed presents a rather special problem as fruit clusters containing a number of seeds take the place of a true seed. Beet clusters can be rubbed (to make them more spherical and then graded in the same way as other seeds). But because the fruit cluster contains more than one seed space, sowing of the clusters cannot give an accurate plant stand, unless 'monogerm' seed is used.

Pelleted seeds

Conventional precision seed drills cannot cope easily with irregular shaped natural seed. By coating an irregular seed with an inert clay material made into a spherical unit it can be easily handled by the seed metering unit of a normal precision drill.

REGULAR OR ROUND PELLETS   Large spherical pellets (about 3–5 mm diameter) intended for precision or space sowing of the seed. They are the largest and most costly (about 10 times the cost of natural seed) of the pellets used for seeding direct into the field.

MINI PELLETS   These are approximately one-third of the weight of a regular pellet but are not completely spherical and are therefore only suitable for semi-precision drilling. In the case of seeds which are almost regular in shape, eg, leeks, the mini pellet can be drilled almost as precisely as regular pellets, so reducing the seed cost to the grower.

SPLIT PILLS   This form of pellet is used for precision seeding into containers, usually peat blocks or Japanese paper pots. Unlike the other forms of pellet the split pill cracks open as the seed imbibes water. This gives a much higher germination percentage and more uniform germination than could be achieved by the other forms of pellet in this situation. The cost of split pills is high (approximately five times the cost of regular pellets) but some of the cost is offset by the lower wastage rate (every 10 peat blocks wasted costs 4p, in addition to the wasted propagating space).

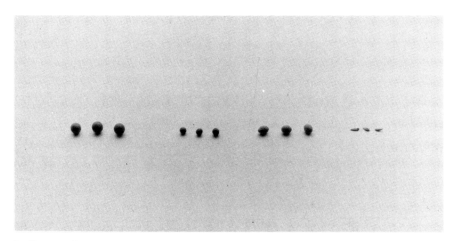

Different forms of pellet compared with natural seed.
Left to right:
  regular pellets, mini-pellets, split pills, natural seed (lettuce)

Pre-germinated or chitted seed

The advantage of pre-germinating or chitting natural seed in a favourable environment has been known for a long time and is frequently practised by amateur gardeners. The difficulty facing the commercial grower in 'handling' the chitted seed is that once the radicle has started to emerge it can be easily damaged.

Machine sowing to obtain a more rapid and uniform crop emergence is possible with fluid drilling using chitted seed in a protective alginate gel, particularly in the case of slow germinating species, like onions and parsnips. These features could, in turn, give more predictable plant densities and earlier maturity, or higher yields as a result of the extended growing season. If a cheap and efficient system could be developed for the separation of germinated and ungerminated seed this would enhance the advantages of fluid drilling.

The fluid drilling system does require a specialist drill and equipment for pre-germinating the seeds. The latter could be dispensed with, if pre-germinating seed became readily available through specialist suppliers. But this is not the case at present.

Cost of different types of seed using lettuce as an example

Natural seed   5.8p/1000 seed
Mini-pellets   21.3p/1000 pellets
Regular pellets   42.9p/1000 pellets
Split pills   £2.0/1000 pills

Techniques used to propagate from seed

FIELD DRILLING   This may be done with a view to later singling. There are two main methods.

(1)   *Random seeding:* thinning of a random drilled crop is difficult as two or more seeds frequently fall in close proximity giving rise to a group of plants. To thin this group to a single plant requires care and skill to minimize damage and disturbance to those plants which are to remain. This type of singling must be carried out manually which is a slow and costly operation.

(2)   *Precision seeding:* this technique still aims to give a plant stand slightly in excess of requirements but the plants are spaced apart making singling a much quicker and easier operation and offering the possibility of mechanical singling. Two forms of spacing may be used when precision seeding a crop for thinning see Figures 7(a) and (b) opposite.

The choice between these two spacing systems will be influenced by the ultimate crop spacing required and the method of singling which is employed.

Figures 7(a) and (b)

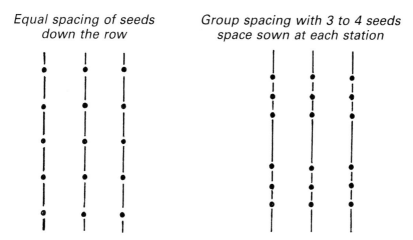

Equal spacing of seeds
down the row

Group spacing with 3 to 4 seeds
space sown at each station

DRILLING TO A STAND When field drilling high density crops, eg, carrot or onions the sowing rate is calculated to give a predicted emergence equal to the required density. The sowing can then be carried out by random or by precision seeder units, the latter offers a far greater accuracy especially where graded or pelleted seed is used.

Achieving the correct plant stand depends on accurate drilling and the ability of the grower to assess the condition of a seed bed and express that condition as a numerical factor, known as the field factor. (See section below.)

Calculation of sowing rate

Crop density may be expressed in a number of different ways. Weight of seed per ha, eg, onions sown at . . . kg/ha. As the number of seeds per kg can vary greatly between different batches, this method can lead to wide differences in crop density. Distance between rows and between plants in the row, eg, Brussels sprouts at 530 mm × 530 mm (21in × 21 in). This method is satisfactory for crops to be singled but row widths cannot be adjusted. Number of plants per metre run at a given row spacing, eg, 26 onion plants/m run at a 300 mm (12 in) row width. This is suitable for crops which are planted or drilled to a stand but it does not give the grower the opportunity to adjust row widths to suit his particular machinery or cultivating methods. 'Plant population' quoted as plants per m² (or plants per sq ft). This is now the most widely used method and allows for variation in row width as the number of plants per metre (or yard) run can be increased to compensate for wider row spacings and vice versa.

It is important for a grower to calculate the number of seeds he must sow per metre run of drill to achieve the required plant population. Where the recommendation is given as 'plant population' (see page 25) the first step is to decide the row spacing best suited to the crop and the machinery which is to be used. Having decided on a suitable row spacing the number of PLANTS per metre run of drill can be easily calculated, as follows.

$$\text{Plants per metre run} = \text{plants per square metre} \times \frac{\text{row width in mm}}{1000}$$

eg, onions to be drilled in rows 300 mm apart at 86 plants/m^2

$$\text{Onion plants per metre run} = \frac{86 \times 300}{1000} = \frac{8.6 \times 3}{1}$$

$$= 25.8 \text{ (say 26) plants per metre run.}$$

To get 26 plants growing per metre run more than 26 seeds must be sown as a number will fail to germinate and some seedlings will fail soon after germination. The two factors which have to be taken into consideration are: (a) laboratory germination – this can normally be supplied by the seed company on request for any given batch of seed and (b) the condition of the seed bed, ie, the physical condition of the soil, the temperature and moisture status. Estimation of the seed bed condition relies on the experience of the grower, who has to give a numerical value to the conditions. This value is known as the FIELD FACTOR. A field factor (Ff) of 1.0 would mean a field germination equal to the laboratory germination which would never be achieved in practice. At the other extreme a field factor of 0.1 would suggest that only 10 per cent of the laboratory germination would be achieved in the field. In these circumstances a grower would not sow. The working area of the scale is between 0.8 for very good seed bed conditions to 0.5 for rather poor conditions of tilth or temperature.

Armed with the laboratory germination figure plus an estimate of the field factor the number of seeds per metre run can be calculated, as shown below:

$$\text{Seeds/metre run} = \frac{\text{Plants per metre run} \times 100}{\% \text{ Lab. germination} \times \text{Field factor}}$$

eg, the onion crop required 26 plants per metre run.
Laboratory germination is 80%
Field factor is estimated at 0.7 (Reasonably good seed bed with moisture and temperature)

$$\text{Seeds/metre run} = \frac{26 \times 100}{80 \times 0.7} = \frac{260}{5.6} = \frac{130}{2.8}$$

$$= 46.4 \text{ ie 46–47 seeds/m run to be drilled.}$$

The seed drill can then be calibrated using a sample of the seed to be sown, so that it delivers the required number of seeds per metre run of drill (see Chapter 11).

FLUID DRILLING   This technique developed by the National Vegetable Research Station in the early 1980s is not yet in widespread use, perhaps because of the high capital cost and the numerous pre-drilling operations required. Fluid drilling can be used for drilling natural seed, but in order to obtain maximum advantage from the system the use of pre-germinated seed is required.

There are a number of distinct stages involved in the preparation of a crop for fluid drilling, each stage, involving various pieces of equipment.

(1)   Germination of the seed. The method employed for smaller quantities of seed consists of suspending seed in warmed water which is constantly agitated and aerated by bubbles of air. This environment provides the conditions required for germination, ie, warmth, moisture and oxygen. In the case of seed which requires light for rapid germination, eg, celery, a suitable wavelength of light can also be provided during this stage using a light source with a predominantly red frequency, eg, incandescent filament bulbs.

(2)   Storage of the seed. Having germinated the seed it is not possible to guarantee suitable field conditions for drilling, therefore storage facilities must be available. By cooling the seed to 0°C it is possible to store most species for up to two weeks, but the seed must NOT be frozen. Accurate control of temperature is essential, high temperatures will allow excess development of the radicle while temperatures below 0°C will damage the chitted seed.

SEED BED SOWING   (for production of 'drawn' or 'peg' plants). When sowing protected seed beds eg, under (cold) frames or tunnels, the use of mechanization is limited and maximum use of available space is required. Seed may be broadcast on to a well prepared seed bed if accurate and uniform density can be achieved. Frequently, the practice of broadcasting gives a variable density resulting in uneven transplants. An additional problem is the difficulty of achieving a uniform covering. Failure to do so results in variable emergence and seedling size.

The alternative is to drill the seedbeds with a small pedestrian operated drill (see picture page 197) which has been calibrated to give the correct density of seed required for the crop. Leeks and brassicas are commonly drilled in this way. An example of the sort of seed rates used for these crops is detailed on page 28.

If seedbeds are used frequently for the same or similar crops, soil borne pests and diseases will build up in the soil (eg, clubroot of brassicas). Prevention is better than an attempted cure, if rotation is very limited

Table 8: Seed rates

	Plants needed per m²	Plants per m run	Seeds/m² in gramms	Seeds/ m run	Comment
LEEKS – *Sown under protection* 50 mm narrow row spacing	900– 1200	45–60	3–6	80–107	These are figures based on seed laboratory germination of 70% and a field factor of 0.8
Sown in open beds 300 mm wide row spacing	450– 550	22–28	2–2.5	40–45	
BRASSICAS – *Sown under protection* 50 mm narrow row spacing	400– 500	20–25	BS 2.5–3.6 Cab. 2.5– 3.0 Caul. 2.0– 2.6	36–45	These are average figures based on an 80% laboratory germination and a field factor of 0.7
Sown in open beds 300 mm wide row spacing	100– 240	30–72	BS 0.7–1.8 Cab. 0.6– 1.6 Caul. 0.5– 1.3	54–130	Seed counts were: 250/gm BS 280/gm Cab. 350/gm Caul.

Key: BS = Brussels Sprouts
Cab. = Cabbage
Caul. = Cauliflowers.

or not possible at all, partial soil sterilization with Dazomet should be carried out as a regular operation at least every second year.

SEED SOWING IN TRAYS Traditionally many early vegetables were raised by sowing in seed trays, then pricked out into frames or containers such as peat blocks. The high cost of labour has almost eliminated this practice, except in the case of celery, which does not have a sufficiently reliable germination rate to justify the technique of sowing direct into blocks or paper pots as practised with other crops.

BLOCK RAISED CROPS Most vegetable crops can now be sown direct into peat blocks, eliminating the need for pricking out. Most power driven block making machines are now fitted with a simple but efficient seeding unit, capable of placing one seed (or pellet) in each block. Regular shaped seed may be used in the natural form, irregular shaped seed should be sown in the form of pill or split pill type pellets. Large seeds, eg, courgettes, runner beans and sweet corn, are not suitable for machine sowing but can be easily hand sown into blocks as they are produced by machine. The only crop which still requires to be pricked out is celery. This does not usually have a satisfactory level of germination when direct sown in pelleted form.

MULTI-PLANT BLOCKS With lower value crops eg, onions and beetroot, more than one seedling must be produced in each block to make block raising economic. To sow several seeds per block with consistent accuracy involves the use of a more complex and costly seeding unit which will normally handle natural seed, placing a pre-set number of seeds in each block.

Is it cheaper to buy or grow your own?
The factors a grower should consider in making a decision are:
(1)   Capital cost of the blocking machine with seeding facility (a modest machine would cost approximately £2,500, 1982) also trays or other handling system for the blocks.
(2)   Availability of labour at propagation time for blocking and managing the seedlings (10,000 blocks/man/hour).
(3)   Adequate propagation area under some form of protection, eg, glass or plastic, heating would be required for the earlier crops.
(4)   If lettuce are to be produced during late spring, summer or autumn, some means of avoiding high temperatures during germination would be essential, eg, adequate space in a cool shed to germinate the seed.
Costs relate to 1982 prices:

Blocking compost/1000 blocks (4.3 cm) 100 litres	£2.63
Split pill seed/1000 blocks	£3.25
Labour input/1000 blocks 1.5 hr @ £1.87/hr	£2.81
Depreciation on machine @ 10 yr write off assuming production of 100,000 blocks/yr	£1.80
Tray for handling blocks – per 1000 blocks £6 written off over 5 years	£1.20
	£11.69*

Cost to buy in/1000 blocks – lettuce £11.50 delivered

*In addition a grower must consider the cost of glasshouse space allocated approximately 2.9 m/1,000 blocks plus the heating cost of early crops which require heat during propagation.
One can see that buying in blocks is probably cheaper than growing your own especially for the smaller grower.

OTHER SYSTEMS OF PROPAGATION   Transplanted crops, particularly container raised transplants, offer much more uniform and rapid crop growth. Unfortunately transplanting has the disadvantage of requiring a very large labour input (around 4,500 plants/operator/hour). Current development work is directed at developing a commercially acceptable automatic and semi-automatic planter, capable of planting 15,000 or more plants per operator per hour.

For a fully automatic planter a plant module which can be fed mechanically into the planting unit is essential. There are three principle modules in use or under development for use in conjunction with the new planting machines.

(1)   *Speedlings (Vegetable Wedges)* – this technique was developed in the USA and involves raising the seedlings in modules of polystyrene cells, each cell in the shape of an inverted pyramid. The compost is normally composed of peat and vermiculite to give a well aerated medium. This system is used by at least one specialist vegetable plant raiser in Britain. Speedlings or similar plant units can be machine planted by the Speedling Brand Model 3,000 transplanter, marketed in the UK by The Springfield Company.

(2)   *Bandolier* – this system is under development. The blocking machine uses unwetted blocking compost to make a set of linked cylindrical blocks, each block is wrapped and linked to the next by a degradable paper film. In common with conventional blocking machines the 'Bandolier' also seeds the blocks as they are produced (8–12,000 blocks per hour).

The planting machine is fully automatic with a work rate of 75 to 80 blocks per minute on each planting unit. Development of this system is a joint project between the NIAE and Tichhill Engineering Co Ltd.

(3)   *The Japanese paper pot ('Honeycombs')* – these hexagonal paper tubes are linked by a water soluble glue. The pots can be filled and seeded by machine. Once moist the individual pots can be separated easily. The system has been in use for many years.

The new honeycomb developed for machine planting forms a chain of linked pots as the honeycomb network separates.

A prototype fully automatic Japanese planter has been successfully used in Europe for sugar beet planting. It is planned to modify the machine for vegetable planting. In addition the Whalehide Company are importing the Lannen semi-automatic/transplanter, developed in Finland for planting paper pots. It is also capable of handling a wide range of container raised plants.

Crop	Natural seed shape	Seeds/per 10 grams (Seeds per ounce)	Minimum EEC standards %germination	%purity	Optimum germination temperature (°C) 5 10 15 20 25 30 35	Seed type normally available
ASPARAGUS		450–600 (1,300–1,700)	70	96		Natural
BEAN–BROAD		6–12 (17–34)	80	98		Natural
BEAN–DWARF FRENCH		18–60 (50–170)	75	98		Graded–sizes A,B,C,D,E Natural
BEAN–RUNNER		6–12 (17–23)	80	98		Natural
BEETROOT		420–1,590 (1,200–4,500)	70	97		Graded–sizes M–P, Q–S Ungraded
BRASSICAS Brussels Sprout		1,760–3,530 (5,000–10,000)	75	97		Graded–sizes H,J Ungraded
Broccoli		2,120–4,580 (6,000–13,000)	75	97		Graded–sizes H,J Ungraded
Cabbage		1,940–3,700 (5,500–10,500)	75	97		Graded–sizes H,J Ungraded
Calabrese		1,410–4,230 (4,000–12,000)	75	97		Graded–size J Ungraded
Cauliflower		2,120–5,640 (6,000–16,000)	70	97		Graded–sizes H,J Ungraded
CARROT		4,940–16,930 (14,000–48,000)	65	95		Graded–sizes F,G,H Ungraded & Pelleted
CELERY		17,640–38,800 (50,000–110,000)	70	97		Natural Pelleted (mini)
LEEK		2,820–4,400 (8,000–12,500)	65	97		Graded–sizes H,J Ungraded & Pelleted
LETTUCE		6,000–12,350 (17,000–35,000)	75	95		Ungraded, Pelleted (regular, mini-pellets & pills)
MARROW		53–92 (150–260)	75	98		Natural
ONION		2,120–3,175 (6,000–9,000)	70	97		Graded–sizes K,L Ungraded & Pelleted
PARSNIP		2,000–3,000 (5,700–8,500)	No standards			Graded–sizes S–U, V–X Ungraded & Pelleted (mini)
PEA		30–90 (80–250)	80	98		Natural
RADISH		700–1,760 (2,000–5,000)	70	97		Graded–sizes K,L Ungraded
SWEDES		2,470–4,230 (7,000–12,000)	80	98		Graded–sizes H,J Ungraded
TURNIP		3,350–5,290 (9,500–15,000)	80	97		Graded–sizes G,H Ungraded
SWEET CORN		35–70 (100–200)	No standards			Natural

Table 9: Summary of Vegetable Seeds

*Natural seed size shown in this table is half the actual size.

Chapter Three

Irrigation

Few growers can contemplate vegetable production without the aid of irrigation. For although Britain has a temperate climate, official drought periods (15 days or more without rainfall) are commonplace. Even rainless periods of as little as one week have been shown to retard crop growth. Irrigation during such (short) periods of moisture stress can greatly increase crop yields.

It is, therefore, important when determining irrigation needs and choosing equipment to remember three factors. Firstly that there are few vegetable growing areas in the UK *which can produce high yielding crops without irrigation.* The UK requirement for irrigation water is shown in Figure 10. Secondly *that vegetables have 90 per cent or more water content* and that their requirement for water may be at a very specific stage of growth, and lastly that the irrigation system used *must be capable of coping with a more than average dry summer.* It should be possible to contemplate budgeting for full irrigation in 15 years out of 20, accepting a certain amount of inadequacy during the drier five years. For detailed climatic maps see *Atlas of Irrigation Need for England and Wales* by W. H. Hogg.

Advantages of Irrigation

Questions like: 'Why irrigate?' 'Is it worth it?', 'What are the advantages of irrigation?' are bound to arise. Here are some of the answers:

SEED GERMINATION   Irrigation is particularly advantageous in the germination of seed as high moisture content is an important requisite in the process. Where pelleted seeds are used, water is essential in order to break down the kaolin coating around the seed, so allowing germi-

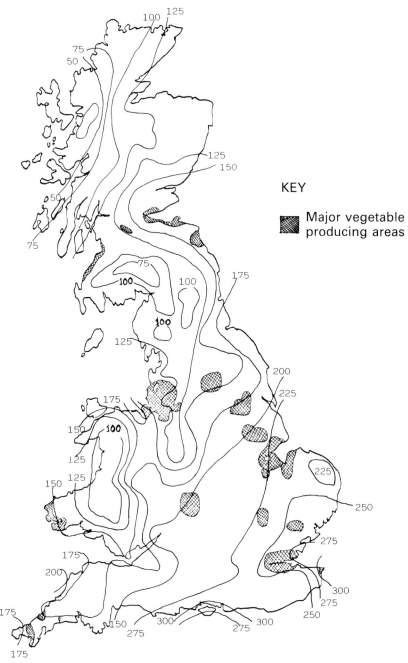

Figure 10 Millimetres of irrigation water needed to prevent the soil moisture deficit exceeding 25 mm from April to September in the fifth driest year in twenty.

nation to occur. Many growers irrigate land a few days prior to drilling to ensure satisfactory germination.

SOIL STABILITY   Moisture helps maintain soil stability. This is particularly the case with lighter sandy soils, where irrigation helps resist wind erosion.

EXTRA YIELD   So much is written about increased yield attributed to irrigation that the grower is understandably confused. Percentage figures are useless unless they are related to a base yield and even more futile without a note of the timing and amount of water applied. The effect of application of water on vegetable plants is obvious enough – immediate response by rapid growth of more and larger foliage. Naturally, leafy crops, like lettuce, spinach and cabbage, are very responsive. Careful timing of irrigation may in turn effect yield in other plant parts – flower parts enlarge (cauliflowers), seeds swell (peas) and food storage organs grow longer and larger (carrots). Timing is where special success is achieved. The outstanding example is the pea crop, where two applications of irrigation, 25 mm at flowering and 25 mm at pod swelling gives massive increase in yields. Water applied before flowering merely sends peas to 'leaf'. If the reader needs convincing further, an example of increased yields by limited irrigation is shown in the table below.

Table 10: Increased yields by limited irrigation

Crop	Yield irrigation applied	Yield from normal rain Tonnes/Ha	Yield from irrigated land Tons Acre	% increase
Cabbage	25 mm three weeks before harvest	54.4 (22.4)	60.4 (24.9)	11.1
Carrot	63 mm applied once at soil deficit of 75 mm	35.6 (14.6)	40.0 (16.5)	11.1
Cauliflower early summer	25 mm just before commencing selective cutting	20.9 (8.6)	28.0 (11.5)	13.4
Lettuce	Soil brought to field capacity in spring before sowing	19.9 (8.2)	25.8 (10.6)	12.9
Peas	25 mm at flowering only	16.9 (7.0)	20.0 (8.2)	15.6

CROP QUALITY   Far too much stress is placed on the increase in yields without reference to quality. Irrigation has been shown to increase the quality of crops, particularly in plants like lettuce and cauliflower. Quality vegetables always find a ready sale, even in periods of glut or when produce is moving slowly in the wholesale market.

CONTINUITY OF CROPPING Irrigation should help the grower to plan better. Periods of drought hold up production and make planning difficult.

OTHER SIDE BENEFITS In addition to continuity of production irrigation may benefit other cultural operations. In dry springs the watering in of nitrogen top dressing may be more effective than allowing that material to waste on the surface. Most residual herbicides are far less effective on dry soils, so irrigation prior to application often helps soil absorption. The harvesting of crops like salad onions, radishes and root crops is made easier in moist or irrigated soils.

Disadvantages of Irrigation

Obviously irrigation leaches out nutrients, and these need replacing. Far more important is the damage to soil structure caused by irrigation, especially where droplet size is large. Panning or capping of soil is commonplace and growers should choose irrigation equipment which minimizes this problem – where droplet size is large (5 mm +) the damage is greatest. Unfortunately the large throw of modern irrigation heads is not conducive to small droplet size. The problem of capping is particularly frequent on silty or sandy loams and it has been demonstrated that emergence of lettuce seedlings can be reduced by up to 35 per cent with medium/large droplets. Heavy droplets on slopes may also cause *gullying and soil erosion.*

Also some disease problems manifest themselves where moisture abounds. Clubroot disease of brassicas is encouraged, particularly if drainage is poor. Botrytis (grey mould) commonly enters crops where heavy water input has caused damage to plant tissue, particularly on lettuces. Not least of all, seedling damping-off disease is especially prevalent when cold nights occur after irrigation has been applied.

CONCLUSION The advantages of irrigation far outweigh the disadvantages. The greater the moisture stress, the larger the effect on yield and the less turgid plants become. Since the prime market requirement for vegetables is succulence, prevention of moisture stress is a must. Drought merely seems to increase the fibrous nature of vegetables, especially in beans, celery and sweet corn, in an irreversible manner. And as for taste, a much more intangible subject, this is said to improve with irrigated crops.

Water Balance

What happens to all the water we receive in the form of precipitation and where does it all go to? The truth of the matter is that most of the UK receives an excess amount of rainfall or snow in winter and an insufficient supply (for plants) during the summer.

The limited supplies of water that remain in the soil surface (the soil reservoir) are affected by the sun's radiant energy to be evaporated from the soil surface or transpired from plants.

It is the imbalance of supply of natural water in summer (April to September), when most vegetable crops grow, that determines how much the grower needs to irrigate. Thus WATER BALANCE is the *relationship between precipitation* on the one hand *and the loss by evaporation, transpiration and drainage* on the other. In percentage terms it is illustrated below for a year round crop in the midlands area of the UK where crop cover is not complete.

Figure 11   Water balance

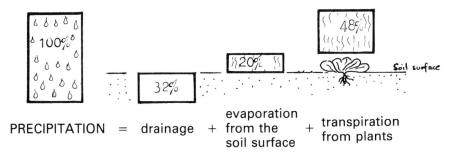

PRECIPITATION   =   drainage   +   evaporation from the soil surface   +   transpiration from plants

Measurement of rainfall and evaporation/transpiration is an important part of knowing how much to irrigate in dry weather. Determining the timing is another matter which is covered later on, under the heading of 'The practical approach to irrigation'.

Irrigation Terms Explained

No student of irrigation can contemplate tackling the subject without an understanding of some of the basic terms, like field capacity, permanent wilting point, available water capacity and soil moisture deficit. Soil contains a number of constituents, the major ones being soil particles and pore space (containing air and water). The amounts of water and air vary considerably according to the season of the year and the input of moisture by rain or irrigation

Figure 12 Diagramatic representation of soil moisture terms

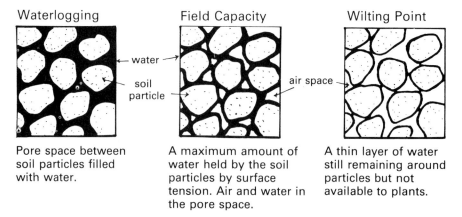

Waterlogging — Pore space between soil particles filled with water.

Field Capacity — A maximum amount of water held by the soil particles by surface tension. Air and water in the pore space.

Wilting Point — A thin layer of water still remaining around particles but not available to plants.

WATERLOGGING   When all air is excluded from pore spaces the soil is said to be waterlogged. This state commonly occurs immediately after heavy rainfall or after flooding with irrigation. It is a situation which is hardly likely to remain stable and one in which few plants can survive.

FIELD CAPACITY (FC)   Under normal circumstances, gravitational pull and suction from lower unsaturated layers encourages drainage from the waterlogged situation. This rapid rate of drainage continues until each soil particle holds a maximum amount of water in a film around its perimeter by suction (called soil moisture tension). Thereafter drainage continues very much slower. This point of maximum water retention by tension is called *field capacity*. It is also the point at which *most water is available to plants*, though it varies markedly with different soils. The ideal, in plant terms, is to keep the soil permanently at field capacity, but this would be impossible in the practicalities of field scale vegetable crops.

PERMANENT WILTING POINT   As further water loss occurs and moisture content falls, soil moisture tension increases. There comes a point where plant roots can no longer take up water against this suction force. Transpiration exceeds plant intake of moisture so the plants wilts and dies. This is called the *permanent wilting point*.

AVAILABLE WATER CAPACITY (AWC)   This is the total volume of water available to plant growth between field capacity and permanent wilting point. It varies with different soils. Also the degree of suction needed for plants to take up water varies with different soils. By looking at the Figure 13 opposite it is possible to see that while the volume of water available is higher in clays than sandy soils, the amount of water easily taken up by plants is higher in sandy soils. So clay soils may need bringing up to field capacity more often than sandy soils to ensure that plants can take up moisture without being put under stress. Figures for available water capacity for different soil types are shown in Table 11. For irrigation purposes, however, soils are merely divided into three categories:

  – Light   (gravelly or sandy soils)
  – Medium   (loams, clays or silty loams)
  – Retentive (deep silts or peaty soils)

The amount of water necessary to bring a soil up to field capacity is called the SOIL MOISTURE DEFICIT (SMD). On medium soils it is common practice in vegetable growing to irrigate when soil moisture deficits reach 25 mm.

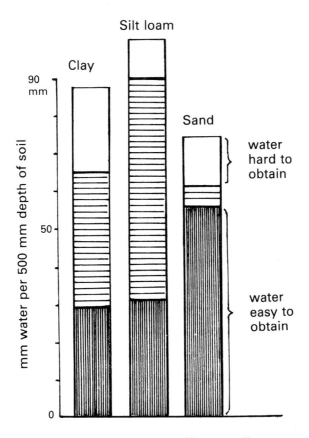

Figure 13   The availability of water in different soils

Table 11: Available water capacity of different soils

Soil type	Available water capacity (mm/500 mm depth of soil)
Coarse sand	41
Sand	75
Loamy sand	79
Sandy loam	88
Silty loam	100
Clay loam	91
Clay	88

Water Sources and Storage

Perhaps the most important aspect of irrigation is finding a ready supply of water and plenty of it. Remember, to apply 25 mm/ha (the minimum worth while average application) involves 250,000 litres of water, so the reservoir of water supply is all important. Having found a suitable source, further enquiry will be necessary to discover whether it can be tapped.

BOREHOLES   Water bearing rock stratas or aquifers can be tapped by sinking a borehole and then pumping the water out. Even assuming that a suitable geological formation is available, permission to sink a borehole for abstraction is required from the appropriate local water authority. Then an abstraction licence has to be paid. Initial cost, too, may be prohibitive. Boreholes cost £40 to £60 per metre to drill out, according to diameter of bore, depth and difficulty of drilling. Abstraction costs about £6 to £17 per 1 million litres (0.22 million gallons). The licences specify the point of abstraction, the land on which water is to be used, the quantity to be removed and the period of usage.

WATER COURSES, RIVERS, STREAMS   Abstraction direct from watercourses is commonly carried out. Again licences are required from the local water authority and these are rarely conceded to new concessionaires. The best approach is to buy up land with an existing licence. With rivers, variability in water level is a major problem, especially as the basis for licencing is that any abstraction should be unlikely to affect necessary minimum flow requirements. That means that abstraction has to be on land adjacent to the river and removal of water should not affect flow lower down the river. Obtaining new licences is becoming increasingly difficult, especially since the water shortage summer of 1976. Certainly in dry summers growers may face restrictions or even total prohibition despite so-called maximum abstraction figures quoted for the season.

OFF STREAM RESERVOIRS   Off stream reservoirs are increasingly being used to store water as an alternative to direct removal from rivers. This consists of an artificial excavated area supplied by a channel intake from a stream, with an overflow channel to take excess back into the course down stream. The idea is to abstract water during winter or excess and to store it for summer use. The construction of these is shown in Figure 14. Earth made reservoirs may be created and made to hold water by smearing the interior with a 75 mm thick layer of heavy puddled clay – keeping it moist all the time until it is filled with water. But expect 10 per cent loss by evaporation and up to 20 per cent by seepage. Use of butyl lining avoids seepage but this at least doubles the cost of the reservoir. Capacities of up to 100 million litres (22 million gallons) can be constructed without civil engineering instruction, particularly if made in natural hollows.

STREAM DAMMING   Technical difficulties and high cost make this impracticable.

WATER TANKS   These are suitable for storage of relatively small quantities of water of up to 227,300 litres (50,000 gal). They are used more in glasshouse units or frame areas for intensive culture.

OTHER WATER SOURCES   Include wells, public water supplies and land drains, but for large scale irrigation they usually do not offer a great deal. Public mains water is fine for seedbeds and frame yards, it is reliable and clean but very costly at £12 per 4,546 litres (1,000 gal). Storage of land drain water in reservoirs has potential but it as yet unexploited.

Water quality

The best source of irrigation water is from a deep borehole, being clean and unlikely to be contaminated by pollution. Careful inspection of river water is necessary, especially if untreated farm effluent is used to spray river side land further upstream or where industry may inject pollutants into the water course. Whatever the source of water, it should be chemically checked for pH and incidence of harmful elements before use.

Distribution of Water

Distribution of water from the water source is usually carried out by pump. The type and capacity of pump will depend on volume of water, distance and gradient to the site.

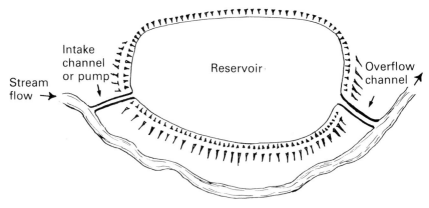

Plan view

To qualify for grant aid from the ministry the reservoir must:–
(a) Have a bank slope of not steeper than 1 in 2½
(b) The water to be used for agricultural or horticultural irrigation purposes
(c) If a butyl liner is to be used a minimum 300 gauge must be used.

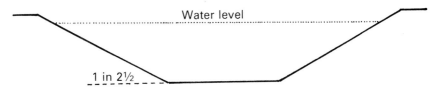

Cross section of reservoir construction

Where a butyl rubber liner is to be used a sheet of approximately 40 m × 29 m will hold about 1,140,000 litres (250,000 galls) water.

Figure 14 Off stream reservoirs

Centrifugal pumps are probably best as they are relatively cheap, have high efficiency and are easy to install. They can pump large quantities of water and are not damaged by overloading or shutting off. They also have very few wearing parts. But centrifugal pumps need priming and only have a maximum lift of 4½ m (14½ ft) which means that large fluctuations in water level make their use awkward. At low working speeds constant checks are necessary to ensure that priming is not lost during operation. Choice of power source will depend on site. An illustration of comparative costs of pumps is given opposite (1981 prices). The next thing is to channel the water from its source to the areas of irrigation. Piped mains must be at least 600 mm (2 ft) below ground level and they should run as direct as possible, with few bends,

Table 12: Comparative costs of pumps

Tractor driven pump	£450 –£750
Electric pump	£3500–£4000
Diesel pump	£3000–£6570

otherwise friction loss will be high. Mains ranging from 100–300 mm (4–12 in) diameter are used according to volume and size of area to be irrigated. A sample layout for an irrigation unit is shown in Figure 15.

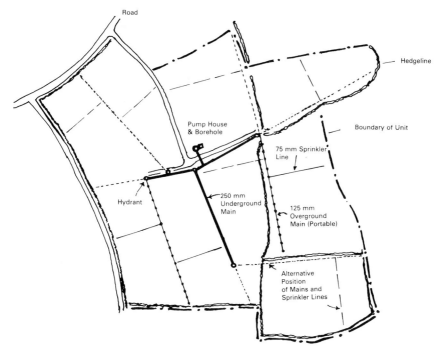

Figure 15 Line layout for a typical sprinkler irrigation system

Which method of application?

The choice of irrigation equipment will depend very much on the crops grown, the area to be irrigated and the amount of labour available. Since high capital investment is involved, the grower would be wise to carry out a 'Which' survey of types of irrigation before purchasing.

In looking at equipment the potential buyer must bear in mind the following four factors. The *droplet size* emitted and its uniformity (1–4 mm). The *area of distribution* of the applicator or series of applicators

– the larger the area the better, but do not sacrifice small droplet size for area covered. The droplets produced by rain guns are too large for many horticultural crops. The *capital cost* – irrigation is one of the most costly investments the grower has to make. The *labour required* to move and maintain the equipment.

Different types of irrigation equipment (see Figure 16 for illustrated details)

There is a wide range of field equipment available varying from low cost sprinkler systems to huge rain guns.

Trickle irrigation is available as layflat tubing and seephoses, both enabling water to be applied at ground level near the rooting zone. They are not really suitable for large scale vegetable production in the UK, but have some use in intensive areas, like frame yards, where they save the labour of having to raise frames to irrigate. Layflat tubing, in particular, suffers from pressure loss the further away from the water source which is usually mains supply.

Sub-irrigation with 'Leaky Pipe' is a new innovation which is being currently tested for intensive vegetable production. Rather like an ordinary rubber hosepipe, it allows water to seep out through minute pores in the pipe. The manufacturers recommend that it is buried 100 mm (4 in) below soil level so that water seeps out at root level. But like trickle irrigation it suffers from loss of water pressure down the line.

Overhead irrigation through sprinklers and oscillating spraylines is the most common approach to large scale vegetable cropping. But water can be lost by evaporation off leaves and soil surface. Speed of application of water can affect both run-off and panning of surface soil. Oscillation of spraylines ensures relatively slow application. Rotary impact sprinklers move slowly round so that the circular pattern is covered in about one minute.

The pattern of distribution is also highly relevant to irrigation planning.

Rotary sprinklers, with a circular pattern, need overlapping by 35 per cent to ensure complete coverage. It also means there is a wide variation in application rate within a small area. The equipment that gives an oblong pattern of distribution is much more adaptable for row crop work. That is why oscillating spraylines are commonly used on small rectangular areas.

STATIC SYSTEMS are usually made more versatile by using gangs of labour to move the equipment at regular intervals, so covering larger areas of land. Equipment is normally moved over 20 sites before returning to the original area. The equipment is usually left on each site for about 5 hours, time enough to apply 25 mm of water, thus working on a 5-day cycle.

Figure 16 Irrigation equipment

TRICKLE IRRIGATION (application rate 0.5–2.0 litres/minute)

Area covered is a long narrow strip or row.

Advantages of trickle irrigation
1. Slow application of water.
2. No soil panning.
3. Useful for frames or propagation beds.

Layflat tubing   *Seephose*

Consists of 50 mm   Consists of stitched
polythene tubing. Water   polythene pipe. Water
emerges from pin pricks.   emerges from stitching.

OSCILLATING SPRAYLINES (application rate
                        150–600 litres/5m length of line.)

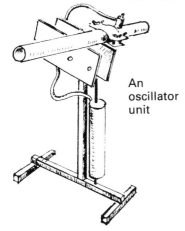

An
oscillator
unit

Advantages of spraylines
1. Slow application of water
   provided by oscillation.
2. Medium to small droplet size.
3. Spraylines can be moved over
   a number of sites.
4. Ideal for small areas of strip crops.

OSCILLATING SPRAYLINES (*continued*)

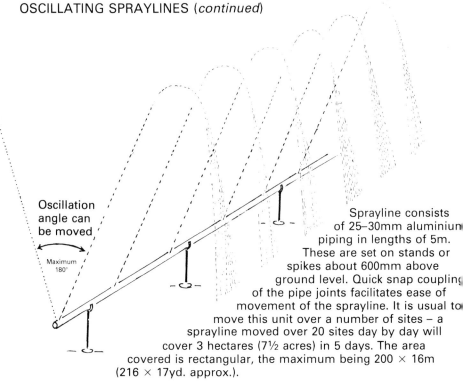

Oscillation angle can be moved

Maximum 180°

Sprayline consists of 25–30mm aluminium piping in lengths of 5m. These are set on stands or spikes about 600mm above ground level. Quick snap coupling of the pipe joints facilitates ease of movement of the sprayline. It is usual to move this unit over a number of sites – a sprayline moved over 20 sites day by day will cover 3 hectares (7½ acres) in 5 days. The area covered is rectangular, the maximum being 200 × 16m (216 × 17yd. approx.).

SPRINKLER IRRIGATION

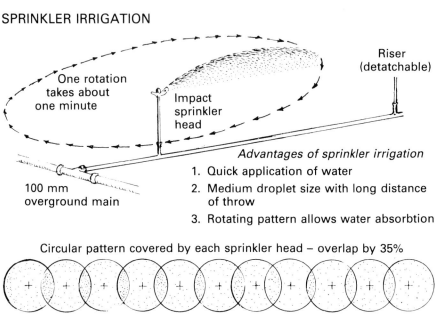

One rotation takes about one minute

Impact sprinkler head

Riser (detatchable)

100 mm overground main

Advantages of sprinkler irrigation
1. Quick application of water
2. Medium droplet size with long distance of throw
3. Rotating pattern allows water absorbtion

Circular pattern covered by each sprinkler head – overlap by 35%

Rotary impact sprinkler head –

Water ejected from nozzle
hits breaker plate, thus
breaking up
water droplets
and deflecting
the plate. The
plate returns
against the
spring so turning
the head in a series
of jarring movements.

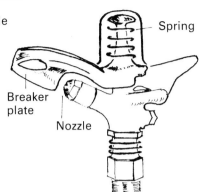

Spring

Breaker
plate

Nozzle

SELF-TRAVELLING EQUIPMENT – SPRINKLERS, RAIN GUNS & BOOMS

The machine is positioned at one end of the plot to be irrigated
(preferably the headland). The hose is then reeled out to the required
length. The machine will then reel in the irrigation unit on its skid (or
wheels), once connected to the water hydrant and the pump has been
started. Move the unit on to another site once reeled back to the drum.

Different types of irrigation heads can be used with
self-travelling devices – sprinklers, rain guns or
booms. Rain guns give the furthest throw
but produce too large droplets.

Coverage – rain guns up to 4 ha.
– sprinklers up to 2.2 ha.
– booms up to 1.8 ha.

Breaker
plate

Nozzle

A rain gun head

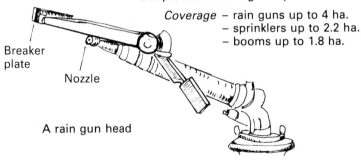

Area covered roughly oblong

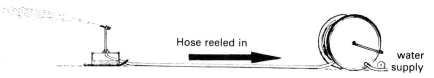

Hose reeled in

water supply

Advantages of self-travelling systems

1. Labour saving – can be operated by one man, unlike most other sprinkler systems.
2. Large area of coverage. Unit easily moved.
3. Relatively low operating pressures, especially when compared with sprinkler lines.

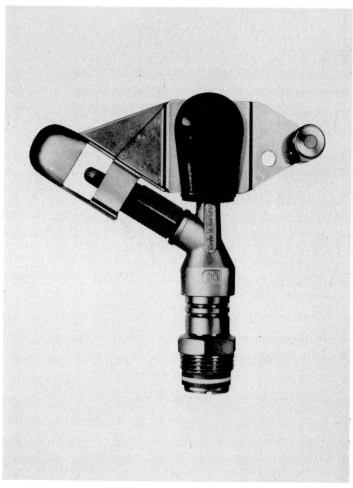

A typical hammer action rotary sprinkler head. Photograph by Perrot Irrigation Ltd.

Table 13: Quick guide to irrigation equipment

Type of equipment	Seasonal capacity (or litres per hour)	Approx. capital cost	Approx. cost per hectare (1981)	Labour needed to apply 100 mm water on 1 ha in hrs	Major manufacturer/ supplier
STATIC TYPES Trickle (Seephose)	11 litres per m/ hour	£43 for 350 m	£1,400	Minimal	Access Irrigation Ltd.
(Layflat Tube)	varies with pressure	£8 for 150 m	–	Minimal	Brydon Fibres Ltd.
Sub Irrigation (Leaky Hose)	9 litres per m/ hour	£40 for 100 m	–	Minimal	J & J Nurseries (Gloucester)
Spraylines	0.15–0.3 ha from 1 line	£750 for 0.3 ha	£225	10	Evenproducts Ltd. British Overhead Irrigation.
Sprinklers (Conventional)	12 ha	£1,011 for 720m line	£210	24	Wright Rain Ltd. Cameron Irrigation Co. Perrot Irrigation Ltd.
('Hopalong')	12 ha	–		17	Wright Rain Ltd.
('Portagrid')	8–16 ha	–	£1,000	7	Wright Rain Ltd.
MOBILE TYPES Rotating Boom (Tractor Mounted 'Laureau')	16 ha	–	–	3	Wright Rain Ltd.
Self-travelling Rotating Boom ('Miniboom')	16 ha	£5,100	£320	3	Wright Rain Ltd.
('Touraineboom')	36 ha	£10,875	£300	2½	Wright Rain Ltd.
Self-travelling Rain guns (small)	16 ha	£4,840	£300	3	Wright Rain Ltd. Javelin Irrigation Ltd.
(medium)	23 ha	£6,552	£285	2½	Perrot Irrigation Ltd.
(large)	64 ha	£11,240	£175	2	

Table 13 tabulates some of the major types of irrigation equipment available to the grower, their relative costs, capacities and labour requirement. This is in no way an exhaustive list but it may be a useful starting guide.

MOBILE Self-travelling sprinklers or rain guns are gaining rapid popularity in vegetable growing circles because large areas can be irrigated in an approximately oblong pattern with a great saving in labour. These have tended to supersede the large rotary spray booms towed behind a tractor which were heavy, cumbersome and expensive. The latest innovation is the use of a rotating boom on a self-travelling system.

A self-travelling fixed-boom sprinkler. Photograph by Wright Rain Ltd.

Irrigation Layouts

Care in the design of a layout is all important if economies of labour and equipment are to be made. In laying out underground mains make sure that all parts of the field you wish to cover can be reached by the equipment and water pressure available.

The basic idea is to divide up the land to be irrigated into units of land of the size which can be irrigated at one complete watering (or day cycle). Many growers look to a 10-day rotation of their equipment before returning to the first site. The use of self-travelling devices enables more flexibility of equipment and labour. Some more useful systems are shown in Figures 17 and 18.

Figure 17 Irrigation layouts
SPRINKLER SYSTEM LAYOUTS – Conventional and 'Hopalong' systems are most popular with vegetable growers. The 'Portagrid' is probably too expensive and few growers like the idea of a permanent layout
of pipes across their fields.

Conventional Layout

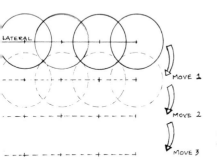

'Hopalong' System
(Conventional layout with a
reduced sprinkler compliment)

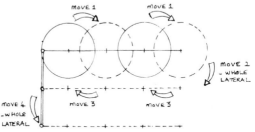

The whole lateral sprinkler line
is moved to a new position on the
line, after sufficient water has
been applied in the first site.

Half the number of sprinklers are
used on each lateral line. Each
sprinkler is then moved to its
adjacent position before the lateral
is moved and the same procedure
repeated

'Portagrid System' (Semi-permanent layout)

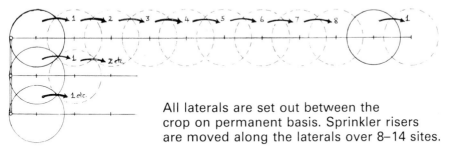

All laterals are set out between the
crop on permanent basis. Sprinkler risers
are moved along the laterals over 8–14 sites.

The Practical Approach to Irrigation

Armed with a full understanding of the principles of irrigation the
grower can decide on a plan of campaign for watering vegetables. It
may be approached any of three ways: *full irrigation*; applying water
when *soil moisture deficit figures* rise above a certain level or using *limited
irrigation* at sensitive periods.

Figure 18 Layouts for self-travelling devices

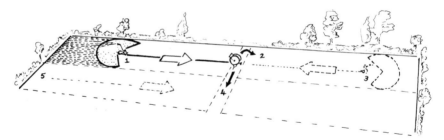

The pipe is unreeled from the
centre of the site to position (1) After
irrigation and reeling in the drum is pivoted 180° to site
(2) The device is unreeled again to site (3) to repeat the process.
The drum is then moved across to a new site (4) before the whole
operation is repeated.

FULL IRRIGATION Returning the soil regularly every day or two to field
capacity on a large field scale is not really practical. To just supply 75
mm of water to a small 6 ha site would take 4,500 cu m (119 million
gal) of water (the capacity of a small reservoir). Full irrigation can only
be carried out on small highly intensive produced crops in frames and
seedbeds where investment for the whole vegetable unit is at stake.

WORKING TO SOIL MOISTURE DEFICIT FIGURES Plants will tolerate a certain degree of moisture stress before crop yields drop away rapidly.
Wait until soil moisture deficit figures reach about 25 mm before use of
equipment. So for self-blanching celery the recommendation is to apply
25 mm of water when there is a soil moisture deficit of 25 mm. The
timing and amount depends on crop type and soil texture. The ability
of different crops to withstand soil moisture deficits varies as does the
water holding capacity of different soils. To work this system means
keeping a water balance sheet. This consists of measuring rainfall
against transpiration figures and balancing them up with irrigation.
The availability of a nearby meteorological station or the recording of
rainfall on your own holding are invaluable in maintaining water balance sheets. They are an important part of any irrigation programme.
In the example water balance sheet (Table 14) there is no soil moisture
deficit. Figures for estimated transpiration are given in evapo-transpiration tables. Later the meteorological office will be able to give actual
figures for transpiration which are used to correct the estimated figures
on a weekly basis.

Table 14: Water balance sheet for irrigation

Date	% crop cover	Weather for the day	Estimated transpiration (mm)	Actual transpiration from Met. Office (mm)	Rainfall received (mm)	Moisture Deficit (mm)	irrigation applied (mm)
July 9	100	Blue skies	4.83		–	4.83	
10	100	Mainly cloudy	2.29		–	7.12	
11	100	Mainly sunny	3.81		–	10.93	
12	100	Blue skies	4.83		–	15.76	
13	100	Blue skies	4.83		–	20.59	
14	100	Overcast	1.27		0.6	21.26	
15	100	Blue skies	4.83		–	26.09	25
		Totals	26.69			1.09	25
Agrometeorological weekly figure for potential transpiration				24.20			
Balancing figures				–2.49	+1.40=(FC)		
Actual Soil Moisture deficit at 15 July							
16	100	Overcast	1.27		0.27	1.00	

Crop cover determines the amount of transpiration.
0–25%   Look up evapo-transpiration tables under different soil types – light, medium and heavy soils.
25–75%   Soil type and weather allowed for in the tables.
75–100% Crop cover – sets of estimated figures for transpiration are given for four weather types . . . overcast, mainly cloudy, mainly sunny, and blue skies.

USE OF LIMITED IRRIGATION AT CROP SENSITIVE PERIODS The use of smaller quantities of water at selected times is the third and most practical approach to irrigation. These moisture sensitive periods are tremendously important because, for relatively small inputs, they give a high return. Two sensitive periods are common to nearly all vegetable plants. Firstly, during establishment at sowing or planting and secondly, two to three weeks before anticipated harvesting date. Legumes are also sensitive at flowering and pod swell. In practice, irrigation will probably consist of a combination of approaches using both limited irrigation techniques and SMD figures. Detailed recommendations are given in the irrigation schedule on page 54.

CROP RESPONSE TO IRRIGATION There is a limit to the amount of irrigation which will continue to bring an increase in viable return from higher yields. In the case of summer cabbage the diminishing returns

Table 15: Irrigation schedule – general recommendations

Crops	Response periods	Time to water	General Recommendations
All crops	At sowing time At planting time	Apr.–Sept.	Bring soil to field capacity
Broad beans	At early flower + pod swell	May–July	Apply 25 mm at 25 mm SMD. Irrigate 25 mm at FLOWERING STAGE
French or dwarf beans	At early flower stage	June–July	At early flower if SMD more than 20 mm. Then 25 mm at 25 mm SMD
Runner beans	Early flowering onward	June–Aug.	At early flower if SMD more than 25 mm. Then 25 mm at 25 mm SMD light soil; 50 mm at 50 SMD on medium soil; 50 mm at 75 SMD retentive soil
Beetroot Carrots	Throughout life	June–Sept.	Where necessary 25 mm at 25 mm SMD. Do not irrigate carrots between sowing and 4 leaf stage
Brussels sprouts	When buttons marble size	Aug.–Oct.	Water well at transplanting, further applications if necessary to establish the crop. Water Brussels sprouts at button marble stage with 25 mm if SMD reaches 40 mm
Winter cauliflower Winter cabbage	Planting to September	July–Sept.	
Leeks	Throughout life	May–Aug.	
Summer cabbage	Throughout life	May–Sept.	Irrigation 25 mm at 25 mm SMD. Then apply 25 mm 10–20 days before cutting expected if SMD reaches 25 mm
Summer cauliflower	20 days before cutting		
Peas	At flowering + pod swell	June–July	Irrigate 25 mm at early flowering plus further 25 mm at pod swell if SMD reaches 25 mm
Spring cabbage (hearted)	20 days before cutting	Apr.–May	Apply 25 mm 10–20 days before cutting expected if SMD reaches 25 mm

Table 15: (*continued*)

Crops	Response periods	Time to water	General Recommendations
Self-blanching celery Summer lettuce Marrows Spinach	Throughout life	July–Aug. Apr.–Aug. May–Aug. May–Aug.	Give 25 mm water at 25 mm SMD. Irrigation of lettuce before 4 leaf stage may reduce plant stand. Blocked lettuce need immediate watering after planting
Salad onions	Throughout life	Apr.–Aug.	Give 25 mm water at 25 mm SMD. Before harvesting to aid lifting
Rhubarb	When pulling has stopped	May–Sept.	Only water if SMD reaches 50 mm. Then apply 50 mm
Radish	Throughout life	Apr.–Aug.	Apply 15 mm water at 15 mm SMD
Turnips	Beginning root swelling onwards	June–July	From root swell onwards give 25 mm water at 25 mm SMD

begin to set in after 75 mm of water have been applied. The response to be expected from irrigation is shown in Table 16. Using this chart extra yield can be calculated for the amount of irrigation applied. In turn this can be converted into extra crop receipts, eg, 25 mm of water applied to 1 hectare of cauliflowers will increase yields by 10 crates per mm of irrigation – 10 × 25 mm = 250 crates. This will bring an increase in crop receipts of 250 × £1.48 a crate = £370. From this has to be deducted the additional costs incurred in producing the extra crop.

Table 16: Irrigation response

Crop	Extra yield tonnes/ha mm
Broad bean	0.04
Runner bean	0.05
French bean (freezing)	0.06
Cabbage (summer)	0.14
Carrots (early)	0.03
Cauliflower (summer)	10 crates
Lettuce (drilled 2 crops)	20 boxes
Onions	0.08
Peas (dried)	0.40
(vining)	0.04
Sprouts	0.04
Potatoes (early)	0.08

Does Irrigation Pay?

The vegetable grower should work out whether the initial capital cost of irrigation is likely to pay for itself. Even then it is a gamble against the most unpredictable of forces – the weather. The tables 17–19 give an approximate guide to the costs of irrigation and the returns . . . and a break-even point has also been calculated to give an indication of which crops are more profitable.

Table 17: The cost of irrigation (including annual running costs) per hectare irrigated (1981)

Costs of setting up and running irrigation are very much determined by the size of area to be irrigated and the system used but the figures below give a rough guide:

| Irrigation source | Total cost of irrigation per hectare/annum | | | |
	up to 20 ha	20–30 ha	30–60 ha	60 ha plus
Direct abstraction systems (using sprinklers, pump and pipework)	£337 (£108)	£315 (£85)	£273 (£69)	£255 (£55)
Stored water systems (using various equipment: pump, pipework and reservoir)	£430 (£101)	£400 (£78)	£350 (£62)	£326 (£49)

Brackets denote the annual running costs of irrigation which are included in the costs of irrigation. These running costs are assessed at maximum usage of equipment and water.

Table 18: Estimate of extra margin in response to irrigation of vegetable crops (before irrigation costs have been deducted)

	Beans broad	Beans dwarf	Beans runner	Cabbage	Carrots (early)	Onions	Peas (dried)	Peas (vining)	Potatoes (early)	Spring Onions	Sprouts
Extra Margin £/ha	166	250	1400	535	135	355	128	130	385	180	230
Water mm/ha in E. Anglia	50	50	*	125	100	100	50	50	125	*	125

Table 19: Estimates of required revenue to break-even on costs by giving an interest rate of return of 15%

Irrigation source	Minimum annual return required to break even in £/ha			
	up to 20 ha	20–30 ha	30–60 ha	60 ha plus
Direct abstraction system	£280	£280	£250	£245
Stored water system	£400	£390	£350	£340

Table 17 shows the total cost of running two types of systems of irrigation – by direct abstraction from rivers, and pumping from a stored water system. The figures are based on a capital cost ranging from £946 for setting up a direct abstraction system to £1,500/ha for a stored water system, with an estimated cost of £1,100/ha for pumps, pipework and water licences. These capital costs have been depreciated over 10 years, the estimated life of the equipment. The running costs, shown in brackets, are based on maximum use of equipment and water.

Table 18 illustrates the sort of response that can be gained from a known amount of irrigation in the drier area of East Anglia.

Table 19. The figures given here show the very minimum amount of revenue required to break-even on the capital investment made. But these are a basic minimum and assume that irrigation is required in the initial years following capitalization. If, due to the haphazard nature of our climate, three wet years were to follow, then these figures would have to be increased by 55 per cent. The figures calculated here are worked on a complex discounting procedure based on the assumption that not every year the total running costs for maximum irrigation will be used – hence the estimate may appear a little lower than you would expect.

So is Irrigation Worthwhile?

At current depressed market prices for vegetables it is clear that capitalization in irrigation equipment, with its very high costs, is a speculative investment. For a handful of crops (potatoes, cabbage, onions and runner beans) irrigation may be profitable but not every crop will bring sufficient return. Despite the pessimistic forecast few growers can really afford to be without some form of irrigation facility. It is the lifeline to success in the germination and harvesting of so many horticultural crops. And in the really dry year the people with irrigation strike it rich.

Table 20: Student summary and memory jogger

What is meant by soil moisture deficit? How does it relate to water application in your area?
Available water capacity = the amount of water available between field capacity and permanent wilting point.
Soil classification determines the amount of irrigation applied and timing.

Breakdown of sources, storage and distribution of water for irrigation

Sources	Storage necessity	Storage type	Distribution determined by	Distribution Equipment
Boreholes	Direct use (no storage required)	Off stream reservoirs	(1) Acreage	Pumps
Watercourses (rivers, streams and lakes)	Storage system required due to limitation on time of abstraction	Dammed Watercourses	(2) Crop ground cover	Pipelines
Mains water		Storage Tanks (up to 454,600 litres) 100,000 galls.)	(3) Labour available	Watering systems
Wells, other sources			(4) Cropping programme	Field crops: (sprinklers, rotating booms, self-travelling sprinklers, rain guns and booms.
			(5) Type of equipment available	Intensive crops: (spraylines)
			(6) Amount of equipment available	Frames and Specialized crops (trickle)
			(7) Accessibility of site	
			(8) Water pressure	

Chapter Four

Brassicas

The British climate, noted for its cool, wet summers and mild winters is ideal for production of most brassicas. Perhaps because of this inherent advantage, Britain is one of Europe's largest producers. The hectarage of major brassica crops in England, Scotland and Wales is: Brussels sprouts 13,554 ha; cabbage and savoys 12,738 ha; cauliflowers (including heading broccoli) 5,850 ha.

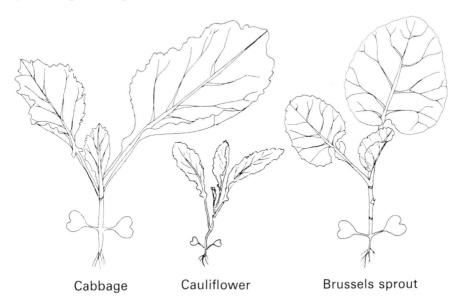

Cabbage   Cauliflower   Brussels sprout

Figure 19 Distinguishing between different brassicas may prove a problem for some people – these diagrams may help. Look at leaf edge, shape and veination.

Brussels Sprouts – *Brassica oleracea var. Gemmifera*

Soils

Medium to heavy soils are preferred for sprout production to obtain an adequate reserve of soil moisture (at least 40 mm per 300 mm or 1⅝in per 1 ft of profile). Organic soils produce over-vegetative plants which do not yield well. Good drainage is also essential. This is more critical where mechanized harvesting results in heavy traffic during the winter period.

Land preparation

A firm soil is required for sprout production, therefore ploughing should be completed before the end of December. If the pH is below 6.5 lime should be applied to raise the pH level to between 6.5 and 7.0. Applications of ground limestone should be made after ploughing and preferably before the end of December. Low pH levels will encourage the development of the soil-borne disease club root.

Nutrition

Fertilizers should be applied prior to breaking the soil down to a seed or transplant tilth. The amount of fertilizer being determined by soil analysis and previous cropping (see Tables 21 and 22). Where a crop is to be direct drilled it is not advisable to apply more than 150 kg/ha of nitrogen in the base dressing. Higher levels can seriously inhibit germination causing an irregular plant stand. Where the nitrogen requirement is in excess of 150 kg/ha the balance should be applied as a top dressing within four weeks of crop emergence.

Plant raising

Sprout propagation may take one of three forms:

(1)   Sowing *under frames or cold structures* from February onwards by drilling or broadcast sowing. Early transplanting (end April) and using early cultivars enables crops to be harvested from August right through to November.

(2)   Sowing *in the open seedbed* from mid March to mid April, with transplanting from mid May to early June gives October to March harvesting.

(3)   *Field drilling* from early April to mid May enables the grower to harvest from early October to March.

   The soil used for raising transplants must be free from soil-borne diseases, particularly club root. A base dressing (see Table 22) should be applied and the pH raised to 6.5–7.0. Seeds can be broadcast in the seedbed or drilled by use of a small drill unit, aiming at a stand of 450

Table 21: Table of recommended fertilizer rates (kg nutrient per ha for transplanted or direct-drilled crops)

Nutrient index (as quoted by ADAS)	Phosphate P_2O_5	Potash K_2O	Magnesium		Nitrogen	
			Sandy soil	Other soils		
0	200	300	90	60	300	If rainfall greatly
1	125	250	60	30	250	exceeds
2	6̲0̲	1̲5̲0̲	NIL	NIL	200	transpiration
3	60	50	–	–	–	within two
Over 3	NIL	NIL	–	–	–	months of applying basal nitrogen, a supplementary top dressing may be necessary, irrespective of base nitrogen levels.

If a soil anaysis is not available use the values underlined in the tables.
Field drilled crops and transplants on light soils – a maximum of 150 kg/ha nitrogen should be applied in base dressing. The remainder as a top dressing within one month of emergence or transplanting.

Table 22: Recommended fertilizer rates for seedbeds (g/m^2 of glasshouse or border soil)

Nutrient index (as quoted by ADAS)	Triple super-phosphate	Sulphate of potash	Keiserite Mg	Ammonium Nitrate N
0	140	140	140	50
1	100	100	100	35
2	100	70	70	1̲5̲
3	70	3̲5̲	N̲I̲L̲	35
4	3̲5̲	NIL	NIL	NIL
5	NIL	NIL	NIL	NIL

If a soil analysis is not available use the values underlined in the table.
(100 g/m^2 = 3 oz/sq yd of soil bed).

plants per m² or 42 per ft². Drilling enables more accurate control of seed densities as well as more uniform covering of seed.

Transplanting

Previously ploughed land should be broken down to a planting tilth with a spring tine cultivator maintaining an adequate level of consolidation without producing a soft and loose tilth (as per a rotavator). Transplants should be rogued for sibs and graded during the pulling operation. Once lifted the plants should be set out in shallow layers in polythene lined trays, each tray being covered with polythene once it is filled. Exposure to wind and bright sunshine must be avoided as rapid desiccation will result. Time between lifting and replanting should be kept to a minimum. If planting is delayed, pulled plants should be stored as cool as possible until planting restarts.

Planting is normally carried out by machine (see planting machinery page 199) and to eliminate another operation a pesticide granule applicator can be fitted to the machine.

Direct seeding

The direct seeded crop requires a larger quantity of seed in a more costly form, ie, graded seed is required. The most economical method is to use the group sowing method. This involves placement of three to four seeds in a group 25–35 mm (1–1½ in) apart at the final spacing (approximately 900 mm or 3 ft along the row). (See 'Field drilling – group spacing' page 24).

Plant densities

The spacing and density of the crop will be influenced by a number of factors:
(a) machinery to be used on the crops
(b) method of harvesting to be employed
(c) the outlet for which the crop is destined
(d) cultivar – modern hybrids perform better at high densities
(e) period over which the crop is to be harvested

Densities may range from the traditional 1.2 plants per m² (900 mm × 900 mm) (36 in × 36 in) to 4 plants per m² (530 mm × 530 mm) (21 in × 21 in). Densities higher than this offer no great advantage. The optimum density for maximum marketable yield is about 3.6 plants per m² (0.33 per ft²). Increasing densities above this level incurs the law of diminishing returns.

The general rule is to use lower densities for hand harvesting or self-pick, giving better access for the pickers. Increased densities favour machine harvesting since this gives longer plant stem lengths resulting in sprouts more widely spaced on the stem and of uniform size. The increased density results in smaller sprouts, much favoured for the freezing trade but not popular with most fresh market outlets.

Cultivars (see Table 23)

Sprout cultivars fall into two main categories – open pollinated forms and F_1 hybrids. Despite the high cost of F_1 seed most modern cultivars are of this type. They offer a two-fold advantage when grown for destructive harvest (single harvest system) – a more uniform plant stand and buttons mature more evenly along the stem length when grown at high densities, ie, above 27,800/ha or 600 × 600 mm spacing (11,250/acre or 2 ft × 2 ft spacing.)

In addition to high cost the F_1 hybrid has the disadvantage of contamination with self-in-bred seed (sibs for short). These are seeds which result from inbreeding of one or other of the parent lines. Sib plants have very low productivity and are best rogued out at a very early stage when lifting transplants. High sib levels can be a serious disadvantage. Many breeders now include an indicator gene in the breeding to give sib plants an easily recognized characteristic such as very glossy leaves.

Herbicide treatment

There is a wide choice of herbicides for use in brassica crops, but treatments may be placed in five categories. A combination of two or more categories are normally required for effective weed control.

PRE-DRILLING OR PRE-PLANTING RESIDUAL HERBICIDES Trifluralin is the main herbicide in this group. It is applied at 2–3 l/ha (28–43 fl oz/acre) after the soil has been broken down to the required tilth and must be incorporated into the top 50–100 mm (2–4 in) by harrowing or rotary cultivation. Failure to do so will result in rapid loss of herbicide due to its volatile nature. Trifluralin is not effective on organic soils and should not be used on light sandy soils.

PRE-EMERGENCE OR PRE-PLANTING CONTACT HERBICIDES Paraquat and diquat mixtures at 3–5.5 l/ha (43–80 fl oz/acre) may be used to control annual weeds prior to seedling emergence or pre-planting. Contact herbicides may damage crops if used too late when seedlings are beginning to emerge.

PRE-EMERGENCE RESIDUAL HERBICIDES These materials are applied to weed free ground soon after sowing. Any delay in application may give an opportunity for weed seeds to germinate and reach a stage where they are not controlled by residual treatment. Most of these residuals give weed control for six to eight weeks after application provided the soil is not disturbed.

Table 23: Continuity of cropping using different cultivars (1982)

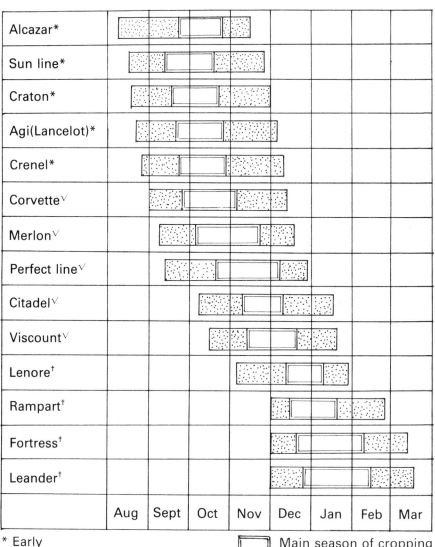

	Aug	Sept	Oct	Nov	Dec	Jan	Feb	Mar
Alcazar*								
Sun line*								
Craton*								
Agi(Lancelot)*								
Crenel*								
Corvette[∨]								
Merlon[∨]								
Perfect line[∨]								
Citadel[∨]								
Viscount[∨]								
Lenore[†]								
Rampart[†]								
Fortress[†]								
Leander[†]								

* Early
∨ Mid
† Late

☐ Main season of cropping

▨ Extension to season

Eg, Chlorthal-dimethyl 6 kg/ha (5.35 lb/acre) – normally applied with propachlor as a tank mix.

Propachlor 7 kg/ha (6.25 lb/acre) – normally used in conjunction with another herbicide to obtain a better weed control spectrum. Normal mixes include chlorthal-dimethyl + propachlor and trifluralin followed by propachlor.

Nitrofen 4.9 1/ha   (70 fl oz/acre) – sprayed within three days of drilling gives good control of annual weeds provided there is a good fine tilth. Not suitable on organic soils. Heavy rainfall immediately after application may cause damage.

POST PLANTING RESIDUAL HERBICIDES   These are applied to transplanted crops as soon as the crop has recovered from the initial transplanting check. It is important that these herbicides are applied before any weed growth starts.

Eg, Propachlor + chlorthal-dimethyl (as opposite)

Propachlor applied after trifluralin has been incorporated pre-planting.

Chlorthal-dimethyl + methazole (Delozin S) at 6 kg/ha (5.35 lb/acre) combines two very effective herbicides. Methazole is absorbed and translocated by weed foliage in addition to having residual properties, so may control young emerging weed seedlings.

POST EMERGENCE OR POST PLANTING FOLIAGE ACTING HERBICIDES   These are often applied as a follow up to residual treatments when weeds are at an early stage of growth.

Eg, Aziprotryne 4 kg/ha   (3.57 lb/acre) – this herbicide is both foliage acting and residual. The crop must have at least three true leaves before treatment, but weeds are controlled only up to three true leaf stage. Aziprotryne is not suitable for use on light soils.

Desmetryne 1.1–1.7   kg/ha (1–1.5 lb/acre) – this herbicide is purely foliage acting. The crop is protected from damage by the waxy nature of brassica leaves. The rate of application has to be adjusted according to the condition of the leaf wax on the crop plant. Lower rates should be used during wet weather. Susceptible weeds are controlled up to 100 mm (4 in) in height.

Singling or thinning

Field drilled crops will require thinning to a specific density, either by machine or by hand. Singling group sown crops to singles is easy whereas the job requires much more skill and judgement in plant spacing when sown by traditional methods.

When singling F_1 hybrid crops any sibs should be removed in preference to F_1 seedlings. Any hand or machine singling operation causes considerable soil disturbance so it should be carried out before the second treatment of a two-fold herbicide programme.

Irrigation – see Chapter 3

Stopping

Stopping consists of removing the growing point from the plant. This accelerates the development of the uppermost buttons. The technique can be used to adjust the date of maturity. Crops sown and planted on the same dates can be brought to harvest stage in a four-week succession by use of four different stopping dates. The effectiveness of stopping to bring forward harvesting date diminishes as the season progresses and is non-effective after the end October.

Timing of stopping is related to harvest date – about four weeks before harvest in August and ten weeks prior to harvest for December crops. Stopping too early leads to 'blowing' of upper sprouts. As a guide, commence stopping when 50 per cent of basal sprouts are 12 mm (½ in) in diameter.

De-leafing

This should be carried out just prior to harvest (two days maximum) otherwise yields will be reduced, especially on early crops. Also, most sprout harvesting machines work best when leaves are stripped in advance. Hand de-leafing can be carried out in several ways – using the hands to break the leaves, or cutting with beet knives and circular cutting blades.

Field harvesting

Field harvests commence from August onwards and the main harvesting systems are:
(1)   Hand harvest – direct picked into nets in the field
(2)   Hand cutting of stems – for machine stripping in the field
             – for machine stripping in the packing shed
(3)   Machine harvesting   – semi-automatic machines usually employ one operator per row to transfer the cut stem to the stripping head
             – fully automatic machines require only one

operator to steer, adjust height of cut and generally supervise as the operation proceeds

Grading and marketing for the fresh market

Where the crop is to be marketed fresh, grading should conform to EEC regulations (see Chapter 11 on Marketing).

Sprouts for processing outlets are graded in sizes, the smaller sprouts (13–20 mm or ½ in–¾ in) attracting the highest prices. Sprouts for processing have to be trimmed, which is carried out manually by casual labour or by machines. Very early crops which command a high price may be marketed in non-returnable trays, of 4 kg (9 lb). The bulk of the crop is marketed in 20 lb in green nets but this will soon change to 10 kg. Sprouts for the supermarkets are packed into 500 g or 1 kg units using a netting sleeve sealed at each end.

Market pack of Brussels sprouts labelled to EEC standards.

Anticipated yield

	Picked over	Single harvest
Average yield –	17.5 tonnes/ha (7.2 tons/acre)	13.5 tonnes/ha (5.6 tons/acre)
Good commercial yield –	22.5 tonnes/ha (9.2 tons/acre)	17.5 tonnes/ha (7.2 tons/acre

Pests and diseases

See pages 82–85 for details of important brassica pests and diseases and Chapter 12 for summary chart.

Cabbage – *Brassica oleracea Capitata*

Cabbage crops are harvested almost all the year round, using different types of cabbage for the various seasons. (For details of cultivars see Table 26.)

Table 24: Continuity of production using different types of cabbage.

	J	J	A	S	O	N	D	J	F	M	A	M
Early Summer	▒	▒										
Summer		▒	▒	▒								
Savoys					▒	▒	▒	▒	▒	▒		
Dutch White						▒	▒	▒				
January King & January King × Savoy Hybrids							▒	▒	▒	▒		
Spring Greens										▒	▒	▒
Spring Cabbage											▒	▒

Soils

Cabbages are tolerant of a wide range of soils. The lighter ones are preferred for early production. Good drainage assumes extra importance for winter maturing and over wintered crops. Impeded drainage not only restricts crop growth but limits the use of harvesting machinery and transportation of winter crops.

Soil pH should be maintained between 6.5 and 7.0 to help suppress club root disease.

Cultivations

As for Brussels sprouts (see page 60).

Fertilizers

The crop responds well to high soil fertility, and bulky organic matter may be incorporated during the primary cultivations, if available. A base dressing applied 10 to 14 days prior to planting or sowing supplies most of the nutrients. The rate of application will depend on soil analysis, soil type and previous management.

Table 25: Recommended fertilizer rates (kg nutrient per hectare)

Nutrient index (as quoted by ADAS)	Phosphate P_2O_5	Potash K_2O	Magnesium		Nitrogen					
			Sandy soil	Other soils	Early Summer	Summer & Autumn	Winter and Savoy Pre Christ.	Post Christ.	Dutch White	Spring greens and cabbage
0	200	300	90	60	250	300	300	150	150	75
1	125	250	60	30	200	250	250	125	125	50
2	60	150	NIL	NIL	125	200	200	100	100	26
3	60	50	–	–	–	–	–	–	–	–
> 3	NIL	NIL	–	–	–	–	–	–	–	–
Top Dressing					60–120	*1	*1	0–75 *2	*1	190–380

If a soil analysis is not available use the values underlined in the table.

*(1) Direct drilled crops or transplants on light soils should not receive more than 150 kg/ha of nitrogen, the balance applied as a top dressing within four weeks of emergence or planting.

*(2) Crops for early harvest should only require smaller rates of top dressing. Crops which will be fully matured at harvest will respond to the higher levels of top dressing, but relate to weather conditions and potential market period.

The nitrogen requirement can be supplied by the base dressing with pre-Christmas maturing crops or may be split between the base dressing and a top dressing. The latter is necessary for post-Christmas maturing crops.

Plant raising

(see Table 26 for sowing dates for year round production) Cabbage plants may be raised in three ways.

CONTAINER GROWN PLANTS Cabbage sown into peat blocks, Japanese paper pots or similar low cost module. Confined to the high value crops such as early summer cabbage.

Production costs are high and a machine capable of planting block or pot raised plants must be available (small scale enterprises may be able to hand plant).

DRAWN OR PEG PLANTS Seed drilled into the border soil under protection or into open seed bed, transplanted bare root.

Widely used for all cabbage crops, enables grading of the plants and pre-planting dips. Reduces the length of time the crop occupies its cropping position.

FIELD DRILLED   The crop is drilled in its final position and singled to the required density early in the crop's life, widely used for spring cabbage (greens and hearted) and Dutch white storage cabbages. Elimination of transplanting and the associated check can be useful with summer raised crops which are subjected to high levels of water stress. It also reduces the high labour input required for planting.

PRODUCTION OF EARLY SUMMER (BLOCK RAISED) PLANTS   Early cultivars which are resistant to bolting should be selected for production of the very early summer crops.

The seed is sown direct into 3.8 cm peat blocks (1½ in blocks) from February 20 to the end of February. The seed is germinated at 12–15°C, once germination has taken place the temperature can be reduced to 10–12°C for growing on (temperatures below 10°C may result in a percentage of the crop bolting) until the end of March. A gradual hardening off should be started two weeks before planting, which is normally in mid April.

DRAWN PLANT RAISING   As per Brussels sprouts page 60.

DIRECT DRILLED CROPS   As per Brussels sprouts page 62, see Table 26 for spacings.

Planting
Planting of container grown plants is normally carried out by machine – for details see Chapter 10, 'Transplanting Machinery'.

Herbicides – as per Brussels sprouts page 63.

Thinning (direct drilled crops) – as per Brussels sprouts page 60.

Irrigation
Irrigation can be valuable for establishment of transplants, and to provide adequate moisture prior to drilling to ensure quick and uniform germination of direct drilled crops. Cabbages respond to irrigation at all stages of growth but maximum response is derived by irrigating three weeks prior to harvest (see Irrigation page 33).

Pest and disease control – see Brassica pest and disease control page 82.

Harvesting
Crops maturing during the summer and early autumn are normally harvested as soon as the plant has a good solid heart. Delay in har-

vesting these crops usually results in splitting of the outer heart leaves which detracts from the quality of the crop.

Crops maturing during the late autumn and winter (October–February) can be harvested as required for marketing. Dutch white cabbage is one of the most temperature sensitive of the winter crops and may be damaged during severe frosts. To overcome this risk the Dutch white crop can be harvested in late October–early November and barn stored to give a regular supply for marketing up to early March.

Spring maturing crops may be marketed before the crop has reached the hearted stage. In this case the time of harvest is largely dictated by the market demand and price. Early harvest will result in a lower total weight per hectare which must be offset by the higher price per kg obtained.

Grading see grading chart page 212.

Packing and marketing

The higher value cabbage crops are normally packed into non returnable wood veneer or composite crates. With between 10 and 14 kg per crate (20–30 lb) according to the requirements of the market. Lower value crops are marketed in green vegetable nets in the same weight range.

Storage

Dutch white cabbage is the only one put into long term storage by the grower. Where this crop can be successfully stored it reduces the risk of frost damage, eliminates traffic in the field during the wettest time of the year and eases pressure on the outdoor labour force (pack shed labour will be required for post storage trimming prior to marketing).

Anticipated yields

	Early (loose)	Mid/late (loose)	Hearted
Spring cabbage			
– Average yield	11.4 tonnes/ha	17 tonnes/ha	19.6 tonnes/ha
	(4.7 tons/acre)	(7 tons/acre)	(8.1 tons/acres)
– Good commercial yield	14.4 tonnes/ha	26.6 tonnes/ha	30.6 tonnes/ha
	(5.9 tons/acre)	(10.9 tons/acre)	(12.6 tons/acre)

	Celtic Type	Winter white	
Winter cabbage			
– Average yield	32 tonnes/ha	60.5 tonnes/ha	
	(13.2 tons/acre)	(24.9 tons/acre)	
– Good commercial yield	64 tonnes/ha	90 tonnes/ha	
	(26.4 tons/acre)	(37 tons/acre)	

	Early summer	Summer	
Summer cabbage			
– Average yield	32 tonnes/ha	54.4 tonnes/ha	
	(13.2 tons/acre)	(22.4 tons/acre)	
– Good commercial yield	50 tonnes/ha	85 tonnes/ha	
	(20.6 tons/acre)	(35 tons/acre)	

Table 26: A guide to cabbage production method for all harvest times

Sowing Date Field Drilled	Sowing Date/ Transplanted	Example of Cultivars	Plant Density and Spacing	Approximate Harvest Date	Comments
N/A	20 Feb. Direct into blocks (slight heat)	Derby Day Hornspi	8.33/m² 300 × 400 mm 12″ × 16″	Early–End June	Best suited to early areas
N/A	Early Feb. Cold Frames	Hispi	6.25–8.33/m² 300–400 × 400 mm (12″–16″ × 16″)	End June– Early July	
	Late Feb. Cold Frames	Goldenacre			
Early April	Mid March Cold Frames	Histona Greyhound	As above	Mid–End July	
2nd–3rd week April	Early April	Hispi Cape Horn	6.25/m² 400 × 400 mm 16″ × 16″	End July Early Aug.	
Mid May	First week May	Histona Buderich	3.70–4.44/m² 500–600 × 450mm (20–24 × 18″)	Mid–End August	
End May	Mid May	Minicole Predena	3.70/m² 600 × 450 mm (24″ × 18″)	Early September	
End May	Mid May	Stonehead Histanda	As above	Mid–End September	
End April– Early May	Mid April	Hidena Bartolo Polinus	1.85–2.78/m² 600 × 600 mm to 600 × 900 mm 24″ × 24″ to 24″ × 36″	October–End December	Dutch white storage cabbage may be barn stored or allowed to stand in the field
Early June	Mid May– Late May	Wiam Erdeno	3.80/m² 650 × 500 mm (26″ × 20″)	October	Savoy cabbages
Early June	Mid May– Late May	Late Green Winter Custodian	As above	November– December	
Early June (5–7 app.)	Mid May– Early June	January King 3 Celtic Celsa	As above	January February Early March	
Early June	Mid May– Late May	Novum Ice Prince Hiversa	As above	Nov. – Dec. January February	Savoy cabbages
Early July– Late July	April	Durham Early Myatts Offenham Compacta	17.54–26.32/m² 380 × 100–150 mm 15″ × 4″–6″	Late July Jan.–Feb. February – March	Spring greens. Not usually transplanted

Table 26: (*continued*)

Sowing Date Field Drilled	Sowing Date/ Transplanted	Example of Cultivars	Plant Density and Spacing	Approximate Harvest Date	Comments
Mid August	End July	Wheelers Imperial Harbringer	11.70/m² 380 × 225 mm 15″ × 9″	Late March –April	Hearted spring cabbage
Mid August	End July	Durham Elf Clipper Myatts Off. Compacta	8.77–11.7/m² 380 × 225–300 mm 15″ × 9–12″	Mid April –May	Hearted spring cabbage

N/A = not applicable

Calabrese – *Brassica oleracea var. Italica*

This vegetable is a comparative newcomer to commercial production, though long grown by the gardener. It is related to the cauliflower and like that crop it produces a central immature flower head, which when harvested gives rise to smaller lateral heads lower down the stem.

Soils
Though tolerant of a wide range of soils, medium to light loams are preferable. Heavy soils are not suitable as accurate plant population cannot be achieved with certainty due to variable emergence. The crop is sensitive to water stress and crops grown on sandy soils will require irrigation during dry periods. The soil pH should be at least 6.5.

Fertilizers
The nutritional requirements of this crop are not so well understood as those of the major vegetable crops, but the recommendations are as follows.

N 180–250 kg/ha P_2O_5 75–125 kg/ha K_2O 100–125 kg/ha

Soils low in Boron should also receive a dressing of Borax or Solubar.

Soil preparation – as for Brussels sprouts.

Plant raising
This crop is almost exclusively direct drilled to a stand because of the high densities which are normally involved. (For calculation of sowing rate see Propagation Chapter 2.)

Sowings may be made from April to late June at approximately 14-

day intervals. The crop will not hold in the field so the area drilled must be related to labour available for harvest, as well as market demand.

Plant densities

For the fresh market the crop may be grown at densities as low as 10–12 plants m^2 (1/ft^2) with rows 380 mm (18 in) to 600 mm (24 in) apart. This results in a large primary head and a long harvest period. Where small primary heads are required a high density must be used – plant populations of 20 plants/m^2 (2/ft^2) will give the maximum proportion of the heads in the 65 mm (2½ in) size range as required for processing or prepacking. The high density crops should be grown on a 1420–1524 mm (56–60 in) bed system with four rows 225 mm (8.86 in) apart in each bed. The 600 mm (24 in) spaces between beds act as paths from which to harvest the crop.

Cultivars

There are a large range of cultivars from which the grower may choose. The requirements of a cultivar for processing are very specific – high yielding, even maturing heads of compact shape which do become open to flower. The most popular cultivar in Scotland is Corvet, but other useful processing calabrese include Premium Crop, Hybrid Gem, Southern Comet and SG 1.

For the fresh market or the self-pick trade the requirements may well be different. Some cultivars, like Dandy, mature over a very short period, while others have a very long period of heading. This gives a much higher yield as much of the production is made up of secondary heads, and cultivars like Southern Comet and Atlantic fall into this category.

Herbicides – as for cauliflowers.

Pest and disease control – as for cauliflowers.

Harvesting

Harvesting usually starts 70 to 100 days after sowing, depending on cultivar and season. High density crops will have only the small primary heads harvested. With low density crops secondary heads will develop and give a longer period of harvest. The season extends from early July until the first frost.

The heads must be cut while still in the tight bud. So twice a week harvesting is essential in warm weather, once per week in cool weather.

To achieve an acceptable rate of work, picking bag or baskets hung from the neck and shoulders should be used so that both hands are kept free for picking.

The picked heads deteriorate very rapidly if they can not be dispatched immediately they should be kept cool – preferably by precooling or placing in a cold store.

Marketing
The crop may be packed into chip baskets with 2 kg (4 lb) per chip or in cardboard or solid board trays with 3–4 kg (6–8 lb/tray).

Anticipated yield
Mean average yield – 2 tonnes/ha (0.8 tons/acre).
Good commercial yield – 5.5 tonnes/ha (2.3 tons/acre).

Pests and diseases – see details on page 82 and Pests and Diseases Chapter 12.

Cauliflower – *Brassica oleracea var. Cauliflora*

The cauliflower was described by Mark Twain as 'a cabbage with a college education', perhaps reflecting the many problems the cauliflower presents during its production. As a crop it is very prone to physiological disorders and is very uneven in its maturity.

The cauliflower crop can be split into five main groups based on production time and varietal group (see Table 28 for cultivars and year round production).

EARLY SUMMER CAULIFLOWERS Alpha, Danish and le Cerf cultivars. The crop is raised in the autumn and overwintered under protection prior to planting out and gives a May–June harvest.

SUMMER CAULIFLOWERS Cultivar groups as above. The crop is spring sown under protection and in open seed beds to mature July–August.

AUTUMN CAULIFLOWERS Mainly based on Australian cultivars which show a distinct curd form. They are more resistant to high temperature induced physiological problems than others grown to mature from September to early November.

WINTER HEADING CAULIFLOWERS (HEADING BROCCOLI) The Roscoff cultivar group. Production of these is confined to very mild areas of Cornwall and Devon.

WINTER HARDY SPRING HEADING Production of this crop has increased greatly in the eastern counties. The crop overwinters in the field to give an April to May harvest.

Early summer cauliflowers

This can be a valuable crop for the small intensive grower who can achieve a very early crop by raising plants in 9 cm (3½ in) plastic pots. A container of this size requires hand planting which precludes larger growers who rely on mechanical planting techniques.

Plant raising

The sowing date for this crop is critical. The late cultivars, like Dominant, should be sown during the last week of September and the early cultivars like Romax Early are sown during the first 10 days of October. Within this range of dates, the latest should be sown first and the earliest last. Earlier sowings merely cause a very high percentage of buttoning.

Seed may be sown in three ways. Sowing into seed trays of seed compost 200–250 seeds per tray – mainly used for crops which are pricked out singly into plastic pots. Sowing direct into peat blocks or Japanese paper pots one seed per module – the labour saving method for large scale production. Sowing seed into border soil of frames or glasshouses for raising drawn or peg plants. These are later maturing but give continuity.

Container type, size and order of maturity

9 cm (3½ in) plastic pots – earliest
7 cm (2¾ in) peat blocks or Japanese paper pots – a week later (approx.)
4 cm (1½ in) peat blocks or Japanese paper pots – two weeks later (approx.)
Drawn plants approximately 10–14 days later than smallest container.

Overwintered plants

The plants are usually overwintered under cold glass. Attempts at overwintering under plastic structures have usually resulted in serious problems with downy mildew (*Peronospera parsitica*). Provided certain routine precautions are taken the plants require little attention during the winter months other than occasional watering. Avoid overwatering and ventilate freely except during frosty weather.

Routine precautions should be taken to control downy mildew, slugs, and mice.

Plants should be ready for planting from early March and hardening off of the plants should be started at least two weeks in advance of the anticipated planting date.

Summer, autumn and winter crops

Plant raising is as for transplanted Brussels sprouts. Field drilling of cauliflower is not widely practised but techniques described for Brussels sprouts would again apply.

Soils

Cauliflowers require a fertile soil and incorporation of farmyard manure (FYM) or bulky organic manure should prove beneficial. Medium texture soils with a good structure and good drainage are preferable, with pH of 6.5 to 7.0 to discourage club root disease. Where possible land should only be cropped with brassicas one year in four.

Table 27: Recommended fertilizer rates for cauliflower (kg nutrient per hectare)

Nutrient index	Phosphate P_2O_5	Potash K_2O	Magnesium Sandy soil	Other soils	Nitrogen Early summer, Summer and autumn	Winter heading	Winter hardy spring heading
0	200	300	90	60	250	75	75
1	125	250	60	30	200	40	40
2	60	200	NIL	NIL	125	NIL	NIL
3	60	125	–	–	–	–	–
4	NIL	60	–	–	–	–	–
>4	NIL	NIL	–	–	–	–	–
Top Dressing	–	–	–	–	See note (i)	60–125 See note (ii)	125–200 See note (iii)

If a soil analysis is not available use the values underlined in the table.
(i) For transplants on lighter soils and all field drilled crops no more than 150 kg/ha nitrogen should be applied in the base dressing. The balance should be top dressed within one month of transplanting or crop emergence.
(ii) Crops for February cutting in frost free areas should be top dressed in late autumn. Crops for harvest after mid February top dress in mid February.
(iii) Top dress during the period January to March.

Spacing (see Table 28)

The optimum density or spacing for cauliflowers varies with cultivar, season and the type of market outlet. Higher densities give smaller curds but tend to give lower curd quality.

Early Summer and Summer Crops:

600 mm × 450 mm – Normal field layout
(24 in × 18 in)

530 mm × 530 mm – Bed system
(21 in × 21 in)

Autumn Crops – large cultivars

685 mm × 685 mm – Field layout
(27 in × 27 in)

600 mm × 600 mm (min) – Bed system
(24 in × 24 in)

– compact cultivars

550 mm × 550 mm (none shown in Table 28)
(22 in × 22 in)

Winter Hardy Crops

670 mm × 670 mm – Most cultivars
(26 in × 26 in)

740 mm × 740 mm – Dutch
(30 in × 30 in)

Weed control

Of all brassicas, cauliflowers are the most difficult crop in which to achieve good weed control as they will not tolerate the normal post-emergence herbicides. It is, therefore, essential to get a good level of weed control, either pre-emergence or immediately post planting. Various methods can be adopted:

FIELD DRILLED CROPS

Example 1

Pre-drilling – trifluralin incorporated into the top 50–150 mm (2.3 1/ ha) (33 fl oz/acre).

Pre-emergence – propachlor applied within three days of drilling (6.75 kg/ha.) (6 lb/acre).

Example II

Pre-emergence – chlorthal-dimethyl + propachlor (6 kg/ha + 7kg/ha) (Dacthal + Ramrod)   (5.3 lb/acre + 6.25 lb/acre).

TRANSPLANTED CROP

(a) Pre-planting – trifluralin (as above) + propachlor post-planting (rates as above).

(b) Post planting – chlorthal-dimethyl + propachlor (rates as above).

(c) Immediately post planting – methazole + chlorthal-dimethyl (Delozin-S) 6 kg/ha (5.3 lb/acre).

This is best applied before the crop recovers from the transplanting check. Slight leaf chlorosis may occur, but the crop should soon grow out of this without any effect on yield or quality.

(d)   Simazine may be used post planting at 850 g/ha (12 oz/acre). This material may cause damage if used on the lighter soils.

Irrigation

Summer and autumn cultivars respond throughout their life. The soil is returned to field capacity when an SMD of 25 mm is reached. If irrigation facilities are limited the best response is approximately 20 days before cutting when up to 50 mm should be applied if the SMD is 50 mm or more.

Winter cauliflowers often require water after planting to help establishment, but are unlikely to require any further irrigation except in very dry seasons.

Harvesting

The cauliflower crop is very variable in maturity and must be selected and cut by hand at regular intervals. The crop may be packed straight into crates, or more frequently into trailers or tractor mounted bulk bins for transport to the packing shed where the crop can be graded and packed. Summer crops in warm weather may require harvesting at least three times a week. While winter crops in cool weather would only be harvested once per week. It is traditional to trim the cauliflowers as they are cut leaving two rows of wrapper leaves to protect the curd.

Grading and packing

For most market outlets the crop requires grading. This may be done in the field or in the pack shed. The latter is easier and more efficient, in addition to offering more favourable conditions for the work force. The crop may be marketed in four grades: extra class, class I, class II and class III. Unless demand is very high class III grade would not be marketed. Many growers do not use the extra class, thus grading is reduced to two classes. Non returnable crates, solid board boxes or composite crates are used for marketing the crop. The number of curds per crate varies with size, the usual counts being 12, 18, 24 or 30 (see grading chart page 214).

Storage

Cauliflowers can be stored in a refrigerated store for a short period (up to one week); temperature should be 1.5°C and relative humidity 90–95 per cent. Curds cut for storage should be cut immediately they are ready (over-mature curds do not store well). Trimming must be very light to allow a light retrimming before market. If using direct refrigerated stores the crop must be stored in polythene lined bins or wrapped in polythene to prevent desiccation.

Anticipated yield

Early summer cauliflower:
- average yield, 1,153 crates/ha (467 crates/acre)
- good commercial yield, 1,565 crates/ha (606 crates/acre)

Late summer/early autumn cauliflower:
- average yield, 1,195 crates/ha (478 crates/acre)
- good commercial yield, 1,672 crates/ha (667 crates/acre)

Late autumn cauliflower:
- average yield, 1,228 crates/ha (497 crates/acre)
- good commercial yield, 1,424 crates/ha (570 crates/acre)

Winter heading cauliflower:
- average yield, 813 crates/ha (329 crates/acre)
- good commercial yield, 1,251 crates/ha (500 crates/acre)

Pests and diseases

By far the most important pest of cauliflower is cabbage root fly – see following pages for details. See Chapter 12 for full chart of pests and diseases.

Table 28: Cauliflowers for year round production

Sowing date	Cultivar	Density & Spacing	Approximate Harvest date	Comments	Planting time
CAULIFLOWER – SUMMER AND AUTUMN					
First 10 days October	Romax Early Starla Alpha	450 × 600 mm (18″ × 24″) to 520 × 520 mm (21″ × 21″)	End May early June	Container grown and overwintered under cold glass	March
Last week September	Corvilia Delta Dominant		Mid-late June		March
Early October	Delira Nevada		Early–mid July	Drilled in border soil, cold glass	March
Early March (cold frames)	King Dominant		Mid–late July		Late April May
Late March (cold frames)	Delira Nevada		Early–mid August		May
Mid–late April or April (frames)	Lecerf Lawyna		Mid–late August		Early June
Early May (frames or open seedbed)	Flora Blanca Parnas Coolabah		Early–mid September	Australian crop	Mid June

Table 28:(*continued*)

Sowing date	Cultivar	Density & Spacing	Approximate Harvest date	Comments	Planting time
CAULIFLOWER – SUMMER AND AUTUMN					
Mid May (open seed bed)	Wallaby Coolabah	600 × 600 mm (24″ × 24″) to 685 × 685 mm (27″ × 27″) depending on curd size required.	Mid–late September	7 week planting harvest	Late June
″	Orco Barrier Reef		October	Flora Blanca cross Australian	Early July
″	Snowy River Late Supreme		Late October November		
WINTER HEADING CAULIFLOWER BROCCOLI					
May	St. Swithian	710 × 710 mm or (28″ × 28″)	Late November	Roscoff	Aim to complete planting by mid July. Plant late cultivars first. Planting too early causes high percentage buttoning. Late planting reduces yield and gives small curds size 180–230 cm 7–9″ tall
May	St. Agnes		Late December	suitable	
May	Lamorna		Late December Early January	for use	
May	St. Hilary		Late January Early February	in the south	
May	Trevean Fourth		Early–mid February	only	
May	St. David		Late February Early March		
May	St. Keverne		Mid March Early April		
May	Trevean Sixth	710 × 600 mm or (28″ × 24″)	Mid April		
May	Seale Hayne No. 5 RxA (5)		Late April	Not a true Roscoff, therefore not fully resistant to ring spot	
May	St. Mark		May	British cultivar – Late	
May	Vision		Early–mid June		
WINTER HARDY SPRING HEADING					
Early–late May (open seed bed)	Preminda	670 × 670mm or (26″ × 26″)	Late March	Very early. Vigorous (Armada Primo)	June
″	Heralda		Early April		Early–mid July
″	Amardo April		Mid April	Good winter hardiness Solid curds	″
″	March Past		Mid April	High % marketable head and high % class I	Early-mid July
″	Aprilex		Late April	Leaves broad and low – gives good curd protection	″
″	Amanda May		Early May	Reliable	″

Table 28: (*continued*)

Sowing date	Cultivar	Density & Spacing	Approximate Harvest date	Comments	Planting time
WINTER HARDY SPRING HEADING					
"	Marketane		Mid May	Heavy Yielding, uniform	"
"	May Star	670 × 670 or (26" × 26")	Late May	Very high marketable yield. Low level of ricey curds.	"
"	Amardo olio		End May– early June	Very white deep curds	"
"	Mirado		Early-mid June	Round loose grained	"

If field drilling, drill 2–3 weeks after sowing date recommended for a transplanted crop.

Brassica Pests and Diseases and Control

Pests

CABBAGE ROOT FLY   (*Erioischia brassicae*) This tiny fly is a pest in the larval stage, which feeds on the main roots causing wilting and death of the plant. Egg laying starts between late April and mid May; which normally coincides with the flowering of cow parsley (acting as a useful time indicator). Of the three generations per year, the first (end April to June) is the most damaging, frequently attacking seedling crops. Later generations damage established plants, and surface root feeding allows rotting organisms to enter which may result in rotting of sprout crops. Control measures are aimed at killing the larvae as they hatch from the eggs which are laid on the soil close to the neck of the plant.

Where cabbage root fly occurs in seedbeds, it is controlled as follows.

If plants remain in seedbed after egg laying starts overall treatments are applied:

Carbofuran at 3 g/m^2 (9 oz/100 sq yd) incorporated as granules into top 25 mm (1 in) of soil.

Chlorfenvinphos at 4.5 g/m^2 (13.3 oz/100 sq yd) granules applied to soil.

Chlorfenvinphos applied at 0.56 ml/m^2 (1.7 fl oz/100 sq yd) immediately after sowing

Diazinon 40% w.p. at 2.25 kg/ha (21 lb/acre) applied at second leaf stage.

Where field drilled plants are concerned, particularly early sown crops – treat at egg laying time (at end of April) as for transplants.

Crops drilled after mid April, should have pesticide granules applied during drilling by use of the bow wave technique.

With transplanted crops *band treatment* is recommended – a granule applicator fitted to a sandwich frame mounted between the tractor and planter or direct on to the planter makes granule application and planting in one operation possible. Best results are obtained by feeding the granules into a Leeds (hollow) coulter set to deliver the granules 50 mm (2 in) below the soil surface in front and exactly in line with the planting share. Alternatively, granules may be placed as a surface band over the plants within a few days of planting.

On small areas hand applicators can be used to spot treat each plant, placing the granules close to the neck of the plant. Hand applicators, are available for chlorfenvinphos, carbofuran, diazinon and fonofos granules.

Materials	Hand applicator rate/1000 plants
Carbofuran	400 g (14 oz)
Chlorofenvinphos	200 g (7 oz)
Diazinon	907 g (2 lb)
Fonofos	200 g (7 oz)

APHIDS The main aphid is the mealy cabbage aphid (*Brevicoryne brassicae*) but the peach potato aphid (*Myzus persicae*) will also attack brassicas. Both pests are important as vectors of virus disease, notably cauliflower mosaic and cabbage ring spot. The cabbage aphid can also cause serious reduction in yield as a direct result of feeding. The presence of aphids, dead or alive, detracts from the market appearance and decreases crop value.

Both pests overwinter on brassica crop plants and weeds. Destroying overwintering hosts before May will help to reduce the problem. And keep seed beds as far away from overwintered crops as possible.

Chemical control may be achieved by the use of pesticide granules or sprays but using granules containing disulphoton or phorate will give control of *both cabbage root fly and cabbage aphid*. Various sprays are available including pirimicarb, dimethoate and chlorpyrifos. The addition of extra wetter helps 'stick' the spray to foliage of Brussels sprouts or cabbage. Control at an early stage of infestation is important.

CATERPILLARS A number of species attack brassica crops, the most common species being the small white butterfly (*Pieris rapae*) and the cabbage moth (*Mamestra brassicae*). Damage is most common from July to October, routine inspection of the crop will reveal tell-tale feeding signs. The pest is easily controlled by a spray of insecticide (trichlorphon, permethrin or triazophos, for example). Alternatively, spraying on the commercially available biological control agent (*baccilus theuringiensis*) can give good results.

Diseases

CLUB ROOT   (*Plasmodiophora brassicae*) This is the most important disease that attacks cruciferous plants and brassicas in particular. As a soil-borne disease it remains in the soil for such long periods that any form of rotation is of little value as a means of control. For the symptoms see the Pest and Disease chart page 251.

In order to control club root, infected land should not be used for brassica growing and should certainly NOT be used for raising brassica plants. Where lightly infested land has to be used, measures may be taken to suppress the disease.

The old treatment of *liming* should not be underestimated. Recent research has shown a high degree of control where calcic limestone was applied at high rates of 15–20 tonnes/ha (6–8 tons/acre). In subsequent years lower applications should be sufficient to maintain a high soil pH of 7.0–8.0. Such levels of lime may induce some trace element deficiencies but these can be corrected fairly easily. With lime at £6 per tonne this gives a control measure costing a minimum of £120/ha (£48/acre). Before embarking on the above control measure consider the possible effect on other crops in the rotation.

In the case of drawn or peg plants, root dips can be carried out prior to planting. The most effective material is calomel (mercurous chloride) (100 g/l or 1 lb/gal of pure calomel) plus a little cellulose paste, eg, wallpaper paste, to help stick the material to the roots. The effects of mercury on the environment are undesirable and it is possible this treatment may be withdrawn.

Alternatively, dip roots in a 1 per cent solution of thiophanate-methyl (Mildothane). Roots should be prewashed and the solution may be increased to a 2 per cent solution if infection is severe.

Block raised plants may be protected by calomel or Mildothane incorporated in the blocking compost. This treatment is more effective in the larger block sizes.

Provisional rates are: Calomel at 50 g (1¾oz) per 1,000 3.8 cm (1½ in) blocks.

Mildothane at 200 g (7 oz) per 1000 3.8 cm (1½in) blocks.

DOWNY MILDEW (*Peronospora parasitical*) The most common of brassica leaf diseases, it is prevalent in conditions of high humidity. The disease can be serious on young brassica seedlings being raised under protection overwinter. Routine sprays of zineb or dichlofluanid from emergence to transplanting are advisable. The disease is rarely serious in the field so field spraying is seldom carried out.

POWDERY MILDEW(*Erysiphe cruciferaum*) This is common in sprout crops, especially in the dry, warm conditions of late summer-autumn. Reduction in yield is small, but the white powdery pustules which develop reduce the quality of the sprouts and may necessitate hand trimming prior to marketing. Sprays of dinocap or fluotrimazole give some degree of control.

Current work done at NVRS concerning *field drilled crops* showing promise is the application of thiophanate-methyl (Mildothane) to the drills immediately in advance of sowing using a compound rig for application, incorporation and drilling.

Areas used for brassica plant raising may justify the cost of chemical treatment or *soil sterilization*. Dazomet will only give control for one season as the disease is not eradicated (cost is approximately £1,500/ha or £607/acre). The most effective single treatment is vaporized methyl bromide costing around £2,500/ha, £1,012/acre. A cheaper but very effective alternative is dichloropropene used at 450 1/ha or 40 gal/acre at a cost of approximately £1,000/ha (£405/acre). The above treatments applied together (dazomet followed by methyl bromide) has succeeded in eradicating the disease but at a cost of approximately £3,000–3,500/ha (£1,215–1,417/acre). For maximum effect, all treatments described require polythene sheeting of the soil surface for a period of four to six weeks.

Chapter 5

Legumes

Most legumes are now grown for the processed trade and over 80 per cent of the total acreage of beans and peas are grown for this market. Growing for processing is often large scale and on contract. Details of traditional and processed crops are included.

Broad Beans – *Vicia faba*

The broad bean has always been a crop of limited demand, but in common with other legumes the fresh market has declined while the demand for the processed crop has increased. It is only the advent of self-pick that has halted the complete decline of the fresh market.

Soils
The crop is very tolerant of soil type provided it is free draining. The lighter soils are preferred for overwintering crops.

Cultivations
The plough is normally used for primary cultivations, but where an autumn bean crop follows cereals chisel ploughing may be used to speed up soil preparations. Secondary cultivations should produce an open or coarse seedbed which is preferred to a very fine one. Excessive consolidation should be avoided.

Nutrition
The pH should be within the range of 5.5 to 7.0 and any acidity below this level should be corrected by liming. Broad beans have a low nitrogen requirement, phosphate and potash being the main nutrients needed.

Table 29: Fertilizer recommendations for broad beans (kg nutrient per hectare)

Nutrient index (as quoted by ADAS)	Phosphate P_2O_5	Potash K_2O	Magnesium Mg Sandy soils	Other soils	Nitrogen N
0	250	250	60	60	60
1	200	200	<u>30</u>	<u>NIL</u>	25
2	<u>125</u>	<u>125</u>	NIL	NIL	NIL
3	75	60	–	–	–
4	40	NIL	–	–	–
Over 4	NIL	NIL	–	–	–

If a soil analysis is not available use the values underlined in the table.

Sowing

For the fresh market, sowing dates are not critical. Sowing commences in November for the overwinter crop and in February or March for the spring grown crop. The autumn sown crop is essential for those wishing to harvest before the normal pea harvest season. Sowing the last week of March gives a post pea harvest suitable for the mature bean canning trade. Later sowings (mid April) are suitable for young soft beans for freezing.

The large seed of this crop cannot be sown by standard seed drills. The seed is best sown by using specialist drills or by bulb or potato planters (see Runner Beans page 94).

Plant densities

A plant density of 14–15 plants/m^2 (1.3–1.4/sq ft) should be the target to aim for. The most common spacing between rows is 450 mm (18 in) which means sowing six to seven beans per metre run (2/ft run). Sowing depth is normally 75 mm (3 in), but under very dry soil conditions drilling to a depth of 100 mm (4 in) is a useful precaution against germination failure through lack of water.

Cultivars

Different cultivars are used for autumn and spring sowings.

AUTUMN SOWING

Aquadulce Claudia – Matures end June, but unsuitable for machine harvesting.

Polar – Matures mid July for freezing, end July for canning. Very hardy in bad winters.

SPRING SOWING

Pax Minica	– Useful new cultivar which matures in mid July. Only suitable for freezing *not* canning.
Three Fold White (Triple White)	– An established white seeded processing cultivar. Matures end July for freezing and early August for canning.
Rowena	– Same maturity dates as Three Fold White, but this is a smaller bean of high quality. Used for freezing and canning.
Beryl	– A very small bean not characteristic of the species. A popular substitute for lima beans. Matures early August for freezing, and mid August for canning.

Weed control

Simazine has been widely used for this crop but has two major disadvantages – damage can occur on some sensitive cultivars and residues in the soil can have an adverse effect on the next crop. The alternative treatments which are now widely used are set out below:

PRE-SOWING HERBICIDE

Trifluralin – incorporated 0–14 days before sowing at 1.7 1/ha (24 fl oz/acre) on light soils, 2.3 1/ha (33 fl oz) on medium heavy soils. This is an unsuitable treatment for soils with over 10 per cent organic matter. Some check to growth may occur on light soils. This treatment needs to be followed by a complimentary herbicide after drilling.

PRE-EMERGENCE HERBICIDES

Trietazine/Simazine (Remtal Sc)
     – Apply any time pre-emergence. Do not use on very light soils. Seed should be at least 25 mm (1 in) below the settled soil after drilling. Use at 1.8–3.0 1/ha (26–43 fl oz/acre).

Terbutryne/Terbuthylazine (Opogard 500 L)
     – Use as soon as possible after drilling and at least three days before emergence. Do not use on very light soils. It is safer than simazine for the cultivar Beryl. Rate 2.3–3.4 1/ha (33–48 fl oz/acre).

Simazine   – Applied immediately after drilling. Do not use on sandy or gravelly soils. Even depth sowing of not less than 75 mm (3 in) is essential. Damage can occur in some conditions and persistence may be a problem.

Do not use on cultivars Beryl, Feligreen and Pax. Rates 1.7–2.2 1/ha (24–31 fl oz/acre) as suspension, 1.7–2.2 kg/ha (1½–2 lb/acre) as wettable powder.

Chlopropham/Diuron (Residuren Extra)
- Spray as soon as possible after drilling and at least seven days before emergence. Dose varies with soil type. Do not use on light or coarse grained soils. Rates are 4.2 – 5.6 1/ha (3–4 pt/acre).

POST-EMERGENCE HERBICIDES

Dinoseb Acetate (Ivosit)
- Apply from shortly after emergence until 150 mm (6 in) high. Avoid spraying in highly humid conditions. Crops with wind damaged leaves or inadequate leaf wax can also be injured. Rate is 5.6 1/ha (4 pt/acre).

Barban (Carbyne)
- Specifically for wild oat or black grass control. Apply when weeds at 1–2½ leaf stage at 3.7–5.0 1/ha (53–71 fl oz/acre). Use low dose where simazine used pre-emergence.

Irrigation

Irrigation from first flowers onwards, using 25 mm of water at a 40 mm SMD, gives a marked increase in yield.

Pinching out

Where the crop is grown on a small scale for self-pick, the growing point can be pinched out when the first flowers are setting. This will encourage the beans to swell and also discourage black bean aphids which feed on the soft growth at the top.

Harvesting

Harvesting for the fresh market is carried out by hand. The swollen pods are picked into buckets, the contents of which are tipped into green nets. On a self-pick scale, the pickers are sold carrier bags into which they pick and the row spacing is wider to allow easier access. Mechanical harvesters, of a similar type to pea harvesters, are used to gather in the crop for processing.

The wholesale market requires broad beans in 28 lb green nets, which will probably be converted to 12 kg nets when the markets become metricated.

Pests and diseases
The most important problems on this crop are black bean aphid and chocolate spot disease. For control see Chapter 12.

Anticipated yield
Average yield – 6.8 tonnes/ha (2.8 tons/acre).
Good commercial yield – 10 tonnes/ha (4.1 tons/acre).

Dwarf French Beans – *Phaseolus vulgaris*

The introduction of efficient machine harvesting has taken this crop out of the hands of the market gardener and into the large scale farmer's fields. Almost the entire UK crop (96 per cent) of a total 9,384 hectares goes for processing.

Soils
This crop is sensitive to soil conditions and ideally should be grown on medium loamy soils of good structure. Sandy soils have insufficient moisture retention which could lead to stringy beans. Heavy soils are not suitable as they are unlikely to give an economic yield.

Cultivations
As with runner beans, over-consolidation and capping must be avoided. The final surface should be as level as possible to facilitate machine harvesting. Use cultivation procedures recommended for runner beans.

Nutrition
As with all legumes, French beans require high levels of phosphate and potash for growth and production of heavy crops (see Table 30).

Sowing
Sowing is normally commenced in late April but this is only subject to adequate soil temperatures prevailing. Minimum soil temperature needs to be 12°C (54°F). Successional sowings can be continued until early June.

A wide range of seed drills will handle French bean seed as it is smaller than those of other bean crops. In selecting suitable drill units, particular consideration should be given to the minimum row spacing which can be achieved and the degree of stress placed on the seeds.

Depth of sowing is normally 25–30 mm (1–1¼in) but under very dry conditions drilling may be as deep as 50 mm (2 in) in order to place the seed into moist soil.

Table 30: Recommended fertilizer rates for French beans (kg nutrient per hectare)

Nutrient index (as quoted by ADAS)	Phosphate P₂O₅	Potash K₂O	Magnesium Mg Sandy soils	Other soils	Nitrogen N
0	300	200	60	60	150
1	250	125	<u>30</u>	<u>NIL</u>	100
2	<u>200</u>	<u>60</u>	NIL	NIL	75
3	125	NIL	–	–	–
4	60	NIL	–	–	–
Over 4	NIL	NIL	–	–	–

If a soil analysis is not available use the values underlined in the table.

Densities

The optimum density is 43 plants/m² (4/sq ft). Where the crop is grown for hand harvest or self-pick, wide row spacings of 400–500 mm (16–20 in) are essential. But for machine harvesting, the spacing between the rows should be reduced as much as the drilling equipment will allow – down to 140 mm (5½ in), while still maintaining the same plant densities. So for 500 mm (20 in) row spacings use 22 seeds/m run (20 seeds/yd), whereas for a close row spacing of 140 mm (5½ in) only 6 seeds/m run (5 seeds/yd) are required. Bed systems allow narrow row spacings as well as easy tractor access to spray the crop (see Appendix 2).

Irrigation

There is no advantage in applying irrigation before flowering. Application of 25 mm (1 in) of water during flowering and another 25 mm (1 in) at pod growth stage will considerably increase yields (see Chapter 3 on Irrigation).

Weed control

PRE-DRILLING   Trifluralin applied 0–14 days before sowing at 1.7 l/ha (24 fl oz/acre). But it is unsuitable for use on light soils or on soils with more than 10 per cent organic matter content.

PRE-EMERGENCE HERBICIDES   Chlorpropham/fenuron (Herbon Yellow) applied after seed has chitted but before emergence to a moist weed free soil surface. Dose varies with soil type and time of year. Use lower rates on light soils and very early sowings. Rates from 22.4–27.0 1/ha (2–2½ gal/acre).

Monolinuron (Arresin) applied immediately after drilling. Dose rate varies with soil type and susceptibility of cultivars – 2.8–4.2 1/ha (2–3 pt/acre).

Diphenamid (Enid 50 W) – only for use on fresh market crops. It is not very effective on organic soils. Use lower dose rates for light soils. DO NOT USE ON CROPS FOR PROCESSING.

POST-EMERGENCE HERBICIDES Bentazone (Basagran) may be applied from when the crop has two trifoliate leaves until visible flower buds are produced. Do not use in temperatures above 21°C (70°F).

Cultivars

The traditional market garden cultivars are still available for hand picking systems or self-pick units. But these are unsuitable for once-over harvest with machines as they become stringy when slightly over-mature.

For processing, the stringless cultivars must be used. Originally, long podded beans were grown but the modern trend is towards the inter-mediate pod length category which produce straight, better shaped pods more suited to the slicing machinery. In selecting cultivars, considera-tion should also be given to disease resistance – notably common bean mosaic, black root and Anthracnose.

LONG PODDED CULTIVARS	INTERMEDIATE PODDED CULTIVARS
Gallatin 50	Groffy
Cascade	Vilja
Blue Bush Lake	Slenderette
Tenderette	BEF

Harvesting

Hand picking is very rarely carried out as the majority of this crop goes for processing. A specialized machine harvester of the pod picker type is extensively used for the job. The harvested produce for processing has to be into the factory within two hours of picking.

A small quantity of the crop is hand picked for the fresh market. These are marketed in a similar manner to runner beans (see page 97).

Anticipated yield

Average yield – 9 tonnes/ha (3.7 tons/acre).

Pests and diseases – see Chapter 12 for pests and diseases of beans.

Runner Beans – *Phaseolus muliflorus*

Botanically this plant is a half-hardy perennial but the grower treats it as a half-hardy annual. It can be grown as a pinched crop or up sticks – either way involves a high labour input.

PINCHED BEANS These crops are grown as a small bushy plant by removal of the growing points. This gives an earlier crop but beans hang close to the ground and, therefore, quality is not so good as the stick grown crop.

STICK BEANS *(supported crop)* This is grown up a support frame-work and produces a better quality crop but later in the season.

Site
Runner beans are very susceptible to wind damage so a sheltered site is essential. The crop is not hardy so avoid frost pockets. For early production mild sheltered areas are desirable.

Soils
A very deep, fertile soil is essential for this crop. The ideal is a medium loam or peat. Heavy soils are unsuitable, however, lighter soils may be used provided regular irrigation is available.

The pH should be between 6.0 and 7.0, except on peat soils where lower pH is advisable (down to 5.5).

Nutrition
Table 31: Recommended fertilizer rates for runner beans (kg nutrient per hectare)

Nutrient index	Phosphate P_2O_5	Potash K_2O	Magnesium Mg Sandy soils	Other soils	Nitrogen N
0	300	250	90	60	150
1	250	200	60	30	100
2	200	125	NIL	NIL	75
3	125	60			–
4	60	NIL			–
1	NIL	NIL			–

If a soil analysis is not available use the values underlined in the table.

Rotation
Unlike most crops it is common practice to grow the beans repeatedly on the same site, especially where a favourable site is available. This

substantially raises soil fertility and enables the support framework to remain in position. If perennial weeds or soil-borne disease become serious then a new site may have to be found.

Cultivation

If available, well rotted farmyard manure should be spread at up to 75 tonnes/ha (30 tons/acre) before ploughing in early winter (a minimum plough depth of 200 mm or 8 in). Fertilizers should be applied after the spring cultivation but prior to breaking the soil down to a seed bed.

Where farmyard manure is used the artificial fertilizer application may be reduced by:
1.5 kg N;   2.0 kg P_2O_5;   4.0 kg K_2O;   0.8 kg Mg per tonne of manure.

Sowing

Very early crop sowings are made on April 8–10. If these early sowings are covered by cloches or low polythene tunnels the crop can be advanced by 10–14 days.

Main crops are sown during the last 10 days of May. Late sowings, up to the end of June, are useful sowings in order to produce high quality beans at the end of the season. But yield is greatly reduced (by up to 50 per cent) with late sowings.

Few growers have the specialist seed drills which will handle a seed of this size. Some improvization is therefore necessary for sowing. On a small scale, and with low density crops, a blunt dibber can be used to make a hole for each seed. On larger areas the most common practices are:
(1)   Using a vegetable planter, with the planting mechanism set to the required spacing. The seed is dropped direct into the furrow. The planting mechanism indicates the correct spacing for the operator.
(2)   Potato or bulb planters with hand fed mechanisms will sow runner bean seed. The seed can be dropped into the furrow in the same way as potatoes. If using a potato planter the ridging bodies must be removed. If the potato planter is fitted with a pesticide granule applicator, disulfoton granules can be drilled below the seeds to provide aphid control during the early life of the crop (but not on very light soils).

Density

LOW TUNNEL CROPS   Under polythene tunnels two rows 450 mm (18 in) apart with seeds 150 mm (6 in) apart down the row.

PINCHED CROPS   Single rows 700 mm–900 mm (27 in–36 in) between rows, seeds 150 mm (6 in) apart down the row.

SUPPORTED CROPS   This is a more complex aspect as the density which gives the highest yield may not be the most profitable. If the crop is grown on a semi-permanent post and wire and string support structure, a density of $10.8/m^2$ (1 plant/sq ft) using twin rows 300 mm (1 ft) apart with 1.2 m (4 ft) paths should give the highest profit, with plants every 130 mm (5 in) down the row. (For details of support systems see Figure 20.)

If the crop is supported by canes, the capital cost of 5.15 plants/m^2 would be prohibitive. Densities between 2.06–4.12/m^2 (0.2–0.4/sq ft) should be considered. These can be achieved with double rows at 600 mm (2 ft) apart, separated by 900 mm (3 ft) paths with a down the row cane spacing from 300–600 mm (1–2 ft), each cane supporting two plants.

Cultivars

There are a wide range of cultivars available. The main requirements are straight and smooth pods, good colour, freedom from stringiness and high yield.

For pinched crops the short podded cultivars are preferable, eg, Kelvedon Marvel and Princeps, as they are less likely to become soiled and distorted. Most main crop cultivars, eg, Streamline and Enorma will continue to crop until killed by the first frost. Those with coloured flowers and seed usually crop more heavily than the white-flowered, white-seeded cultivars which are used particularly for processing.

Herbicides

A pre-sowing or pre-emergence herbicide suited to the weed spectrum should be used plus a post emergence herbicide.

PRE-SOWING OR PRE-EMERGENCE

Dinitramine (Cobex) 0–14 days before drilling at 1–1.5 1/ha (¾–1 pt/acre).

Chlorpropham + Fenuron (Herbon Yellow) – delay application until seed has chitted 22.4–27.0 1/ha (2–2½ gal/acre). Lower dose on light soils or soils with high water table.

Diphenamid (Enid 50W) use 6.7–9.0 kg/ha (6–8 lb/acre). Apply lower dose on light soils.

POST-EMERGENCE

Bentazone (Basagran) applied at first to second trifoliate leaf stage at 3.0 1/ha (43 fl oz/acre). Do not apply when the temperatures are above 21°C (70°F).

Training

PINCHED CROPS   Pinch out the growing point after the first pair of true leaves, when the plants are about 200 mm (8 in) tall. The lateral shoots which result are again pinched at the first or second pair of leaves. Thereafter all shoots should be pinched at regular intervals of approximately 10 days. The operation may be speeded up on established plants by using a small grass hook or curved vegetable knife to top the new growth as an alternative to hand pinching. Correct and regular stopping is vital with this crop, otherwise growth becomes excessive and yield is greatly reduced.

SUPPORTED CROPS   (for details of support systems see Figure 20). During the early stage it is advisable to go through the crop twice per week to ensure the shoots are climbing the support. Any stems failing to do so should be attached to the support by a wire twist tie. Once the shoots have started climbing they require no further attention until the majority are approximately 300 mm above the top of the support. At this stage it is worth while to stop the shoots by chopping them off with a hedge knife or slasher. This makes picking off the uppermost beans much easier.

Pollination

Runner beans require insect pollination. In many areas there will be adequate natural pollinators but in more intensively farmed areas, particularly in the east of the country, it may be necessary to introduce honey bees to get adequate setting of the crop. Two-and-a-half hives per hectare (one hive per acre) should be adequate.

Irrigation

If maximum yield is to be achieved the crop must receive adequate water. Irrigation should be started when the first flowers are at the green bud stage. Very sandy soils should be returned to field capacity at a 25 mm SMD. With loamy soils or very fine sands, 50 mm of water at 75 mm SMD should prove adequate.

Harvesting

PINCHED CROPS   Cropping usually commences during the first or second week of July and continues to mid August. If supplies are short picking may continue longer, but because of the lower quality of pinched crops they are usually abandoned when the supported crop is in full swing.

SUPPORTED CROPS   Picking usually starts during the first week of

Figure 20   Different support systems for runner beans

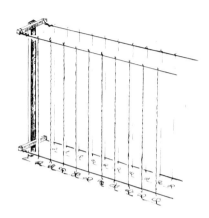

Posts, wire and string system

Posts with cross
pieces every 3 m (9–10 ft).
Posts 3 m (9 ft) long, 2.1 m (7 ft)
out of the ground.

Wires set 300 mm (1 ft)
apart, lower wire
225 mm (9″) above
ground level.

Strings every 130 mm
(5″) along the wires.

Distance between posted
rows 1.2 m (4 ft).

Triple cane support system

Canes 2.4 m long (8 ft) pushed
in ground 450 mm (18″) and tied
in threes at the top.

Distance between canes 600 mm (2 ft).

Distance between rows of canes
900mm (3 ft).

Continuous cane support

Canes 2.4 m long (8 ft) pushed in
ground 450 mm (18″) and tied in
twos at the top. A further set of
canes are positioned along the
top of the apex of the canes in
a single row for rigidity.

Canes 300 mm apart (1 ft) in
the row and 600 mm (2 ft) between
the rows.

Distance between rows of canes
900 mm (3 ft).

August, but this can be forwarded by 10–14 days by starting the crop under tunnels or cloches or by the use of transplants.

Picking should be carried out frequently so that pods do not become over-developed and stringy. The frequency will depend to some extent on season and weather conditions. Picking is the most labour intensive and therefore expensive stage of the crop.

The beans are normally laid into the picking basket in one direction so that transfer to the market pack can be made quickly and easily. Selection and grading of the crop should be carried out by the picker.

Market packs vary according to season and market requirements. Early in the season the crop may be marketed in chip baskets holding 4–6 kg or 8–12 lb. Main crops are mainly marketed in waxed board or solid board trays holding 6–9 kg or 12–20 lb. All the beans should be laid in the same way to form an attractive market pack.

Storage

The crop may be held in store for a short time provided the beans are surface dry (maximum of seven days) at an air temperature of 4.4°C with a relative humidity of 90–95 per cent. An ice bank cooler is ideal.

Anticipated yield

Average yield – 13 tonnes/ha (5.4 tons/acre)

Pests and diseases

For details of bean pests and diseases see Chapter 12.

Peas – *Pisum sativum*

The market for the pea crop has changed radically in the last 20 years. For the purposes of statistics the outlets are split into two main groups: fresh peas and dried peas.

The fresh pea market includes peas sold in the pod, but these have declined to a very low level (10 per cent). Canning of fresh peas, too, is on the decline reaching a peak in the mid 1970s. It is the use of peas for freezing that is now the major outlet.

Dried peas still form an important part of the industry as these are used for animal feed and canning (still 60 per cent) and exports (10 per cent). Split peas for human consumption only account for 5 per cent of the crop. Most of this crop is grown in the drier south-eastern area of the country.

Soils

Peas grow successfully on a wide range of soil types but the extremes should be avoided. Well drained soils are essential and they should be stone-free to aid drilling and harvesting. Avoid growing peas or other legumes on the same land for more than one year in five because of carry over of soil-borne diseases.

Cultivations

Autumn ploughing is desirable to enable early sowings in the spring. In spring work down the frost mould to a medium fine seed bed, deep enough to allow drilling to a depth of 50 mm (2 in). Over consolidation, as with other legumes, should be avoided. Never create a very fine tilth which merely impede drainage and aeration, especially if heavy rains occur before germination.

Nutrition

After soil analysis has been carried out any nutritional deficiencies should be corrected. Manganese deficiency, seen as marsh spot on peas, should not be overlooked, particularly on organic and alkaline soils.

Peas are a short term crop and require nutrients readily available at the start for rapid growth. Base dressings with high levels of potash are required as deficiency results in a serious reduction in yield. Response to phosphate is less obvious though still very necessary. Peas also benefit from small quantities of nitrogen to help establishment, especially with early sowings. Once established, the bacteria (*Rhizobium*) in the root nodules provide the crop with nitrogen.

Application of the base dressing is usually broadcast since combined drilling of fertilizer with seed can cause scorch to germinating shoots and roots. Sideband placement of fertilizer seems to have little advantage.

Table 32: Recommended fertilizer rates for peas (kg nutrient per hectare)

Nutrient index	Phosphate P_2O_5	Potash K_2O	Magnesium Mg Sandy soils	Other soils	Nitgrogen N
0	<u>50</u>	150	60	30	NIL*
1	25	<u>40</u>	<u>30</u>	NIL	NIL*
2	NIL	NIL	NIL	NIL	NIL
3	NIL	NIL	–	–	–
4	NIL	NIL	–	–	–
Over 4	NIL	NIL	–	–	–

If a soil analysis is not available use the values underlined in the table.

*For the early crop when spring rainfall has been high 25 kg/ha nitrogen should be included in the base dressing.

Peas thrive well at a pH range of 6.0–7.5. But beware of overliming on organic soils as this may result in the unavailability of manganese.

Sowing

Peas which are to be mechanically harvested require sowing at high densities in close rows. Row widths should be between 100 mm (4 in) and 200 mm (8 in), the spacing being determined by the form of drill available. The crop should be drilled 50 mm deep to ensure adequate soil moisture is available and to keep the seed below soil acting herbicides (see weed control page 103). A light harrow usually follows the drill to ensure adequate covering of the seeds, and in dry conditions the field can be rolled to depress stones and clods, giving a flat surface for more effective residual weed control and easier harvesting. Do not roll the seedbed in wet conditions. Rolling can be delayed until the peas are 50–75 mm (2–3 in) high.

Drilling starts in February and continues until early May. For dried peas, early drilling is advisable, but only if the land is in a suitable condition.

For vining peas, continuity of harvest at the optimum stage (a consistent tenderometer reading) of pea maturity is essential. Succession can only be achieved by basing the sowing dates on accumulated heat units (AHU's). This results in a long interval between the sowings in the early part of the season and only a matter of days between sowings in May.

Cultivars

Pea cultivars have improved steadily during the last two decades, giving additional earliness, improved quality, more disease resistance and higher yields. The main problem with processed peas is 'lodging' (the collapse of a plant as a result of wind, rain or the sheer weight of the crop) just prior to harvest, which makes harvesting difficult and induces disease in the humid micro-climate produced by a 'lodged' crop. Modern plant breeding has produced three new forms of pea to overcome the 'lodging' problem – leafless, semi-leafless and tare leafed peas.

The leafless pea is the most open and stands the best at harvest. This results in fast maturation from the vining stage to the dried pea stage, which is a distinct advantage for the latter but makes the leafless form less suitable for the vining crop, eg, Filby.

The semi-leafless pea matures much more slowly than the leafless type, therefore a number of vining cultivars of a semi-leafless type are in the development stage, eg, Eaton.

Tare leafed peas can be produced for vining or dry harvesting. The leaf is much finer and thinner than standard cultivars, therefore giving good standing ability. The first cultivar released in this group was the marrowfat dried pea Progreta.

Examples of useful cultivars:

Dried peas	Vedette	standard
	Marco	standard
	Filby	leafless
	Progreta	tare leafed.
Vining peas	Sprite	standard early
	Banff	recent introduction – early
	Eaton	semi-leafless
	Puget	standard main crop
	Jof	new main crop
	Multistar	new main crop

Where peas are grown for processing the cultivar will usually be specified by the processor or choice will be made by agreement between the grower and the processor.

For the fresh market or the 'pick-your-own' trade there are also a large number of cultivars to choose from. It is essential to keep to the dwarf types for field production. The cultivars set out below have been found to perform well and give a good spread of harvesting for the fresh market and 'Pick-Your-Own'.

Feltham First	first early
Progress No. 9	second early
Early Onward	early-mid season
Onward	mid season
Sleaford Phoenix	late-mid season.

Plant densities

Target population for the various types of peas are set out below:
Dried Peas – Small Blues 95/m^2 (9/sq ft)
– Large Blues 70/m^2 (6½/sq ft)
– Marrowfats 65/m^2 (6/sq ft)
Vining Peas – 110/m^2 (10 sq ft)

To calculate seed requirement the formula set out below may be used:

$$\frac{10,000 \times \text{target population per m}^2}{\text{No. of seeds/kg}} \times \frac{100}{\text{Laboratory} \times \text{Field germination \% factor}}$$

= Seed requirement
(in kg/ha)

The accuracy of the calculation depends on a precise assessment of the field factor. Modern developments of vigour testing may give a guide as to what percentage of laboratory germinated seed would germinate in the field.

Irrigation

The irrigation of peas is well documented in Chapter 3. This crop serves as the classic example of huge response as a result of the timing of irrigation (flowering time and pod swell). If soils are dry prior to late sowings of vining peas, irrigation before sowing may assist germination and plant establishment.

Weed control

There are a wide range of herbicides available for peas and only the most important are covered here:

PRE-EMERGENCE HERBICIDES   (before 5 per cent crop emergence)
Trietazine/Simazine
    – Unsuitable for crops drilled shallower than 25 mm (1 in). Cultivar Vedette susceptible to damage. Rate of use 1.8–3.0 1/ha (26–43 fl oz/acre).
Terbutryne/Terbuthylazine
    – Use as for broad beans. Not suitable for highly organic soils, minimum sowing depth 25 mm (1 in). Rate 2.3–3.4 1/ha (33–49 fl oz/acre).
Aziprotryne – Applied normally pre crop emergence but can be used post emergence up to the weeds having two true leaves. Not suitable for soils with more than 10 per cent organic matter. Minimum sowing depth 25 mm (1 in). Rate of use 4.0 kg/ha (3.5 lb/acre).
Prometryne – Use at least three days before crop emergence. Do not apply on light or organic soils. Rate of use 2.8–3.4 kg/ha (2.5–3 lb/acre).
Chlorthal – Dimethyl + Methazole (Delozin S)
    – One of the few *safe* pre-emergence treatments for early peas on light soils. Use 6 kg/ha (5.4 lb/acre).

POST-EMERGENCE HERBICIDES
Bentazone/MCPB
    – Spray when crop has three pairs of true leaves after mid May until flower buds are visible. DO NOT use on cultivars, Surprise or Vedette or any crop pre-treated with TCA. Rate of use 7.5 1/ha (106 fl oz/acre).
Dinoseb Acetate
    – Apply shortly after emergence until crop is 150 mm (6 in) tall. DO NOT use on cultivars, Surprise or Vedette. Rate 5.6 1/ha (4 pt/acre).

Harvesting

The fresh pick market is only a very small part of the total pea crop. For the wholesale market, once over destructive harvesting is practised, the pea haulms are pulled up by hand and the swollen pods picked off direct into sacks. A good picker will be able to harvest 250 kg in a day. For very early fresh peas, 5 kg (12 lb) may be picked into Dutch trays lined with blue paper. The self-pick trade has given some resurgence to the fresh crop and for this trade polythene carrier bags or polythene sacks are commonly sold to pickers. Again once over destructive harvesting is used.

Machine harvesting, which has so revolutionized the cropping of peas, is currently changing from the original two-stage harvesting system to a single operation. Originally, growers used a cutter-windrower and a vining machine to harvest the pods, whereas the modern 'pod-picker' harvester removes the peas direct from the standing crop. Although a good deal of foliage is also removed the amount of haulm passing through the machinery is far less, which means a higher operating speed and better vining efficiency.

The vining crop is only harvested when it reaches the optimum stage (optimum tenderometer reading). Then the crop has to be harvested within two days and the peas themselves must reach the processing factory within four hours of being vined.

Pea Midge damage.

Anticipated yields

	Dried peas	**Vining peas**	**Fresh peas**
Average yield	3.75 tonnes/ha	5.6 tonnes/ha	16.9 tonns/ha
	(1.48 tons/acre)	(2.3 tons/acre)	(7 tons/acre)
	(Podless yield)	(Podless yield)	(in the pod yield).

Pests and diseases See Chapter 12 for details of pea pests and diseases.

Chapter Six

Alliums

The 'Alliums' include such crops as dry bulb onions, leeks, salad onions, chives, shallots and garlic. The first three mentioned crops are of major horticultural importance, whereas chives, shallots and garlic are of such minor importance that they are not dealt with in this book. Garlic really requires warmer climates than can be offered in the UK.

Dry Bulb Onions – *Allium cepa*

This crop was little grown in Britain 30 years ago. Production was originally carried out using spring sowings for an autumn harvest, but further developments make autumn sowing to give a mid summer harvest a possibility.

Soils
Onion production is usually carried out on the brick earth or silty soils which are well drained. Peat is almost as good but tends to retard maturity and ripening. As soils get further from these ideals they are progressively less suitable.

Level sites which are stone free are preferable as this makes drilling, lifting and sorting easier. Good drainage is important for all onions but it assumes greater importance for the overwintered crop. The pH level should be between 6.5 and 7.5 for mineral soils and 5.4 to 6.5 on peat soils.

Cultivations
If necessary, subsoil during dry weather in the autumn prior to sowing the crop. Ploughing should be carried out in the early winter for a spring

sown crop to allow weathering. For autumn sown crops plough as early as the rotation permits.

The secondary cultivations should prepare a firm, fine level, and clod free seedbed to allow accurate drilling.

Nutrition

Where farmyard manure is available it may be spread before ploughing at up to 75 tonnes/ha (30 tons/acre) provided it is well rotted. Where manure is used the fertilizer application may be reduced by 15 kg/ha nitrogen, 20 kg/ha phosphate, 40 kg/ha potash and 8 kg/ha magnesium for every 10 tonnes of manure/ha used.

Table 33: Recommended fertilizer rates for onions (kg nutrient per hectare).

Nutrient index	Phosphate P_2O_5	Potash K_2O	Magnesium Mg		Nitrogen N	
			Sandy soils	Other soils	Fen peat	Other
0	300	300	90	60	60	100
1	250	250	60	30	30	80
2	200	200	NIL	NIL	NIL	60
3	125	125	–	–	–	–
4	60	60	–	–	–	–
Over 4	NIL	NIL	–	–	–	–

For autumn sowings top dress with nitrogen during late February or early March – 50 kg/ha on Fen peats and 100 kg/ha N on other soils. If high levels of rainfall are experienced during winter then a further 50 kg/ha N may be applied. If this is the case the total dressing should be split, the first half in January and the second half during late February or Early March.
If soil analysis figures are not available use the values underlined in the table.

Manganese deficiency may be a problem on organic soils, especially at high pH but it can also occur in light soils which are over limed. The application of a foliar spray of manganese sulphate at 9 kg/ha (8 lb/acre) plus wetter should be applied as soon as there is enough leaf area to absorb the spray. In severe cases further spray may be necessary.

Cultivars

The onion cultivars fall into two major groups – the autumn sown cultivars which over-winter, and the spring drilled cultivars. The main difference between the two groups is the daylength required to induce bulb formation. Onions are sensitive to daylength and once the required length is experienced bulb formation is initiated.

The autumn sown cultivars are primarily of Japanese origin, though some European cultivars are available. They require an intermediate daylength to induce bulb formation and are resistant to bolting when overwintered. They are not suitable for spring sowing. The spring drilled cultivars are mainly developed from the traditional Rijnsburger type though some cultivars of Polish origin are also available. Bulb formation in this group requires long days, they are NOT suitable for autumn sowing.

A few examples of cultivars which have been found to perform well in the eastern counties are set out below in order of maturity.

AUTUMN SOWN CULTIVARS

Extra Early Kaizuka	Early, flat to semi-flat bulb, lower than average yield, thin skin.
Express Yellow (F₁Hybrid)	Early semi-flat bulb, thin skin.
Imaie Early Yellow	Mid season, high yield, globe shaped bulb, average skin thickness.
Keep Well (F₁Hybrid)	Mid season, very high yield, elongated globe, above average skin quality and colour.
Senshyu Semi Globe Yellow	Late, high yield bulbs, average globe shaped with dark skins.

SPRING SOWN CULTIVARS

Early   (80 per cent of tops down by mid August)

Adina	Pale colour, thin skinned.
Sublima	Straw colour with average thick skins.

Early Main Crop   (80 per cent of tops down by end August)

Hyper (F₁Hybrid)	Straw coloured skins.
Maxima (F₁Hybrid)	Dark straw coloured skin, stores well.
Rijnsburger-Wijbo	Pale-straw coloured skin.

Main Crop   (80 per cent tops down by early to mid September)

Hydeal (F₁Hybrid)	High yield but below average storing ability when barn stored.
Hygro (F₁Hybrid)	High yield, straw coloured skins, high dry matter, average storage capacity.
Rijnsburger-Balstora	High yield, darkish bulbs with very good skin quality, stores very well.
Rijnsburger-Robusta	Darkish skin, stores well.

Drilling

Ungraded seed is frequently used to avoid the high cost of graded seed. The crop is normally field drilled in rows not more than 450 mm (18 in) apart. Alternatively, double rows or scatter bands may be used at row spacings of 500 mm (20 in). Row spacing will also be influenced by drilling and harvesting machinery. The density used will be largely determined by the size of bulb required and the estimated yield. The most widely used density is 96 to 100 plants/m^2 which gives bulbs of 40–50 mm diameter at a yield of 45 to 50 tonnes/ha. The table below shows how bulb size can be manipulated by plant density and this in turn effects yield.

Table 34: Plant population (plants/m^2) at harvest

Yield (t/ha) Anticipated	Bulb Size (mm) Required						
	20–30	30–40	40–50	50–60	60–70	70–80	80–90
10	100	40	20	13	7	5	3
15	150	60	30	20	11	7	5
20	200	80	40	27	14	9	7
25	250	100	50	33	18	12	8
30	300	120	60	40	21	14	10
35	350	140	70	47	25	16	12
40	400	160	80	53	29	19	14
45	450	180	90	60	32	21	15
50	500	200	100	67	36	23	17
55	550	220	110	73	39	26	19
60	600	240	120	80	43	28	20
65	650	260	130	87	46	30	22
70	700	280	140	93	50	32	24
75	750	300	150	100	54	35	25
80	800	320	160	107	57	37	27

*NB The figures in the table are for the required plant population at harvest. Plant losses between emergence and harvest commonly amount to 15–25 per cent of those emerged.

Drilling normally starts in March but good soil conditions are essential and drilling should be delayed if soil conditions are not suitable.

Drilling is usually carried out with a precision drill of the belt or cell wheel type. Drilling depth should be just enough to cover the seed (12 mm or ½ in) but uniform depth is important to ensure uniform emergence.

The time of drilling for autumn crops is critical and rapid germination is essential. Drilling early August is required in the north and late August in the south. The sowing rate is slightly higher than for an equivalent spring crop to allow for winter losses. These losses are much higher in northern parts where they may be up to 10 per cent.

Herbicides

SPRING SOWN CROPS ON MINERAL SOIL   At this time of year germination and early growth are slow therefore a good *pre-emergence* weed control programme is essential (main weeds are knotgrass, redshank, fat hen, mayweed and annual meadow grass).

The most effective treatment is a tank mix of propachlor + chlorthal-dimethyl (Ramrod + Dacthal) applied immediately after drilling. If necessary this can be followed by paraquat (Gramoxone) before crop emergence.

The residual life of propachlor is short, therefore a second application four to six weeks after the first is advisable to ensure a good level of control up to the first true leaf stage. (No herbicides with any foliage action should be applied between emergence and the post crook stage – see Figure 21, page 114).

Post-emergence chloridazon + chlorbufam (Alicep) can be used at the first true leaf stage to maintain weed control through to the two-and-a-half true leaf stage when the foliage acting herbicide ioxynil (Totril) or ioxynil + linuron (Control-Lin Onions) can be used if the first post emergence treatment proves inadequate.

RATES OF APPLICATION OF HERBICIDES:

Pre-emergence herbicides

Propachlor (Ramrod flowable)	9 1/ha (6½ pt/acre)
Chlorthal-dimethyl (Dacthal)	6 kg/ha (5.4 lb/acre)
Paraquat (Gramoxone)	2.8 1/ha (if required) (2 pt/acre)
Propachlor (Ramrod flowable) second treatment	6 1/ha (4¾ pt/acre)

Post-emergence herbicides

Chloridazon/chlorbufam (Alicep)	4.5 kg/ha (4 lb/acre)
Ioxynil (Totril)	2.8 1/ha (2 pt/acre)
Ioxynil + linuron (Control-Lin Onions)	0.84 kg/ha (¾ lb/acre)

SPRING SOWN CROPS ON ORGANIC SOILS These soils absorb herbicides thus reducing their effectiveness and causing shorter residual life. Higher rates are usually necessary and some changes of material may be desirable. The following programme is recommended for these organic soils.

Pre-emergence (Applied just before emergence to control weeds emerged before the crop). A tank mix of:

*Propachlor (Ramrod flowable)	9 1/ha (6½ pt/acre)
Chlorpropham (Herbon CIPC 40)	8.4–11.2 1/ha (6–8.2 pt/acre)
Paraquat (Gramoxone)	2.8 1/ha (2 pt/acre)

*If propachlor is used without the addition of CIPC increase the dosage of propachlor by 50 per cent.

A back up application of propachlor (Ramrod flowable) may be applied four weeks later at 6 1/ha (4¼ pt/acre).

Post-emergence application at the two true leaf stage of:
Ioxynil (Totril)   2.8 1/ha (2 pt/acre)
OR Cyanazine (Fortrol)   2.8 1/ha (2 pt/acre)
The post-emergence contact herbicides may be repeated as necessary.

AUTUMN DRILLED CROPS   The same basic herbicide programmes can be used for autumn drilled crops on the respective soil types with the exclusion of paraquat. As autumn crops germinate more rapidly the use of paraquat is of little or no value.

Ramrod flowable	9 1/ha (6½ pt/acre)
Dacthal	6 kg/ha (5.4 lb/acre)
Gramoxone	2.8 1/ha (if required) (2 pt/acre)
Ramrod flowable second treatment	6 1/ha (4¼ pt/acre)
Alicep	4.5 kg/ha (4 lb/acre)

Irrigation

Irrigation is not widely used on the bulb onion crop as soils of reasonable wetter holding capacity are normally used. Where the crop is grown on soils with low available water capacity it responds to 25 mm of irrigation at a 25 mm soil moisture deficit throughout its early growth. Do not irrigate after July as ripening of the bulbs will be delayed.

Sprout suppressants

It is essential that the crop is sprayed with maleic hydrazide (Vondalhyd or Mazide 36) 10 to 14 days before harvest as modern harvest techniques do not allow the transfer of natural growth inhibitors into the bulb.

Harvesting

Traditional systems have now been replaced by 'direct harvesting' which is the only technique that gives consistently good results under all weather conditions. The onions are topped to approximately 75 mm (3 in) above the bulbs. A period of two to six hours is allowed for drying of the leaf debris before undercutting and lifting. The crop must be taken direct to store after lifting.

The crop trailers are tipped into hoppers outside the store and the crop is then carried into the store by a system of conveyors. A pre-cleaner removes unwanted soil and debris which would impede air flow in the store. A moving head conveyor will also help to avoid concentrating soil or trash in cones below the discharge point.

Storage (see Figure 22)

The onion store should be designed so that it consists of three separate bays which can be filled independently. The ventilation ducting should be arranged so that all the airflow can be directed into one bay at a time for the initial drying, then divided equally for the later stages.

DRYING (STAGE I) This stage is designed to remove surface moisture. Drying should commence as soon as loading has started, using a temperature of 30°C (86°F) and an airflow of 425 m³/tonne (250 cfm/ton). This will be achieved by directing the total fan capacity into the one bay. Stage I will take approximately three days. When complete the onions on the top of the stack will be surface dry. It is essential that this stage is carried out properly and immediately after loading.

Onion store showing slatted underfloor ventilation ducts in foreground.

CLOSING THE NECKS (STAGE II) Intermittent ventilation is adequate during the early stages as the airflow will be required for drying the second and third bays. When all three bays are surface dry the airflow should be divided between all three bays 170 m³/hr/tonne (10 cfm/ton) recirculating the air to maintain a relative humidity of 70–75 per cent. This stage is necessary to ensure closing of the necks to seal the bulbs.

AMBIENT AIR COOLING (STAGE III) Once stage II is complete the onion stack should be allowed to cool gradually. By the end of October it should be possible to start ambient air cooling. The stack is cooled by

Figure 21   Different stages in the growth of onions and leeks

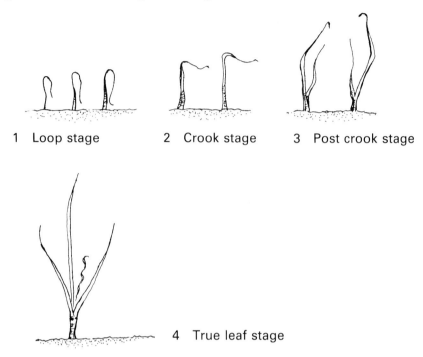

1   Loop stage   2   Crook stage   3   Post crook stage

4   True leaf stage

Figure 22   Different stages in drying and storage of onions

Stage I: Initial Drying

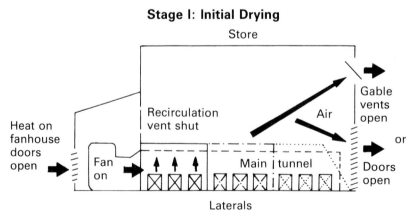

1. This is a three stage operation. The first batch is put into the bay nearest the fan,
   as this is drying the second bay is loaded, and so on. Laterals are open 24 hours a
   day. Drying takes 3–5 days at a drying temperature of 30°C (86°F).

End of Initial Drying

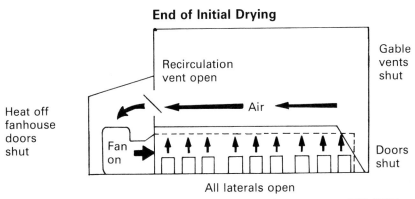

2. Whole stack surface dry and rustling. Minimum stack temperature 26°C (80°F). Humidity about 30% and rising. Fan on 24 hours a day. This is the end of stage I and the start of stage II.

Stage II: Final Drying of Necks

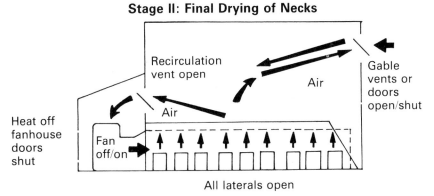

3. Humidity maintained at 70–75% by partial introduction of outside air. Stack temperature 21–24°C (70–75°F). Once necks are dry (10–15 days) the fan is switched on intermittently to keep stack dry. (No further heated air is recirculated).

Cooling and Winter Management

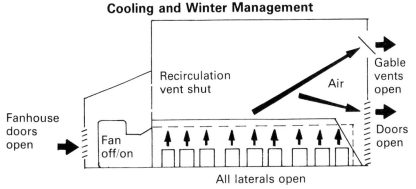

4. The crop is cooled (stage III) by using a fan to draw in air whenever the outside air temperature is 3°C (5.4°F) or more below stack temperature. The whole system is operated by a differential thermostat with an override thermostat to switch off the fan if the outside temperature drops to minus 2°C (28.4°F).

blowing in outside air (at 170 m³/hr/tonne) whenever the outside temperature is 3°C (37°F) or more below stack temperature. The fan MUST be operated by a differential thermostat system as the largest temperature differences are usually during the night. To prevent the stack from freezing, an override thermostat must be fitted and set to cut the fan off when the outside temperature falls to −2°C (28°F).

It is essential that control systems are set correctly and are operating properly. Checks may be carried out by comparing store performance with the current ADAS computer simulation data.

Grading and packing onions

Onions are normally packed in 56 lb nets (this will probably be converted to 25 kg when the pack is metricated). For grading of onions see Table 56 page 216.

Anticipated yield – Average yield – 35 tonnes/ha (14.4 tons/acre).

Pests and diseases – See Chapter 12 pests and diseases chart for details.

Production from onion sets

Due to the high cost of sets and the likelihood of carry over of pests and diseases, production of onions by this method on a commercial scale is no longer a viable proposition.

Production of onions from multi-plant blocks (the growing of several plants in a peat block)

This is a fairly recent innovation to onion growing. Its main advantages are: earliness of maturity (approximately two weeks earlier than drilled crops); more accurate plant populations which enable more accurate bulb size; an increase in yield of about 15 tonnes/ha or 6 tons/acre; easier weed control and lower herbicide costs. The one disadvantage of the system is the increase in establishment cost.

Plant raising

This is usually undertaken by a specialist plant raiser as heated glasshouse space is required. The seed, preferably graded, is sown between Jan 20 and Feb 5 at seven to eight seeds per block (38 mm or 1¾ in size) to give a plant stand of approximately six plants/block at harvest. Seed should be covered with sand or peat/sand compost to prevent the emerging radicle from pushing the seeds out of the block. After seeding the blocks are placed in a temperature of 15°C (58°F) for two weeks. The plants can then be grown under cold glass. From the crook stage the plant should be ventilated as much as possible to give a sturdy plant.

Planting
This should be carried out in early April or by the middle of the month at the latest. A density of 10 block/m² or 1/sq ft (100,000/ha or 40,800/ acre) with six plants per block will give a crop which is approximately half 40–60 mm grade and half 60–80 mm grade. If a higher percentage of 40–60 mm grade is required, increase block density to 12.5/m² (2/sq ft), for more 60–80 mm grade, reduce density to 8.5/m² (0.8 sq ft). This should give approximately 75 per cent in grade. Planting rates are approximately 1,500 blocks/man hour with manual planting machinery.

Efficient moving of plants to the field is essential. The most efficient way is to use caged pallets which will enable movement of 70 trays per pallet or 8,500 to 12,000 blocks, depending on size.

Herbicides
Do not apply herbicides to planted crops until the plants have hardened off, approximately 10–14 days after planting. After this the normal residual or residual/contact programme should be applied according to soil type (see drilled crops).

Block raised crops can only be justified if the additional costs can be covered (though quality is usually better). This will require approximately 6 to 10 tonnes extra yield depending on the current price per tonne.

Leeks – *Allium porrum*

The UK is largely self-sufficient in the production of this crop, as our consumption is lower than that of most other European countries. It is basically a winter vegetable, though production for late summer harvest is increasing.

Soils
The crop is fairly tolerant of most soil types, though the coarser sands are best avoided as grains lodge in the leaf sheaths making them less palatable for the consumer. Very heavy soils make lifting much more difficult so if a choice is to be made then good medium loams or organic soils are best. Good drainage is essential for crop growth and to enable ease of lifting. The crop is not very tolerant of acid soils and the pH should be kept above 6.5 (optimum 6.5–7.5). Analysis might show that lime is required. If so, spread it before breaking down the plough mould.

Cultivations

Deep ploughing is desirable as the leek is a deep rooted crop which grows best in a well aerated soil. The crop responds well to bulky organic matter even on fertile soils. Applications of up to 70 tonnes/ha (28 tons/acre) should be applied if available. This should be ploughed in during autumn and early winter. Where bulky organic matter is used later than the above time it must be well rotted.

During secondary cultivations the use of rotary cultivators (rotavators) should be avoided as aeration is greatly reduced after the soil has settled, particularly if heavy rain falls.

Nutrition

The nutrient requirements for the crop are set out below (Table 35). But where farmyard manure has been used the fertilizer dressing should be reduced by 15 kg/ha nitrogen, 20 kg/ha phosphate, 40 kg/ha potash and 8 kg/ha magnesium for every 10 tonnes of manure/ha used. It is not advisable to reduce phosphate application below 50 kg/ha or potash below 75 kg/ha.

Table 35: Recommended fertilizer rates for leeks (kg nutrient per hectare)

Nutrient index	Phosphate P_2O_5	Potash K_2O	Magnesium Mg Sandy soils	Other soils	Nitrogen N Fen peats	Other soils
0	300	300	60	60	60	100
1	250	250	30	NIL	30	80
2	200	200	NIL	NIL	NIL	60
3	125	125	–	–	–	–
4	60	60	–	–	–	–
Over 4	NIL	NIL	–	–	–	–

If a soil analysis is not available use the values underlined in the table.

Cultivars (Leeks)

A number of points should be considered when selecting leek cultivars: season of harvest; market requirement; disease resistance (Rust) etc.

EARLY CULTIVARS   (Autumn Harvest)

Swiss Giant Colonna	High yield, long stem with medium green flag.
Odin-Long Stanton	High yield, long medium green flag.
Titan	Early, high yielding, long stem with medium dark flag.
Tropia	Late Autumn harvest. Very long, tendency to bulb. Medium green flag.

MID SEASON   (January-March)

Autumn Mammoth – Snow Star	High yield, almost free from bulbing, medium long stem, mid green flag.
Autumn Mammoth – Otina	High yield, almost free from bulbing, medium long stem, mid to dark green flag.
Swiss Giant – Albinstar	High yield, little bulbing, medium to long stem, medium green flag.

LATE SEASON   (April-early May)

Monument	High yields, short stem, medium green flag.
Genita	High yields, medium stem, medium green flag.

Production methods

The leek crop can be raised in three ways:

(a)   multi-plant blocks (for early crops, particularly)
(b)   bare root transplants (for early crops and tight cropping schedules)
(c)   direct drilled (mainly for mid season and late crops)

Transplanting is a costly operation in terms of man and tractor hours. However, transplanting gives a better quality crop and enables earlier harvest when prices are better, while late planted crops can use the land occupied by early brassica crops. For the English market, transplanting of bare root leeks also gives a more blanched stem.

Leeks raised by multi-plant block method, showing four plants growing in a group.

Plant raising

Early cultivars may be sown from the beginning of February onwards, direct into blocks for the multi-plant block or into protected seed beds under glass or polythene tunnels. Later crops can be sown in open seed beds from mid March onwards.

The seed may be sown broadcast or drilled at row spacings of 80–150 mm (2–6 in). Sowing rates vary between 3–6 g/m^2 ($^1/_{10}$–$^1/_5$ oz/yd^2) giving 900–1200 plants/m^2 (84–112 ft^2) for high density seedbed under protection. Lower rates of 2–2.5 g/m^2 ($^1/_{15}$–$^1/_{12}$ oz/yd^2) give 450–550 plants/m^2 (42–51 ft^2) and these are used for seedbeds drilled at the wide row spacings of 300 mm (1 ft) (see Chapter 2 p. 28). Drilling enables easier distribution and covering of the seed. The optimum depth is 12 mm ($^1/_2$ in).

For multi-plant blocks each block will require five to ten seeds depending on the laboratory germination percentage and the estimated field factor for block raising (usually about 0.9). Three to five plants are required per block. The production of multi-plants in blocks requires specialized machinery and is, therefore, undertaken by specialist plant raisers.

Good weed control in the seedbed is essential as leek seed is slow to germinate and the upright growth habit of the plant does not suppress weed growth even at high densities.

Seedbed herbicides

Chlorthal dimethyl + propachlor (Dacthal-Ramrod) applied 7 + 6 kg/ha (6.3 + 5.4 lb/acre) as a tank mix immediately after drilling and covering has been completed.

OR

Chloridazon + chlorbufam (Alicep) used at 3.4–4.5 kg/ha (3–4 lb/acre) applied before emergence. If necessary this material can be used post-emergence once the plants are beyond the crook stage (see Figure 21).

Where tunnels or frames are repeatedly used for leek plant raising, soil sterilization with Dazomet is advisable. This will help avoid the build up of pests and diseases in the soil and will also give a large degree of weed control.

Transplants should be ready for planting in 13 to 15 weeks and every effort should be made to complete transplanting within 17 weeks of sowing or serious reduction in yield may result.

Planting

This may be undertaken in one of three ways. Small areas may be hand planted. One worker makes the holes with a leek dibber and the plants are dropped in the holes by a second worker. Alternatively, tractor mounted multi-dibbers are available. These have an output of approximately 15,000 holes per hour but the plants still have to be dropped into the holes afterwards by hand. Use of mechanical multi-dibbers or hand planting have the advantage of deep planting which gives a good length of blanched stem. Finally, in the case of the planting machine, the leek can be planted by a conventional planting machine but planting is not as deep as with the multi-dibber machine.

It is still a common practice to trim back the roots to 44 mm ($1^3/_4$ in) and foliage to approximately $^2/_3$ of the leek prior to planting as this makes handling much easier. However, recent Dutch research has suggested that this can reduce yield by up to 13 per cent.

Transplanted leeks are normally planted on the bed system at similar row spacings to the field drilled crop – five or six row beds at 250–300 mm (10–12 in) between rows. No earthing up is required since deep planting ensures adequate blanching.

Precision drilled leeks to a stand of 10 plants/metre run.

Field drilled crops

The crop can be direct drilled in late March or April using graded natural seed or mini-pellets. As the uniformity of the leek mini-pellet is very good there is no need for absolute precision. The more expensive regular pellet has little to offer the grower.

The rate of seeding should be calculated from the required plant stand, using the formula given in Chapter 2. Drilling is normally done with a belt, cup or vacuum type precision drill (see Chapter 11) at a depth of 12 mm (½ in).

Densities

Densities of 20–50 plants/m^2 (2–5 sq. ft) should be aimed for as below 20 plants/m^2 yields will start to drop. The high densities are most suitable for pre-pack leeks while the low density caters for the fresh market. Even the fresh market outlets are looking for smaller leeks so growers should aim for the higher density plantings.

The row spacing for direct drilled crops grown in beds is 250–300 mm (10–12 in) using five to six rows per bed. Alternatively leeks can be sown in 450–500 (18–20 in) wide rows and this system allows earthing up to be carried out in late summer, which increases the length of blanching.

Weed-control

Because germination and early growth are slow, coupled with the lack of foliage cover, the crop is very susceptible to weed competition. Most crops will require two herbicide applications, and late season crops may require three herbicide treatments in addition to the use of paraquat pre-sowing or pre-emergence.

FIELD DRILLED CROPS *(pre-emergence herbicides)*

Paraquat (Gramoxone) applied at 2–5 1/ha (1.5–3.5 pt/acre) is frequently used to control annual weeds which emerge before the crop. Alternatively the 'stale seedbed' technique (see weed control Chapter 12) is commonly used to germinate weeds, which can be sprayed with paraquat. In addition to paraquat a pre-emergence residual herbicide is required. The most useful ones are set out below:

Propachlor + chlorthal-dimethyl (Ramrod + Dacthal) 7 kg + 6 kg/ha (6.3 lb + 5.4 lb/acre) respectively for use on mineral soils only. This herbicide is soil acting only, therefore, must be applied before weeds germinate. It is a very safe material to use on leeks.

Chlorthal-dimethyl + methazole (Delozin S) applied at 4 kg/ha (3.5 lb/acre). These materials are soil acting with some foliage action, and they can be used again post-emergence.

Chloridazon + chlorbufam (Alicep) applied at 3.4 kg/ha (3 lb/acre) are soil and foliage acting. Risk of injury on very light soils is high if rain follows application. Seedling weeds are killed when very small.

Once the above treatments start to break down a *post-emergence herbicidal treatment* will be required. Where ridging is carried out a post emergence treatment should follow.

Irrigation
This may be necessary for establishment of transplants after planting. The crop has no particularly sensitive stage, so irrigation can be used throughout the crop's life (May-August). Irrigation of 25 mm (1 in) is normally applied at the following soil moisture deficits: low AWC soil – 25 mm; Medium AWC soil – 50 mm; high AWC soil – 75 mm.

Harvesting
Most leek crops are still harvested by hand, though all but the smallest of growers use a tractor mounted undercutter (see Figure 31, page 206). The vibrating share undercutter, driven from the tractor PTO, is much more effective than the simple static share. It also reduces tractor wheel slip during undercutting.

A top puller harvester can be used where row spacings are wide enough for the machine. For these machines extra workers are required to stack the leeks in one direction as they are discharged. A random stack of leeks is very difficult to handle at the trimming and washing stage.

Preparation and packing
The rough trimming is frequently carried out in the field but there is an increasing tendency for this work to be carried out in the packing shed. The leeks are hand skinned which involves the removal of the damaged or discoloured outer sheath and this is followed by trimming of the roots and leaves. Then the leeks are washed. Many growers have spray washers fitted with power trimmers which trim both leaf and root to a uniform length just prior to the leek entering the washing cabinet.

The trimming and packing requirements differ between England and Scotland. For the English market the leaves are normally trimmed to half the length of the stem and at least $^1/_3$ of the stem should be blanched, with roots trimmed back to at least 12 mm ($^1/_2$ in), the crop is then packed loose in 4–8 kg (9–18 lb) solid board trays.

The Scottish market requires more leaf and a leek of $^1/_2$ leaf and $^1/_2$ stem is acceptable. Blanching of the stem is less important and there is a tendency to leave more root on the plant. They are then bundled into 1 kg (2 lb) bundles, these bundles arc then packed in trays or crates of 4–8 kg (9–18 lb).

For the *pre-pack market* the root must be removed completely (this has to be done by hand) and the leaves are trimmed back hard to give 200–300 mm (8–12 in) overall length. The leeks should be 50–150 g (2–5 oz) in weight and the pack usually consists of a polythene sleeve or an overwrapped tray of 500 g (about 1 lb).

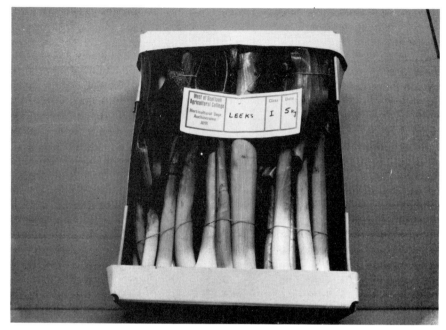

Market pack of leeks labelled to EEC standards.

Anticipated yield

Average yield – 23 tonnes/ha (9.2 tons/acre).

Pests and diseases

See Chapter 12 for details of pests and diseases of leeks and onions. Particular note should be made of rust disease which is a major problem of the leek crop.

Salad Onions – *Allium cepa* and *Allium fitulosum*

This is an important high value horticultural crop, which is mainly confined to the traditional market garden areas because of the very high labour requirement for harvesting. The major areas of production are Worcestershire, Kent, Surrey, Bedford and Essex. The total area is about 975 ha which is divided almost equally between the overwintered and summer crops. In addition to labour constraints the continuing spread of white rot disease is also reducing production on some soils.

Soils

Light soils are desirable for this crop as this eases lifting and washing.

Good drainage is essential, especially for the winter crop, but soils should have good moisture retention as well. Bulky organic manures are rarely used before this crop. If they are necessary for soil improvement they should be incorporated before the preceding crop where possible. Onions are not tolerant of acid soils, therefore the pH should be 6.5 on mineral soils and 5.4 on organic or peat soils.

Nutrition

The nutrition of the crop needs to be adjusted according to the season of production in respect of nitrogen and potassium and the recommendations are set out in the table below.

Table 36: Recommended fertilizer rate for salad onions (kg nutrient per hectare)

Nutrient index	Phosphate P_2O_5	Potash K_2O	Magnesium Mg		Nitrogen N
			Sandy soils	Other soils	
SALAD ONIONS – WINTER*					
0	250	250	60	60	25
1	225	225	30	NIL	NIL
2	200	200	NIL	NIL	NIL
3	125	125	–	–	–
4	60	50	–	–	–
Over 4	NIL	NIL	–	–	–
SALAD ONIONS – SUMMER AND AUTUMN					
0	250	125	60	60	125
1	225	100	30	NIL	75
2	200	75	NIL	NIL	50
3	125	50	–	–	–
4	60	25	–	–	–
Over 4	NIL	NIL	–	–	–

*A top dressing of 50–125 kg/ha N should be applied in spring. If soil analysis figures are not available use the values underlined in the table.

Cultivars

Two species of allium can be used to produce the salad onion crop. *Allium cepa* the species also used for the dry bulb onion crop, and *Allium fitulosum*, the Japanese bunching onion.

ALLIUM CEPA This was the first species used for salad onions, and the only cultivar found to be suitable for commercial production was White Lisbon. A more hardy strain of White Lisbon has been selected and bred for the production of overwintered crops. It is known as Winter

Hardy White Lisbon but the name is frequently shortened to Winter Hardy. The species has a dark green leaf which contrasts with a white stem base giving an attractive product. Unfortunately this species starts to bulb during the longer days of summer. Bulbing detracts from the quality of the crop and also reduces its holding capacity. As the degree of bulbing increases, the longer harvesting is delayed.

ALLIUM FITULOSUM A more recent introduction, this species has a paler green foliage and a larger seed (and the seed count per 10 g is much lower). The principal advantages of this species are its freedom from bulbing and the potential for growing the same cultivars for both summer and overwinter crops. A limited range of cultivars are available. The better known ones are Ishikuro and Asagi Bunching.

Cultivations
The technique used will vary greatly for this crop as it is frequently fitted into very tight crop production programmes. The aim is to produce a firm, level seedbed with even moisture content. A good tilth is essential for uniform emergence and also improves the action of residual herbicides.

Drilling
AUTUMN DRILLED CROPS This crop is normally sown on three dates between mid July and mid August, though small areas may be sown as late as the end of August to early September in mild areas. The earliest sowings should aim for a density of 270 plants/m^2 (25/sq ft) while the later sowings should aim for a higher density of 350 plants/m^2 (32/sq ft).

SPRING DRILLED CROPS This crop is drilled at a higher density than overwintered crops and 430 plants/m^2 (40/sq ft) should be aimed for. The first sowings are made as soon as soil conditions are suitable and continue until approximately the middle of June.
The drilling depth for all salad onions is 10–12 mm (about ½ in).

SPACING of the crop varies with the equipment used. The most common is as follows: single rows at 200–225 mm (8–9 in) spacing is most suitable for bed systems; for field systems double or triple lines can be sown with lines 25 mm (1 in) apart and 300–380 mm (12–15 in) between row centres.

Weed control
Good weed control is essential in this crop as it has little ability to

suppress weeds and they greatly inhibit harvesting. Where the crop is slow to germinate paraquat applied at 2–5 1/ha (1.5–3.5 pt/acre) pre-emergence will control early germinated weeds. During the summer when germination is more rapid the seedbed can be prepared 10–14 days before sowing and paraquat applied to the germinated weeds pre-sowing (the stale seedbed technique). In addition to paraquat a residual herbicide should be applied pre-emergence. The two most successful ones are: Chloridazon + chlorbufam (Alicep) applied at 3.4 kg/ha (3 lb/acre); and Chlorthal-dimethyl + propachlor (Dacthal + Ramrod) used as a tank mix at 7 + 6 kg/ha (6.3 + 5.4 lb/acre).

Irrigation
During dry periods irrigation pre-sowing may be required to obtain even germination. It may also be required pre-harvest to enable easier lifting. The crop does not have a moisture sensitive period. 25 mm (1 in) irrigation from April to August at 25 mm SMD will improve growth rate.

Harvesting
The crop is harvested when the stems are 6 to 12 mm (¼-½ in) in diameter. It is usual to undercut by machine and then by workers employed on piece work bunch the leeks in the field. They remove 'tagging' (dead leaves and debris) and weeds as they work. The bunches usually weigh approximately 85 g (2¾ oz) and contain a handful of some 10–15 salad onions in each bunch. A good worker will be able to bunch about 200 bunches in an hour. The bunches are then taken into the packing shed for spray washing and trimming. If the latter is required it is carried out after washing or by means of a mechanical trimmer on the washing machine. The individual bunches are then banded together in bundles of 10 or 12.

The crop is frequently packed wet, therefore the trays used must be waterproof. Wooden tomato trays are frequently used or an equivalent sized tray of waterproof solid board with four bundles per tray. The crop should be free from soil and yellowed leaves once packed.

Storage
The crop has a very limited storage life, but to even out supplies or hold Friday liftings for a Monday market the crop can be stored at 0 to 1°C (a maximum of three days). Rapid cooling is essential if the crop is to be stored. It should be harvested, washed and cooled in the shortest possible time. The market trays can be stacked in store provided there is adequate air circulation and the depth of onions in the tray is not more than 100 mm (4 in).

Pests and diseases – see Chapter 12

Major pests and diseases of alliums

ONION FLY   The only major pest of the allium group is the onion fly, *Delia antiqua*. Damage occurs as a result of the larvae of the fly tunnelling into the onion bulb or the base of the plant. The leaves become soft and yellow in colour and the plant begins to wilt at the very slightest sign of moisture stress. When the attack occurs on young onions or leeks, the plants are frequently killed. In some areas Dieldrin is still used as a seed dressing but there is now widespread resistance among onion flies to this pesticide. In areas of resistance, diazinon, applied as granules or as a spray, gives good control.

WHITE ROT   Currently the most serious disease of the allium group is undoubtedly white rot, *Sclerotium cepivorum*. The disease persists for long periods in the soil and there is no satisfactory control measure. The plants start to rot at the base with an obvious white fungal growth in which black sclerotia can be seen.

Where possible alliums should not be grown in infested land and the widest possible rotations should be used to avoid occurrence of the problem.

Seed dressings of iprodine ('Rovral') have proved useful for salad onions, where the high sowing rate enables a large amount of chemical to be added to the soil. Seed dressings are, however, not satisfactory for other allium crops as they tend to have much lower sowing rates.

Sprays of iprodine may be applied down the row as a preventative or curative (in the early stages) treatment but it is very costly and would probably only be worth while in order to save an infected crop.

ONION SMUT *Urocystis cepulae*   This is also a soil-borne disease which remains viable for at least 15 years but the plant is only susceptible during the first two to three weeks after germination. After this, the cotyledon becomes resistant and provides a barrier to infection. Infected plants develop dark coloured spots or streaks on the cotyledons and the disease sometimes spreads to the true leaves. Eventually the epidermis above the spots becomes silvery in appearance and then bursts releasing spores into the soil.

Susceptible crops should not be drilled in infected soil, though a few preventative treatments have shown promising results. Trickling 40 per cent formalin solution in the seed drill before covering has long been used as a control for small areas. Also the use of ferbam and thiram applied with a potash resin sticker to form a seed dressing has also shown promise.

Where plants are raised in peat blocks in an environment free from the disease, the resulting plants should be immune by the time they reach the planting out stage. This is probably a more satisfactory method of control than the use of chemicals on crops sown direct into infected soil.

Chapter Seven

Root Crops

Beetroot – *Beta vulgaris* var. *Esculenta*

Beetroot is an important fresh crop but the expansion of the freezing and pickling trade has changed the emphasis. The long beetroot were once much favoured in the south, being more suitable for storage, whereas globe beet were much favoured in the north and used for early bunching and pickling. They are, however, smaller and less heavily yielding. Despite this, most of the beetroot grown are of the round type.

Soils
The aim is to produce high quality, tender, deeply coloured beetroot, free of fibre. Best roots are grown on sandy loams and silts which have been manured for a previous crop. Beetroot commonly follows March cleared leeks or April cropped spring greens in the rotation.

Preparation of land
On no account should fresh manure be applied to the land before sowing beetroot. On the other hand, land short of organic matter encourages scab, a condition which occurs on alkaline soils too. Prepare soil by ploughing, harrowing and rolling to a medium fine tilth. A soil pH of 6.0 is required but beware of too high pH.

Nutrition
Beetroot requires a very general fertilizer with, perhaps, a slight emphasis on potash. Excess nitrogen should not be applied before seeding.

Densities and spacings
The beetroot seed consists of a cluster of seeds held together by a hard

Table 37: Recommended fertilizer rates for beetroot (kg nutrient per hectare)

Nutrient index	Phosphate P_2O_5	Potash K_2O	Magnesium Mg Sandy soils	Other soils	Nitrogen N
0	250	300	60	60	250*
1	200	250	<u>30</u>	NIL	200*
2	<u>125</u>	<u>200</u>	NIL	NIL	150
3	60	125	–	–	–
4	NIL	60	–	–	–
Over 4	NIL	NIL	–	–	–

If a soil analysis is not available use the values underlined in the table.
*No more than 150 kg/ha of N should be applied as a base dressing. The remainder should be applied as a top dressing soon after emergence.

corky substance, which contains a natural germination inhibitor. Germination is, therefore, somewhat sporadic and may take days to several weeks. Each seed cluster may well produce several seedlings. Soaking seed in thiram solution has been found to wash out inhibitors as well as provide a useful fungicide against diseases carried on the seed, such as *Phoma betae*.

The seed is usually drilled to a stand, rates depending on the final crop use.

Table 38: Seed densities for drilling beetroot

Beet crop	Density/sq m	Plant population/ha
Early bunching	53.8 (5/sq ft)	538,180 (217,800/acre)
Baby pickling	161.4–215.2 (15–20/sq ft)	1,614,000–2,152,000 (653,400–817,200/acre)
Fresh	47.62 (4.4/sq ft)	476,200 (192,716/acre)

For the early bunching crop row spacings should be between 300–380 mm (12–15 in). At a spacing of 280 mm (11 in) a stand of 20.3/m (6.2/ft) row of plants is required. The standard spacing for the fresh market is also 380 mm (15 in). When the Fernhurst bed system is used 280 mm (11 in) row spacing is used with six row beds (for fresh consumption).

If beetroot is to be used for baby pickling (and freezing) much closer row spacings ensure small tender beet. Rows at 50 mm apart either in four row or six row mini-beds are used. Plant stands of 20–26/m (6.2–8/ft) of row are required.

Sowing

Seed is sown from end of March for earliest crops for bunching. Maincrop beetroot is sown from April to end July in the south and end April to early July in the north. Depth of drilling is 25–38 mm (1-1½ in) but during dry weather drilling can be as deep as 50 mm (2 in) to ensure moisture reaches the seed clusters. Rates of drilling vary according to seed size and type. Use of rubbed seed means that the seed cluster has been smoothed to a regular shape and therefore allows more accurate drilling. Mono-germ seed, where only one seedling germinates, is now becoming popular to achieve accurate stands.

Calculate the seed requirement by using known laboratory germination figures and field factor figures as described in Chapter 2.

Very early sowings may lead to 'bolting' of the crop. Long cultivars need warmer soil temperatures, so never sow these until May.

Cultivars

Special emphasis is placed on cultivars which are resistant to 'bolting' (the situation causing beetroot to run to seed during the first growing season). Standard bolting resistant round cultivars include Avon Early and Boltardy. The standard long varieties are Cheltenham Greentop and Cylindra.

Weed control

PRE-DRILLING HERBICIDES Cycloate/lenacil (Ro-neet/Venzar) are incorporated into the top 20–50 mm (1–2 in) of soil by harrowing before sowing – but not after April 15. Use 2.8–5.6 1/ha (2–4 pt/acre) Ro-neet and 0.49–1.05 kg/ha (½–1 lb/acre) Venzar as a tank mix. Do not use on soils with more than 50 per cent organic matter or on soils lighter than loamy sand.

PRE-EMERGENCE HERBICIDES Chlorpropham/fenuron (Herbon Yellow) residual herbicide applied at 22–27 1/ha (2–2½ gal/acre) as soon as seed has chitted. Use low dosage rates on light sands and soils with a high water table.

Ethofumesate (Nortron) applied as soon as possible after drilling at 5–10 1/ha (3.5–7 pt/acre) OR at two fully expanded true leaves (rate of use 5 1/ha or 3.5 pt/acre). Tank mixes lenacil (Venzar) or chlorpropham/propham/fenuron formulation (Herbon Gold) are carried out pre-emergence.

Lenacil (Venzar) is used immediately after drilling or pre-drilling on organic soils at 1.1–2.8 kg/ha (1–2½ lb/acre) or 2.2–3.4 kg/ha (2–3 lb/acre) on organic soils, lighter than loamy sand and heavier than sandy clay loam. A moist fine tilth is essential for this residual to be absorbed by soil. Drill deeper than 18 mm (¾ in). Its residual life is six months, and longer on organic soils.

POST-EMERGENCE HERBICIDE   Metamitron (Goltix) – This is applied at 5 kg/ha (4.5 lb/acre) post-emergence when crop has two true leaves. If weeds beyond cotyledon stage add Actipron at 5 1/ha (3.5 pt/acre).

Irrigation

Irrigation is not widely used for this crop except to induce early varieties to mature quicker. Use 25 mm irrigation at 25 mm SMD for these early crops. Excessive addition of water on main crop can lead to production of large coarse roots.

Harvesting

The bunching beet season lasts from June to July. The beet foliage is trimmed and roots bunched in sixes and tied. The bunches are then packed in Dutch trays or in units of 10 bunches. Care must be taken not to bruise these young beetroot. The season for topped beet starts from end July and continues until next May.

Lifting is done during dry weather. On light soils for early crops the job of lifting can be carried out by hand. For the later market the beet is topped about 25 mm (1 in) above the crown with a forage harvester and harvested with a digger elevator and put in trailer or bulk bins. The beet can then be washed. The most popular sized root for the fresh market is 100 mm (4 in) in diameter. Beets are sold loose in red nets of 12 kg (28 lb) or loose in crates.

Storage

Beetroot can be stored in clamps the same way as potatoes. The roots are stacked tops outwards and covered with straw and soil to be sold from December onwards. A more modern approach is to harvest beet-

Figure 23 'Clamping' beetroot in a bulk bin by surrounding the unit with straw bales. Note that the inside of the bin is lined with polythene.

oot into bulk bins, then a clamp of the bulk bin is formed in the manner hown in Figure 23. Nowadays, of course, refrigerated cold stores enable long term storage to be used.

Anticipated yield Average yield – 36.5 tonnes/ha (15 tons/acre).

Pests and diseases See Chapter 12 on pests and diseases.

Carrot – *Daucus carota* var. *Sativa*

After brassicas and peas, carrots are the next most important horticultural crop grown in the UK. Most of the 14,542 ha are grown on a large farm scale, using a high degree of mechanization, with a few early punched carrots being grown intensively in favoured areas.

There are two distinct markets – the WARE trade sold mainly through the wholesale market or by self-pick, and the PROCESSING market for which carrots are mainly grown on contract. The cultivars and plant densities used for each are very different. Not surprisingly, the processing trade is more demanding in quality and uniformity of carrot grown. Considerable attention to detail is required to produce quality carrots otherwise the chances of failure are high. There are three prerequisites to success:

1) An adequate stand of carrots based on correct seed rates and good cultivation.
2) A high level of weed control during growth.
3) Good control of carrot fly which can so easily reduce a crop to an unmarketable level.

Soils

To ensure unrestricted root development a well textured sandy loam is considered ideal. Sandy soils may also be used but here the texture of the subsoil is important – those overlying sands or gravels may present a problem with drying out. Stones complicate mechanical operations, poor structured soils cap easily in wet conditions, making germination a problem, while shallow soils may cause 'fanging' of roots. Peaty soils are also used in the Fens but these present difficulties with herbicide application. Stone free soils with a minimum depth of 380 mm (15 in) and a water holding capacity of 37 mm per 300 mm depth (1½ in per ft) overlying moisture bearing subsoils, are required.

Any site chosen must take into account mechanical operations which play a vital part in this crop. The soil must take heavy equipment and should be well drained so that autumn or winter mechanical operations do not cause excessive damage.

Rotation

Close cropping may cause problems with the soil-borne diseases and pests, violet root rot and carrot root eelworm for which there is no real control. Carrots are commonly rotated with cereals and potatoes over a five-year rotation.

Cultivation

Ploughing should be completed by the end of February, but during a wet winter late ploughing followed by rolling to firm the surface is adequate. Subsoiling prior to ploughing may be necessary if a compaction or soil pan is suspected. If the soil is very acid (below 5.5) part of the lime required should be ploughed in, the remainder being used after ploughing, but before the end of February. The required minimum pH is 6.5 for mineral soils and 5.8 for peat soils.

In working down the soil to a firm, fine, clod-free level surface, remember to use wheel track eliminators to remove wheelings created by tractor cultivations during preparation of the seedbed. Tractor wheel compaction causes uneven germination – so for all cultivations work in one direction only. The bed system (see Appendix 2) of growing avoids these problems.

The use of the stale seedbed technique (see p. 234 Chapter 12) is continually used with later sowings to reduce annual weed populations.

Fertilizer application

Apply fertilizers, except the nitrogen part, at least one month before sowing during the ploughing operation. The nitrogen can then be applied after drilling or even emergence. However, many growers prefer to use the simpler approach of applying a compound fertilizer just before the drilling operation. Since the growth of the crop is far more demanding than most others, soil analysis is a *must* to assess fertilizer needs. The requirement of carrots is for high levels of phosphate and potash.

Trace element deficiencies can cause problems on carrots, notably boron, copper and manganese. Boron is commonly deficient on sandy soils, especially where the pH is above 6.5 and this can be identified by soil analysis. Correct deficiency by applying Borax at 22 kg/ha (20 lb/acre) as a solid dressing or use Solubor as a spray at 11 kg/ha (10 lb/acre) to the seedbed before drilling. Copper, often deficient on reclaimed heathland and peat, can be rectified by a foliar spray of copper oxychloride at 2.2 kg/ha (2 lb/acre) during the mid season. Manganese deficiency may be a problem on peat soils and soils of high pH, but this can only be diagnosed by leaf analysis. Where 20 mg/kg or less of manganese are found in dry leaf matter then deficiency should be rectified by a foliar spray of manganese sulphate (9 kg/ha in 200–300 l of water or 8.0 lb/acre in 44–66 gal of water).

Table 39: Recommended fertilizer rates for carrots (kg nutrient per hectare)

Nutrient index	Phosphate P_2O_5	Potash K_2O	Magnesium Mg Sandy soils	Other soils	Nitrogen N Fen Peats	Other soils
0	250	250	60	60	60	100
1	200	200	30	NIL	40	75
2	125	125	NIL	NIL	NIL	NIL
3	60	60	–	–	–	–
4	60	60	–	–	–	–
Over 4	NIL	NIL	–	–	–	–

If a soil analysis is not available use the values underlined in the table.

Cultivars

A well grown top quality carrot should have a uniform deep orange core and flesh with a smooth skin. The many hundreds of varieties available fall into major category groupings, each having a distinctive shape and satisfying different market outlets. Selecting a suitable variety is very important, though the buyers of the processed crop normally make recommendations to their growers. The groups are shown below in order of maturity.

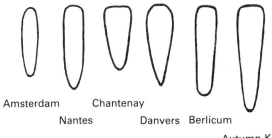

Amsterdam	Chantenay
Nantes	Danvers Berlicum
	Autumn King

Figure 24 Carrots grouped by their shape

AMSTERDAM FORCING   Small, cylindrical and very early. Grown mainly for early bunching, fresh market or pre-packing.
NANTES   Medium size, with slight shoulder and taper. Grown for fresh market and pre-packing.
CHANTENAY   Small to medium size carrot which has good core colour. Widely used for canning (small carrots are used whole, medium sized roots for slicing and large for dicing).
DANVERS   Heavy yielding carrots, mainly used for canning and slicing.

BERLICUM   Long cylindrical carrots of good colour, widely used for ware, pre-pack and freezing markets. Some also used for sliced canning. AUTUMN KING   Heavy yielding, large tapered carrots, usually with inferior core colour. Chiefly grown for the late ware market, but select cultivars for colour and frost resistance.

Production cycle

All-year round production of supply can be achieved in the manner shown below.

Table 40: All-year round marketing of carrots

Month required for market	Sowing date												Production technique
	Jan	Feb	Mar	Apr	May	June	July	Aug	Sep	Oct	Nov	Dec	
JUNE		▓											Field grown under plastic mulches.
JULY–SEPT		▓	▓										Field grown for early crop.
OCT–MAY				▓									Field grown, soil or straw covered after November.
JUNE				▓									Field grown and cold stored.

Seed and seed treatment

Seed is commonly dressed with HCH/captan or HCH/thiram. The HCH gives some protection against the first generation of carrot fly and the fungicides (thiram and captan) discourage seed rotting. But the powdered coating may affect seed flow so check the drill carefully. Also many processors restrict the use of HCH because of risk of taint.

Plant densities

Plant densities are very important in growing carrots, especially for processing where a uniform root size is required. Recommended densities for the varying crop outlets are shown in Table 41.

Quality of seed used

Because of the variation in seed numbers and the variation in percentage germination with different stocks, calculation of seed requirements based on final density required should be carefully worked out (see

Table 41: Carrot densities for different outlets

Crop outlet/use	Approx. shoulder diameter	Density per sq m	(per sq ft)
Carrots for bunching (early)	12–25 mm (½–1″)	540	(50)
Carrots for freezing	20–25 mm (¾–1″)	430	(40)
Small roots for canning whole/small pre-pack	18–32 mm (¾–1¼″)	376	(30–40)
Medium sized roots for pre-packing	32–43 mm (1¼–1¾″)	161	(15)
Large roots for slicing or dicing	greater than 45 mm (1¾″ min)	55–110	(5–10)
Large roots for maincrop ware yield	25–70 mm (1–3″)	100	(9)

Chapter 2). Graded seed is particularly useful since it ensures more accurate seed counts and more accurate calculation of seed requirement. Large variations in seed size and germination percentages can alter seed requirement by as much as 100 per cent.

Drilling – patterns of growing

The seed is normally drilled to a stand at a depth of 10–12 mm (approximately ½ in).

The seed rates will be affected by row spacing, the density required and the harvesting system chosen. Many row systems exist and some are illustrated on page 140 giving approximate plant densities. The newer mini-bed systems (three four-row mini-beds to a bed, and two six-row mini-beds to a bed) are becoming popular for dense sowings for bunching or small carrots for freezing and pre-packing. The old single row system is virtually confined to large carrot production.

The most vigorous carrots grow at the edge of beds, so to ensure uniformity of root size increase the sowing rate of outer rows on the beds by about 15 per cent.

The mechanical harvester available may determine which row spacing the grower can use (see details noted against each system). Basically, harvesters are of two types – top lifting and digger elevator types. *Top lifting types* lift single rows or beds at minimum row spacings of 375 mm (15 in) and foliage width of not more than 100 mm (4 in). The machine is tractor mounted, light and leaves tops and stones behind. It can only be used on wide row spacings and once foliage dies down it cannot be used at all. *Digger elevator types* ('hoovers') although heavy, are more versatile, lifting both beds and individual rows. However, stones and clods may carry over in to the elevator. A topper on the front of the

Figure 25 Row spacings for carrots

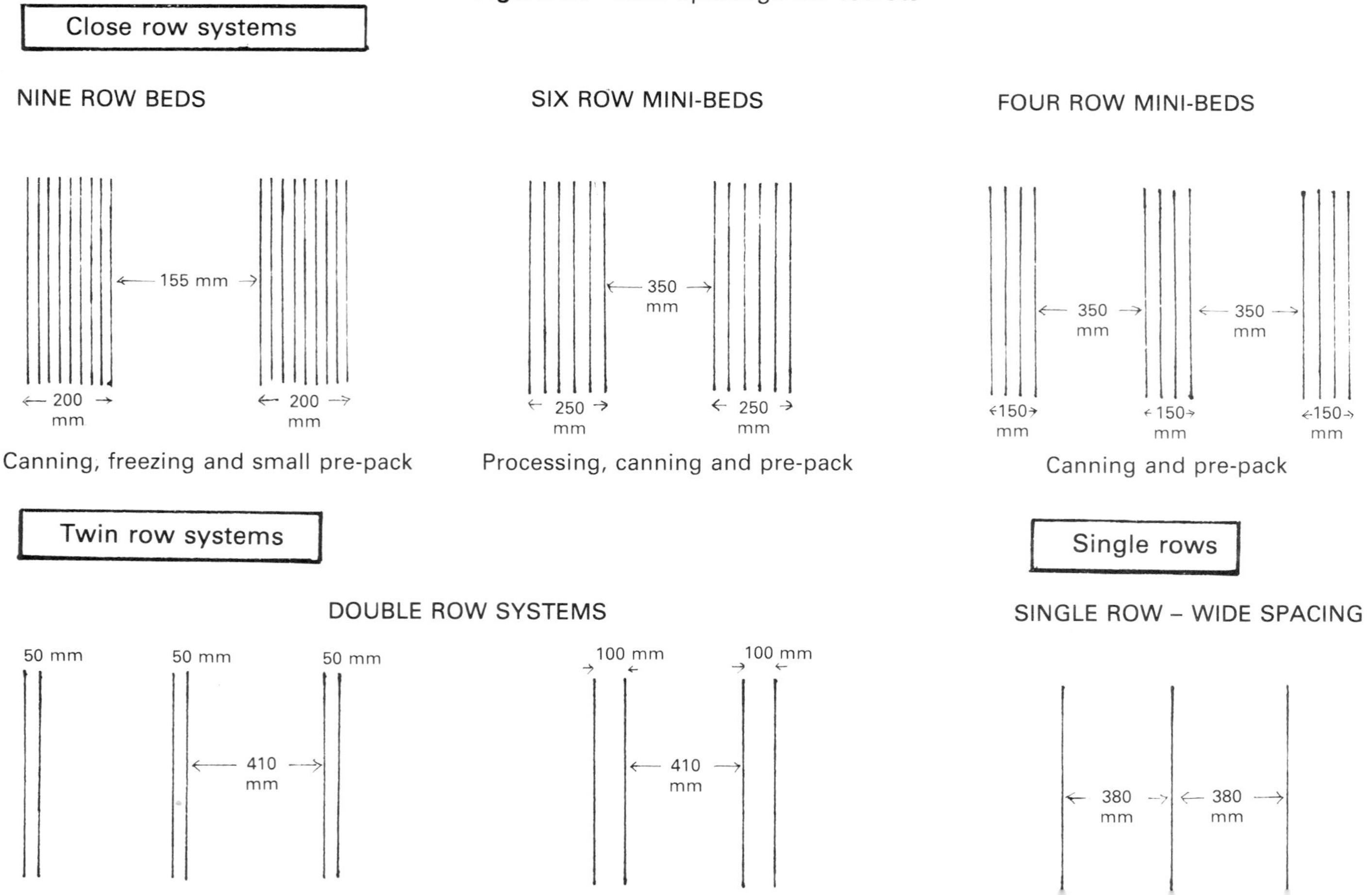

machine removes leaves before lifting.

Drilling should only be carried out when the soil is adequately moist for germination. On light land in dry conditions pre-irrigate a day before drilling – but beware of capping soil with excessively large droplets.

Even distribution of seed down the rows and an even spacing between the rows is important to achieve an uniform root size. Using graded seed with French chalk to aid the flow enables greater accuracy and better uniformity. Recent work suggests that in close row systems the carrots in centre rows are smaller. It is therefore suggested drilling at different rates, decreasing the rate slightly in the centre rows or increasing the size grade of seed used. Semi-precision drills are extensively used for sowing close row spacings (300 mm or 12 in and less) and bed systems. Multi-purpose cereal drills are still used (pneumatic/centrifugal mechanisms or fluted roller types) but it is difficult to maintain seed sowing at such shallow settings. Rowcrop or root drills with rotary perforated plate and agitator mechanisms are also used. But precision drilling units with cell wheels, or of the belt type, are the most effective and can be mounted in tandem to achieve close row spacings.

Plastic mulching
The maturity of early carrots can be advanced by using perforated plastic mulches like Xiro, but row systems must be adjusted to suit the machinery for laying the mulch. The mulch should be removed when the crop has about seven true leaves.

Temperature and the growth of carrots
Many growers do not realize the important part that temperature has to play in the development of carrots. Germination temperature is critical to success since carrots rely on the store of food within the seed to generate initial roots, the quicker the seed germinates the better the chance of success, and the less the chance of the seed rotting from soil borne fungi.

Temperature also affects premature bolting. Carrots are most prone to 'bolting', or running to seed in their first year, at the five to eight leaf stage. Periods of low temperatures (frost levels) cause bolting. Bolted carrots are tough, small and unmarketable.

Finally, carrots depend on adequate temperature for their colour and shape. The best coloured carrots are produced when temperatures at growth are 15–20°C (59–68°F). Above or below this level carrot colour develops slowly and tends to be rather yellow. Root shape most typical of the variety is also produced at similar temperatures, the ideal being 18°C (64°F).

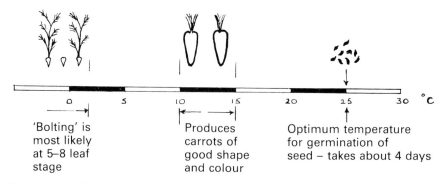

'Bolting' is most likely at 5–8 leaf stage	Produces carrots of good shape and colour	Optimum temperature for germination of seed – takes about 4 days

Figure 26   The effect of temperature on the growth of carrots

Weed control

Growing carrots is only as successful as the level of weed control that can be maintained. For this is a slow germinating crop and weed seedlings can so easily choke out the young carrots.

Treatments include:

PRE-DRILLING RESIDUAL   Triallate incorporated in soil pre-drilling at 3.5 l/ha (2½ pt/acre) for control of couch or black grass.

PRE-EMERGENT CONTACT   Paraquat or paraquat/diquat applied at 2.8 l/ha (2 pt/acre) to young germinating annual weed seedlings. Apply just before carrots germinate.

POST-EMERGENCE RESIDUAL   Linuron applied at 1.1 kg/ha (1 lb/acre) will control germinating annual weeds. Apply within four days of drilling. Double the rate for peaty soils.

Chlorbromuron applied at 1.1 kg/ha (1 lb/acre). Use as above but unsuitable on peaty soils at this stage.

or

POST-EMERGENCE RESIDUAL   Linuron – rates as above, apply after two true leaf stage.

Chlorpropham + Pentanochlor – apply at 5.6 l/ha (4 pt/acre) at two true leaf stage. Prevents seedlings germinating but also has some contact action on small existing weeds.

Prometryne – apply at 2.2 kg/ha (2 lb/acre) at two true leaf stage. Again has residual action plus some contact effect.

Chlorbromuron – apply at 1.65 kg/ha (1½ lb/acre) when weeds first emerge but only after crop has reached two leaf stage. Double rate for peaty soils.

POST-EMERGENCE CONTACT   Pentanochlor – apply 5.6 l/ha (4 pt/acre) at first true leaf stage to control a wide range of annual weeds, including annual meadow grass.

Irrigation

Carrot production is viable in most years without irrigation on sandy soils, provided the subsoil is not too free draining. If irrigation is necessary, never irrigate (a) between sowing and four true leaf stage, as seedlings can be 'swamped' and soil capping may inhibit germination, or (b) in the latter stages of the crop after a long period of drought as this causes splitting. For details of irrigation timing see Chapter 3.

Harvesting and storage

Crops for ware purposes are often lifted as and when required by the market. To protect roots from frost 150 mm (6 in) of soil is earthed up over the rows and these are lifted from January onwards. For bed grown crops use 300 mm (1 ft) depth of straw laid loosely over the crop in November to December to protect roots. Clamping, the old way of covering a heap of unwashed carrots with soil, enables roots to be maintained until end of March. Crops for processing are rarely field stored as they are usually lifted by December. Lifting of the crop is carried out by a digger-elevator or a top lifting harvester. The carrots are loaded into a nearby trailer before going to the packing shed. A system is needed to harvest, load up trucks and transport carrots to the packhouse. This will vary according to manpower available and type of machinery used.

CONTROLLED TEMPERATURE STORAGE is carried out for long term storage. Lift under good weather conditions, do not wash, remove any damaged roots and store in polythene-lined bulk containers of 500–1,000 kg (1,102–2,205 lb) at 0.1°C (95–98 per cent humidity). Where icebank cooling is carried out in the store the standard bulk bin without polythene lining may be used.

Marketing and grading

The majority of this crop is sold in orange nets of 28 lb (this will probably be changed to 12 kg when the wholesale markets become metricated). Roots are normally washed and graded into one of three grades (see Table 56).

The early crop may be bunched, and in this case the worker discards any mis-shapen, insect damaged or diseased roots while pulling the crop. Irrigation is commonly used prior to lifting to help 'pull' the crop. A good worker will lift 300 bunches an hour where carrots are grown at close spacings. A handful of 10–12 carrots are placed in each bunch and these are laid flat, 20 bunches to a tray, after the roots have been washed.

Anticipated yield

	Early crop	Main crop
Average yield	23 tonnes/ha	40 tonnes/ha
	(9.5 tons/acre)	(16.5 tons/acre)

Pests and diseases

By far the most important pest of carrots is carrot fly as this can make a crop completely unmarketable. Special reference is made to carrot fly and methods of control in the section below. For other pests and diseases of carrots see Chapter 12.

CARROT FLY – *PSILLA ROSAE*   This is such an important pest of carrots, celery and to a lesser extent parsnips, that it warrants special attention. In carrots the pest can cause almost 100 per cent loss of the crop.

The adult flies, no longer than 2–3 mm, are on wing from late May. They lay eggs in the soil at about the time cow parsley begins to flower. The young larvae hatch and immediately start feeding on the carrot roots, entering the side of the carrot and working towards the carrot core. Initially, damage is seen as minor wilting and later carrot foliage turns red and bronze. When lifted, large patches of the flesh are eaten leaving rusty brown marks and making the roots completely unsaleable. The second generation of fly occurs from July to September. A third generation may occur in November.

Control of the fly is vital to the crop and annual protective treatments are recommended (see Table 42).

Parsnip – *Pastinaca sativa*

Like many other crops, the production of parsnips has changed in recent years to take into account mechanization and market trends. Parsnips are now required nearly all year round with earliest crops being produced from July onwards in small quantities. The main demand in the fresh market occurs over winter, and builds up from November onwards after parsnips have been frosted. It is this frosting which gives them the sweetness that makes them so tasty. Mechanization of every stage of production has enabled this crop to be economically viable despite relatively low market prices.

Parsnips fall into three basic categories: wedge shape, bulbous and long, tapering broad-shouldered types (bayonet).

The long tapering roots are the traditional market varieties but these present problems with mechanical harvesting, the roots breaking off partway down because of their taper. The bulbous and wedge shape varieties are much easier, particularly if not grown too large. A 40–100

Table 42: Chemical control of carrot fly

CHEMICAL	RATE	COMMENTS ON USE
First generation fly control		
Gamma HCH	42–62 g/kg of seed ($^2/_3$–1 oz per lb)	Use a seed dressing. High rate used on peaty soils
*Phorate (as Phorate 10%)	28–34 kg/ha (25–30 lb/acre) – broadcast. 17–28 kg/ha (15–25 lb/acre) – bow-wave	Use as granules applied at drilling time, either broadcast or bow-wave. Higher rates used on peaty soils.
Disulfoton (as Disyston FE 10%)	21 kg/ha (19 lb/acre) – broadcast. 11 kg/ha (10 lb/acre) – bow-wave	Use as granules applied at drilling time, either broadcast or bow-wave.
Chlorfenvinphos (as Birlane 10%)	22 kg/ha (20 lb/acre)	Use as granules applied broadcast.
Diazinon (as Basudin 5%)	36–45 kg/ha (32–40 lb/acre)	Use as granules using bow-wave system at drilling time. Higher rates used on peaty soils.
Second generation (assuming Phorate granules are applied bow-wave for first generation)		
Chlorfenvinphos (as Birlane 24)	10 l/ha (7 pints/acre)	Use as foliage spray for all crops lifted from September–mid November. Repeat spray in early October for crops lifted from late November onwards.

* Also controls aphids on carrots.

mm (2–4 in) diameter root suits the pre-pack trade. The processors, on the other hand, require very large parsnips of 150 mm (6 in) diameter across the shoulder and above.

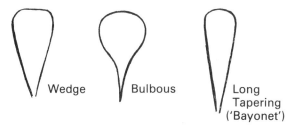

Wedge Bulbous Long Tapering ('Bayonet')

Figure 27 Categories of parsnips

Soils

Deep stone free soils (sands, sandy loams or fen peats) are ideal, similar to those required by carrots. Free drainage and ease of mechanical lifting during winter months are the pre-requisites for success. The soil should contain a minimum water holding capacity of 125 mm per metre depth (5 in per 3 ft), and overlying moisture bearing subsoils.

Nutrition

The nutrition of parsnips is very similar to carrots, with a high requirement of potash and phosphate. The soil pH should be 6.5 and above for mineral soils and 5.8 for Fen soils.

Table 43: Recommended fertilizer rates for parsnips (kg nutrient per hectare)

Nutrient index	Phosphate P_2O_5	Potash K_2O	Magnesium Mg Sandy soils	Other soils	Nitrogen N Fen peats	Other soils
0	250	250	60	60	60	100
1	200	200	30	NIL	40	75
2	125	125	NIL	NIL	NIL	NIL
3	60	60	–	–	–	–
4	60	60	–	–	–	–
Over 4	NIL	NIL	–	–	–	–

If a soil analysis is not available use the values underlined in the table.

Preparation of seedbed

The land for parsnips should be prepared by deep ploughing in the autumn, subsoiling where necessary. The land left in a rough state will then become frosted and the base dressing can then be applied before final cultivation so that it can become evenly incorporated during the final cultivation. Harrowing followed by rolling will probably be necessary to obtain a satisfactory seedbed. Recent work has shown that this crop is extremely sensitive to compaction created by tractor wheelings. Either use wheel track eliminators to overcome the problem or grow parsnips by the bed system.

Plant densities and spacing

The standard row spacing is between 380–460 mm (15–18 in) depending on the size of the parsnip. Older large cultivars, like Hollow Crown, require wider spacings than the newer, smaller canker-resistant varieties. For the fresh market, densities of 20/sq m (2/sq ft) are suggested, which at a row spacing of 460 mm means nine plants/m run (3/ft run) of row. For processing, 30 plants/sq m (3/sq ft) would be required, which, at the standard 460 mm (18 in) row spacing means 14 plants/m run of row.

For the pre-pack trade smaller roots are required and densities of 40–60/sq m (4–6/sq ft) are preferable. Row spacings are still maintained at 380–460 mm but the number of plants in the row increased to 16–19/m run (5–6/ft run).

Seed sowing

This is difficult seed to sow, since it is an unusual flat shape. It can be drilled to an approximate stand using a precision drill of which the vacuum type is most suitable. Both graded and extra cleaned seed help with precision drilling. Adding French chalk to the seed helps better flow in the drill. Precision seeding can be carried out using pellets but the expense of this seed can rarely be justified unless returns are high. Sowing starts as early as February in favourable situations, but the main crop is drilled in the first two weeks of March. Depth of drilling is shallow at 12 mm (½ in).

Cultivars

The breeding of cultivars in recent years has been towards canker resistance as this is a most disfiguring disease. Also for harvesting purposes a shallow crown is useful. But in this last feature, the yielding qualities of newer parsnips tend to be lower than the traditional parsnip. A list of cultivars and their qualities is given below. Choice will depend on market use.

Table 44: Parsnip cultivars and their qualities

	Size/shape	Yield	Canker resistance	Suitability
Alba	Small thin wedge	Low	Very resistant	For pre-packing and canning
Albino	Large wedge/ bulbous	High	Moderate	Fresh market
Avon Resister	Small bulbous	Low	Very resistant	Pre-pack market
Lisbonnais	Large long/ tapering	High	Poor	Fresh market
Offenham Reselected	Large bulbous/ wedge	High	Highly resistant	Fresh market
Unicorn	Medium wedge/ bulbous	Average	Highly resistant	Fresh market
White Gem	Large wedge/ bulbous	Very High	Moderate	Fresh and processing

Thinning

Where drilling cannot be carried out accurately, thinning by hand at the first true leaf stage may be necessary to achieve the required plant stand.

Weed control

The weed control in the early part of the crop is important since the seed is very slow to germinate. Paraquat may be used on a prepared stale seedbed for control of annual germinated weeds.

PRE-EMERGENCE HERBICIDES   Chlorpropham + fenuron (Herbon Yellow) – apply as a soil acting herbicide when seed has chitted at 22–27 1/ha (2–2½ gal/acre). Lower doses are used on light silts, sands and soils with high water table.

Chlorbromuron (Maloran 50 WP) – apply as a split application, the first spray within four days of drilling, the second at two true leaf stage. Alternatively, a single application post-emergence at two leaf stage at 1.1–3.4 kg/ha (1–3 lb/acre) can be used. This is a foliage and soil acting herbicide. Dosage rate varies with soil type.

Linuron – use within four days of drilling and/or after first true leaf stage. Damage may occur on light soils. Dosage rate varies with soil type and brand used.

POST-EMERGENCE HERBICIDES   Pentanochlor (Herbon Solan) – apply from first fully expanded cotyledon onwards at 5.6 1/ha (80 fl oz/acre) and, if necessary, repeat four weeks later.

Pentanochlor/chlorpropham/metoxuron (Herbon Brown + Dosaflo) 3 1 + 3 1/ha (43 + 43 fl oz/acre) applied after fifth true leaf stage.

Trifluaralin – as for carrots.

Harvesting and marketing

Harvesting begins as early as July but only in small quantities otherwise prices fall rapidly, making the low yields uneconomic to lift. Since this is a low value crop most parsnips are lifted at maximum yielding time (October–November) onwards, as and when required for market. Parsnips can be lifted with a digger elevator harvester ('hoover') or a top puller harvester. The latter can only be used while foliage is still present in summer or early autumn. The market requires washed roots, 'fanged' roots being discarded. These are known as 'chumps' when they are sold during times of shortage in the market. Good quality roots for fresh market, 40–130 mm (1½–5 in) wide, are sold in white nets of 12 kg (28 lb).

For the pre-pack trade strict control over root sizes are maintained, the smaller roots being preferred. Ideally 40–65 mm (1½–2½ in) diameter roots are required.

Storage

Although parsnips can withstand frost, they are commonly lifted and stored in unheated barns for two to three weeks. Best prices are obtained during periods of prolonged frost when lifting becomes impossible. Hence the reason for anticipating periods of cold by short term storage.

Anticipated yield

Average yield 23 tonnes/ha (9.16 tons/acre).
Good commercial yield 28 tonnes/ha (11.5 tons/acre).

Swedes – *Brassica rutabaga*

The swede is commonly considered to be a root crop yet it is a brassica, the root being the swollen hypercotyl of the plant. Swedes are extensively grown on a farm scale as they lend themselves to farm rotations. The majority of the crop is grown in Devon, East Anglia and the west of Scotland. Since it is a low value crop minimal work is carried out – even the cost of fertilizer has to be reckoned with.

Soils

The swede requires highly moisture retentive soils and the crop tends to be grown on heavy loams or in areas where summer rainfall is relatively high (ie, Devon and the west of Scotland). This helps production of a fleshy easily cooked swede, as against a rather fibrous root and discourages brown heart.

Swedes are very prone to boron deficiency (brown heart). This commonly occurs on sandy soils and can be induced by growing on alkaline soils above pH 6.5, especially in dry summers. Liming will be required if the pH falls below 5.5

Nutrition

Swedes have a high requirement for phosphate and potash, but it is doubtful whether the value of the crop can warrant high rates of use of these somewhat expensive fertilizers.

If soil analysis shows that boron levels are low, Borax can be applied to the soil just before ploughing at 22 kg/ha (20 lb/acre). Alternatively, Solubor may be sprayed on to the seedbed at 11 kg/ha (10 lb/acre).

Table 45: Table of recommended fertilizer rates for swedes (kg nutrient per ha)

Nutrient index	Phosphate P_2O_5	Potash K_2O	Magnesium Mg Sandy soils	Magnesium Mg Other soils	Nitrogen N
0	250	250	60	0	100*
1	200	200	<u>30</u>	NIL	50*
2	<u>125</u>	<u>125</u>	NIL	NIL	NIL*
3	60	60	–	–	–
4	60	60	–	–	–
5	NIL	NIL	–	–	–

*For early bunched turnips add 50 kg/ha N to the nutrient values.
If soil analysis figures are not available use the nutrient values underlined.

Land preparation

Land should be ploughed in autumn to allow the soil to be well frosted over winter. Any lime should be incorporated after ploughing time.

Cultivars

Doon Major is a cultivar of exceptional uniformity. High yielding cultivars are: Laurention; Marian; Ruta Otofte.

Drilling

Drilling commences early to mid March in the milder west and south, and at the end of May in the cooler north and east. Seed used should be graded for precision drilling. Treatment of seed with Thiram will protect against disease. The seed is drilled to give a seed every 50 mm (2 in) down the row, with a row spacing of 380 mm (15 in). Later thinnings will ensure the correct density of 17 plants/m^2 (1.6/ft^2). The seed is drilled to a depth of 18 mm (¾ in).

Chopping out

Chopping out can be carried out by hand or by selective machine thinning two to three weeks after germination. Machine thinning rarely gives 100 per cent results and hand finishing will be required. Thinning is to singles every 150 mm (6 in) down the row for late August, early September harvested crops. A closer thinning distance of 100 mm (4 in) is required for late October, early November harvest.

Weed control

Weed control is still extensively carried out by steerage hoe. The row spacing is relatively wide and easily managed.

The herbicides used for turnips (see page 148) can also be used on swedes.

Harvesting

From August onwards the crop is machine harvested by a digger elevator harvester. The roots are taken by the trailer load to the packhouse. Topping is carried out prior to harvest by means of a forage harvester or similar machine.

The crop is now sold for both pre-pack and wholesale markets. The pre-pack trade require small roots not more than 150 mm diameter (6 in) and they are graded into two sizes 80–130 mm (3–5 in) and 130–150 mm diameter (5–6 in). Swedes for the wholesale market are normally packed in red nets of 28 lb (12 kg). Grading is minimal, being confined to removal of diseased, small or bolted roots.

Storage

Storage, which commences from October onwards in traditional clamped heaps covered with straw and soil, is still used by many growers as a means of supplying the market with the crop overwinter. The storage of swedes in bulk bins in the manner illustrated for beetroot (see page 134) is a more up-to-date approach to the job. The value of the crop does not warrant refrigerated storage techniques.

Anticipated yield

Average yield 32 tonnes/ha (12.8 tons/acre).
Good yield 68 tonnes/ha (28.3 tons/acre).

Pests and diseases

Swedes suffer from most brassica diseases including club root but the most important problems are brown heart (see earlier) and powdery mildew. The use of Triademefon at 14-day intervals will give good control of powdery mildew. This disease is a real problem in drier areas on light soils. Mildew resistant cultivars, like Ruta Otofte, help to overcome the problem. For details of control of brassica pests and diseases see Chapter 12.

Turnip – *Brassica rapa*

The turnip is a very similar vegetable to the swede. In Scotland some confusion arises in the terminology, since both swedes and turnips are called 'turnips'. Their culinary use is very similar, mainly in soups or as a vegetable. Turnips are much smaller and rarely exceed 100 mm in size and their production can be carried out overwinter. So the major marketing time for the crop is late winter and early spring and summer when swedes are not available.

This crop tends to be an intensively grown crop, commonly grown by market gardeners as a spring catch crop. The time from sowing to harvesting is between six to ten weeks, according to season. The cultivation of the crop, however, is very similar to that of the swede. It requires moist, cool conditions for growth.

Soils

The crop will grow on a wide range of market garden soils but not on heavy clays. For earliness, fertile, sandy loams or silts are commonly used. The soil pH should be between 5.5–6.5. If below this level, rectify by the addition of lime which can be harrowed in before sowing.

Nutrition

As for swedes.

Land preparation

The land should be ploughed and subsoiled and worked to a fine tilth, otherwise clods may shelter flea beetles (always a pest on this crop). Bulky manuring is best carried out on a previous crop, not directly before sowing turnips.

Cultivars

A number of different types allow cultivation all year round.

SMALL – ROUND FOR EARLY SPRING AND SUMMER HARVEST (APRIL–JULY)

| Milan White Early Snowball Milan Purple Top Forcing | } Early white skin and flesh. Roots small. |

Tokyo Cross – fast maturing (35 days) from June sowing but bolt if sown early.

TYPES OF MAINCROP SOWINGS FOR HARVEST JUNE ONWARDS

| Golden Perfection | (globe shape) yellow skin and flesh which is winter hardy. Medium size. |

| Manchester Market Model Winter | } Longer roots suitable for July sowings and winter use. |

Seed sowing

The earliest crops are grown under glass or frames. For outside crops, perforated polythene film is used (Pholene and Xiro) and drills are sown towards end January to early February at a close row spacing (75 mm or 3 in), with seed sown approximately 25 mm (1 in) apart along the row, giving a high density sowing. For outside crops seed is precision drilled at 25 mm (1 in) apart along the drill with a row spacing of 380 mm (15 in). Later chopping out will thin the crop to a density of 34 plants per sq m (3.2 per sq ft).

Chopping out

Chopping out is not carried out under Xiro, because once laid the film cannot easily be moved. With outside crops the job is carried out by hand or machine to thin to singles at 75 mm apart.

Weed control

PRE-SOWING TREATMENT for control of wild oat and couch grass is as follows: Couch grass control – autumn or spring applications of TCA incorporated up to seven days before drilling at 11 kg/ha (10 lb/acre). High dosage rates of 34 kg/ha (30 lb/acre) will give a high level of control, but four weeks must be allowed before drilling.

Wild oat control – Triallate (Avadex BW) applied at 3.5–4.2 1/ha (2½-3 pt/acre) and then incorporated into the top 20–30 mm (¾–1¼ in) of soil by harrowing the soil to a depth of 75–100 mm (3–4 in).

PRE-SOWING TREATMENT for control of annual weeds is as follows: Trifluralin applied at 2.3 1/ha (33 fl oz/acre) and incorporated 0–14 days before drilling. This treatment can be used as the first stage of a weed control programme, but it is not suitable for use on very light soils or soils with a high organic matter content.

PRE-EMERGENCE HERBICIDES Propachlor – applied after drilling and before weed emergence at 7 kg/ha (6.3 lb/acre). This may be used alone, as a supplement to the Trifluralin treatment or as a tank mix with chlorthal-dimethyl (see below). A slight check to growth may occur on light soils. The dose should be increased by 50 per cent on organic soils.

Propachlor + chlorthal-dimethyl (Dacthal) – this tank mix gives a wider spectrum of control than propachlor alone. Use as for propachlor – rates of use, 6 kg/ha (5.4 lb/acre) chlorthal-dimethyl, and 7 kg/ha (6.3 lb/acre) propachlor.

Nitrofen – applied within three days of drilling at 14 1/ha (10 pt/ acre).

POST EMERGENCE TREATMENTS There are few materials recommended for post emergence treatment of turnips and swedes as the crop usually competes effectively with the weeds. The weeds which develop tend to occur late in the life of the crop, and these are usually grasses.

Diclofop-methyl (Hoegrass) – can be used to control wild oat, black-grass and ryegrass. Apply at 3.5 1/ha (2½ pt/acre) when grass weeds have three leaves.

Alloxydim sodium (Clout) – this has limited clearance for use in northern England and Scotland for control of wild oat and volunteer cereals. Apply at the one to three leaf stage of the weed before tillering starts, using 1.25 kg/ha (18 oz/acre). If tillering has commenced use 2 kg/ha (1¾ lb/acre).

Harvesting

Harvesting of Xiro crops will begin from early April onwards, outside crops on early soils being available towards the end of April. Early turnips are commonly pulled, washed and bunched in threes, sixes or eights with a rubber band. About 75 mm of leaf stalk is left, with the root for tying together.

With the cost of bunching ever rising, many growers send the early crop loose in Dutch trays (5 kg or 10 lb to a tray).

Anticipated yield

Average yield (maincrop) 24 tonnes/ha (9.6 tons/acre).

Pests and disease

The major problem on this crop is the pest flea beetle which shot-holes the foliage of turnips and can markedly reduce yields. For control see pest and disease chart Chapter 12.

Chapter Eight

Salad Crops

Salad crops, of all the many vegetables crops grown, are the most labour consuming and therefore tend to be grown by the highly intensive smaller units. They are also crops which are more difficult to handle on a vast field scale. The market price for salads is prone to great fluctuation and such crops therefore are far riskier to grow. Naturally, the returns for salad crops reflect the weather at the time they are sold – in good summers and dry sunny weather prices are usually good. During wet, cool summers, prices may be so low as to make it not worth while harvesting the crop.

The crops covered in this chapter are celery, lettuce and radish, all highly perishable crops grown by the market gardener, rather than the farmer.

Celery – *Apium graveolens*

Traditionally, celery was grown on the deep fertile peat soils, where wide spacings were used to enable earthing-up which induced blanching of the petioles and protected the crop from frost at the end of the growing season. This traditional type of production is still important on the fen peat soils. It is usually referred to as 'trench' or 'white earth' celery.

The self-blanching crop did not become established until the late 1960s (in 1965 only 5 per cent of the total acreage was self-blanching) but it now accounts for 44 per cent of the total area.

Soils
Trench celery can only be grown successfully on deep fen peat soils, while the self-blanching crop can be grown on most soil types, provided

they are deep and fertile. They also need to have high moisture retention as well as being freely drained.

Cultivations

Where possible, bulky manure should be spread at up to 80 tonnes/ha (32 tons/acre) prior to ploughing. Secondary cultivations should break down the soil to give a deep fine tilth which is only slightly consolidated. On fen peats no manure is needed.

Nutrition

Lime and fertilizer recommendations should be based on the results of soil analysis. For the self blanched crop these materials are usually rotavated into the soil to a depth of 150–200 mm (6–8 in) several days before planting. Celery is sensitive to acidity therefore acid soils should be limed to raise the pH to 6.6–6.8.

Table 46: Recommended fertilizer rates for self-blanching celery (in g/m²)

Nutrient index	Phosphate P_2O_5 Triple super -phosphate	Potash K_2O Sulphate of potash	Magnesium Mg Keiserite	Nitrogen N Ammonium nitrate base dressing (liquid feeding to follow*)	OR	Base dressing fertilizer (40%) (solid top dressing to follow)
0	170	200	150	40		80
1	150	150	125	20		60
2	125	100	100	NIL		40
3	100	50	75	–		20
4	70	25	50	–		NIL
5	50	NIL	NIL	–		–
6	25	NIL	–	–		–
Over 6	NIL	NIL	–	–		–

Top Dressing	Where solid top dressings are used apply 35 g/m2 ammonium nitrate for May and autumn harvested crops
	For June/July harvested crops apply 50 g/m² about eight weeks after planting.

*Liquid feeding commences three weeks after planting. Feed with every watering using 90 g/litre ammonium nitrate or 70 g/litre of urea diluted 1 in 200 which gives 150 ppm nitrogen.
Where heavy farmyard manure is applied (100 tonnes/ha or 40 tons/acre) then no nitrogen base dressing is required if liquid feeding is to be practised.
In sites where the K:Mg ratio rises above 4:1 apply 100 g/m² keiserite irrespective of the Mg level in the soil.
Where no soil analysis is known use the rates underlined in the table.

Plant raising

Unlike many other vegetable crops, direct sowing into the field or into peat blocks rarely gives satisfactory results. New techniques, such as field drilling by fluid drilling are being developed but are not yet widely adopted. Currently, however, the old way of sowing in seed trays under heated glass is still used.

Always start by using thiram treated seed to reduce the risk of celery leaf spot. Sowing may commence in mid February (for very early areas)

Table 47: Recommended fertilizer rates for trench celery (kg nutrient per hectare)

Nutrient index	Phosph- ate P_2O_5	Potash K_2O			Nitrogen N			
		Fen peat & loamy peat	Peaty loam	Moss peat	Fen peat & loamy peat	Peaty loam	Moss Peat	Top Dressing
0	200	400	300	400	NIL	50	100	100
1	150	350	275	350	NIL	50	100	100
2	125	300	250	300	NIL	50	100	100
3	100	250	200	250	–	–	–	–
4	60	125	60	125	–	–	–	–
Over 4	NIL	NIL	NIL	NIL	–	–	–	–

If soil analysis figures are not available use the values underlined above.

and continue to mid April. The seed is sown into trays of an open seed compost (many growers use large shallow trays instead of standard seed trays) at a rate of 400–500 seeds/standard seed tray. Celery seed requires light for germination, therefore, the seed should not be covered (a *very* light cover is occasionally used but light must be able to penetrate this). Trays should be covered with slightly opaque or clear polythene to prevent drying out during germination. Germinate under heated glass or in a germination cabinet at 15–20°C (59–68°F). Temperatures below 10°C (50°F) may result in a high percentage of 'bolting'.

Artificial illumination may be used to reduce the propagation time. Do not use illumination to bring forward the planting date, since planting before mid April in early areas (late May in late areas) may result in a very high percentage of bolting. With static lighting use 5,500 lux (500 lumens/sq ft) throughout the 24 hours. Where mobile lighting rigs are used, double batches can be given 11,000 lux (1,000 lumens/sq ft) for 12 hours each.

The crop is usually pricked out into 3.5–4.3 cm square peat blocks. It is then grown on under heated glass at 12–15°C (54–59°F) for about four weeks and hardened off in preparation for planting.

Planting

The plants may be planted by hand on a small scale or by a planting machine capable of working with peat blocks. Where the self-blanching crop is machine planted, the bed system should be used to achieve the necessary plant spacings – distances from 250 mm × 250 mm (10 in × 10 in) to 300 mm × 300 mm (12 in × 12 in) are required. Trench celery is planted at 125–150 mm (5–6 in) apart in the row with 1.5 m (5 ft) between rows.

Planting must be carried out before any root restriction occurs with the top of the block level with the soil surface.

Cultivars

With self-blanching types for early production, by far the most popular and suitable cultivar is Lathom Self Blanching because of its high resistance to 'bolting'. Another useful cultivar is Avonpearl, but since this does not have the 'bolting' resistance of Lathom's it is never sown before mid to end March.

Green celery cultivars are very tender and sweet, but because they do not blanch there is market resistance to them. The best known cultivar is American Green.

Traditional trench celery cultivars, which require earthing up, are pink or white in colour. They include: New Dwarf White (early); Cambridge White; Hopkins Fenlander (White) and Cluseed Resistant Pink.

Herbicides

POST PLANTING SOIL AND FOLIAGE ACTING HERBICIDES   Linuron – can be applied at the one to two leaf stage or when established after planting. Most young weed seedlings are controlled up to the cotyledon stage. Treatment during hot weather may cause some scorch. DO NOT plant lettuce on the site in the same season. Use 1.1–2.2 kg/ha (1–2 lb/acre) or Liquid Linuron which is also available.

Promtryne (Gesagard 50 WP) – Is used when the crop has two true leaves or when transplanted crops are established. Repeat treatments may be used. The rate is 2.3 kg/ha (2 lb/acre).

Pentanochlor/chlorpropham (Herbon Brown) – Is applied after fully expanded cotyledon stage and when transplants are established (10–21 days). This controls annual grasses both pre- and post-emergence.

POST PLANTING FOLIAGE ACTING HERBICIDE   Pentanochlor (Herbon Solan) – Is applied at crop growth stage (as above) and gives useful control of fat hen, redshank, annual nettle, fumitory and orache.

Earthing (trench celery crops only)

The first earthing takes place when the plants are 230 mm (9 in) high in July. Earthing may be carried out with a hiller plough or a purpose made butterfly ridger. It is necessary to hand finish the ridges and the men usually follow the ridge down the field to pack and finish it.

The second earthing is carried out when plants reach 380 mm – 450 mm (15 in – 18 in) some 14–21 days after the first earthing. The third and final earthing is carried out 21 days after the second.

Irrigation

Irrigation immediately after planting is desirable during dry periods and during growth. Irrigation should be applied at a 25 mm SMD returning the soil to field capacity.

Blanching

Where the self-blanching crop is grown on a small scale, straw spread down the wheel track to the depth of the crop three to four weeks before harvest will induce blanching of the edge plants.

Harvesting

The crop should be sufficiently uniform to allow a once over harvest with the majority of the sticks in excess of 500 grams (1.1 lb). The plant is cut by hand at, or just below, soil level. Any discoloured or damaged outer leaf petioles should be removed, the butt neatly trimmed to remove any trace of roots and the leaves on the top of the plant cut back to give 280–380 mm (11 in–15 in) overall length.

If crops are heavily soiled due to rain splash or difficult harvesting conditions, the sticks should be spray washed and well drained before packing. Where the crop is in a clean condition it can be packed as it is cut.

Quality self-blanching celery is dropped into shaped polythene 'sleeves' before packing sticks into a fibre board box or tray.

Containers for celery vary from solid board trays to composite crates. The most popular system is to pack the celery vertically in solid board boxes, with anything from 9 to 30 per container. (See below).

No./ container	Size	Weight		
30 ⎫ 24 ⎬ 18 ⎭	Small 150–500 g	260–340 g 340–420 g 420–500 g	(10–12 oz) (12–15 oz) (15–18 oz)	There should be few plants this small
15 ⎫ 12 ⎭	Medium 500–800 g	500–650 g 650–800 g	(18–23 oz) (23–28 oz)	
9	Large above 800 g	over 800 g	(over 28 oz)	

When labelling up the boxes, the type of celery should be marked, eg, Trench, S/B (Self Blanching), Green or Pink.

Anticipated yield

Self blanching celery:
    average yield – 6,000 crates/ha (2450 crates/acre)
    good commercial yield – 8,500 crates/ha (3470 crates/acre)
Trenched celery:
    average yield – 1,500 crates/ha (612 crates/acre)
    good commercial yield – 2,250 crates/ha (918 crates/acre)

Market pack of celery labelled to EEC standards.

Pests and diseases
See pests and diseases chart Chapter 12.

Lettuce – *Lactuca sativa*

Unlike many crops which tend to be produced in specialist areas, lettuce production is widespread. The demand for lettuce is relatively unpredictable as it is related to the prevailing weather. Good weather induces people to eat salads thus demand rises and vice-versa.

Soils
Lettuce growing is confined to the medium to light soils. The lightest soils are preferred for early season production. Special care must be taken with soils which have a high silt content as these cap easily and the emergence of drilled lettuce can be seriously suppressed.

Nutrition
Lettuce has a low requirement for nitrogen despite being a leafy vegetable. This crop has a high requirement for phosphate and potash. A soil pH of 6.5 to 7.0 is required.

Cultivars
There are three main forms of lettuce:
COS   Tall thin heads usually dark green in colour.
CRISP   (Iceberg) approximately spherical heads, and crisp leaves, with a crinkly margin.

Table 48: Recommended fertilizer rates for lettuce (kg nutrient per hectare)

Nutrient index	Phosphate P₂O₅	Potash K₂O	Magnesium Mg Sandy soils	Mg Other soils	Nitrogen N
0	300	250	60	60	125
1	250	200	30	NIL	100
2	200	125	NIL	NIL	75
3	125	60	–	–	–
4	60	NIL	–	–	–
Over 4	NIL	NIL	–	–	–

If soil analysis is not available use the values underlined in the table.

CABBAGE (Butterhead) the most common type grown, approximately spherical heads, may be light or dark green depending on cultivar.
Popular cultivars include:

COS	Lobjoits Green Cos – old cultivar, large cos type, late season.
	Valmaine – uniform cultivar of medium size, which has resistance to mildew.
CRISP (Iceberg)	Great Lakes – high yielding, large lettuce for early to mid season.
	Pennlake – a compact, uniform, mid season lettuce.
	Webbs Wonderful – reliable, large, crisp lettuce. Traditional and old cultivar which is still very popular.
CABBAGE (Butterhead)	Suzan – large, early to mid season lettuce, reliable cultivar.
	Reskia – large, early cultivar which is rather pale in colour, but is resistant to five races of mildew.
	Avon Defiance – large, late cabbage lettuce which has great resistance to downy mildew and grey mould.

There are differences in crop spacing and packing but other crop production techniques are basically the same.

Drilled crops

Lettuce is normally precision drilled using pelleted seed as few precision drills will handle natural lettuce seed accurately. As the crop is grown at a relatively high density, regular spaced precision drilling is normally used. A seed spacing of 75–100 mm (3–4 in) is usually adequate, allowing later singling to 300–350 mm (12–14 in) for cos or crisp lettuce, and 250–300 mm (10–12 in) for cabbage lettuce.

Cultivations

Ploughing is normally used for primary cultivations, though where lettuce are grown in an intensive rotation a rotavator may be used to achieve a faster turn round between crops.

Secondary cultivations should leave a level and firm tilth for planting or drilling. But avoid excessively fine tilths, especially on soils with a high silt content, as capping can greatly reduce emergence of lettuce.

Plant raising

Apart from direct drilled crops which are later singled, lettuce can also be raised in peat blocks. The block raised crop gives earlier maturity in the early season, reduces the length of time the crop occupies the site and makes continuity of production much easier. But the block raised crops are more expensive to produce.

Production of transplants

The seed is sown direct into the block (38 mm or 1½ in size) using pelleted or natural seed. The earliest sowings for mild areas may be made in November under cold glass or in January under heated glass.

It is essential that lettuce seed is NOT exposed to high temperatures during germination as this will induce dormancy in most of the seed resulting in very poor and erratic germination. During the winter and early spring, lettuce can be germinated under glass, though it is advisable to cover blocks with polystyrene sheets to prevent localized heating during sunny weather. During late spring, summer and autumn, the seed is best germinated in a cool shed or store where temperatures do not exceed 15°C (59F).

Once the radicle has emerged from the majority of the seeds, the blocks can then be transferred to the glasshouse. Production of a suitable transplant in heated glass will take about five weeks during the winter to three weeks during spring and summer. A plant of approximately 50–75 mm (2–3 in) in height is required.

Density and spacing

Most lettuce crops are grown on a bed system, using a 1,830 mm (72 in) module. Six rows can be accommodated across the width of a bed (five rows for large crisp or cos-type lettuce). Plant spacing down the row for planting or singling field drilled crop should be 300 mm (12 in) for Butterhead and small crisp cultivars, and 350 mm (14 in) for cos and large crisp cultivars.

Weed control

It can be difficult to keep an acceptable level of weed control in lettuce. Careful consideration should be given to the likely weed spectrum when choosing a herbicide.

(1) Drilled crops

PRE-DRILLING HERBICIDES

Trifluralin — Applied at 1.2 l/ha (17 fl oz/acre). Not suitable for use on sandy or organic soils, where germination and early growth may be checked.

Propyzamide — Incorporated into the top 20–30 mm (¾–1¼ in) (see below).

PRE-EMERGENCE HERBICIDES

Chlorpropham — Sprayed at 2.8 l/ha (2 pt/acre). Apply immediately after drilling. Damage or check to growth can occur on light soils, especially if spraying is followed by heavy rain. Build up of groundsel and mayweed is a problem since these weeds are resistant.

Propham/diuron (Herbon Pink) — Applied at 22–33 l/ha (2–3 gal/acre) immediately after drilling. More dependable under dry conditions than other pre-emergence materials. Use lower dose on light soils and in early season when conditions are cold.

PRE- or post-EMERGENCE HERBICIDES

Propyzamide (Kerb 50 W) — Use at 2.25–2.8 kg/ha (2–2½ lb/acre). This may be applied at any time until six weeks before harvest. This material should be applied to a moist, weed-free soil. During dry weather irrigate prior to application or use the higher dose rate. Groundsel and mayweed are resistant. Use only one application per crop, do not use pre-emergence or post-emergence if used pre-drilling.

(2) Transplanted crop

PRE-PLANTING HERBICIDES

Trifluralin — As above.

Propyzamide — As above.

Chlorpropham — Applied a few days before planting direct on to the seedbed. Keep soil disturbance to a minimum during the planting operation. Use a lower dose on light soils (see previous page).

Prophamdiuron (Herbon Pink)
– Incorporated into the top 20–30 mm (1–1½ in) immediately after application (see previous page).

POST-PLANTING HERBICIDE

Propyzamide – Apply as detailed earlier. Use immediately post planting or or up to six weeks before harvest.

Singling

Precision seeding, using pelleted seed, has made the job of thinning lettuce to singles relatively easy. Thinning is carried out to a spacing of 300 mm (1 ft) for cabbage lettuce and wider spacings of up to 350 mm (14 in) for crisp and cos lettuce. 'Doubles', or two seedlings close together, rarely form hearted lettuce so ensure these are never left. The job of thinning is usually carried out by hand.

Irrigation

Lettuce require irrgation throughout the life of the crop and the recommendation is to apply 25 mm of water at an SMD of 25 mm. It is particularly important to use irrigation equipment which produces a small droplet size since larger droplets have been found to damage lettuce and reduce yield.

Harvesting

Outdoor crops are not sufficiently uniform to clear the crop in one cut. Selective cutting is required, so harvesting only those lettuces with solid hearts. Skilled operators should be able to cut the lettuce in such a way that old discoloured leaves are left on the soil. Any further trimming is carried out as the crop is cut. A good worker cuts and packs 46 boxes an hour (cutting and sleeving lettuce is 396 lettuce/hour). Depending on market requirement and current price, the heads may be packed in perforated plastic bags prior to packing the lettuce in boxes.

Single layer boxes are now widely used. The lettuce is packed butt uppermost with 9, 12, 15 or 18 lettuce per box, depending on the size of the heads. Where double layer trays are used the first layer should be packed with the butts downwards and the second layer with butts upwards.

Cos lettuce are not polythene bagged and may well require a different market box. They look best when packed vertically (9–15 to a box) in a deep box, though they can be laid flat in the traditional shallow lettuce trays.

Grading
For grading requirements see Table 56 page 215.

Anticipated yields

	Cabbage lettuce	Crisp lettuce and cos lettuce
Average yield	7,640 crates/ha (3,180 crates/acre)	8,886 crates/ha (3,700 crates/acre)
Good commercial yield	9,030 crates/ha (3,762 crates/acre)	10,500 crates/ha (4,375 crates/acre)

Pests and diseases
See pests and diseases chart Chapter 12.

Radish – *Rhaphanus sativus*

There is a common misconception that radish is a quick and easy catch crop which will grow anywhere without too much effort on the part of the grower. Quality radish can only be produced with attention to detail. The degree of growing skill is just as demanding as other crops and the job is not made easier by the fact that markets are not always able to absorb random spot crops.

Soils
Radish can be grown on most soils but light to medium, moisture retentive soils are desirable. Heavy clay soils are more likely to produce mis-shapen roots while very light soils can cause splitting unless frequent irrigation is available. Good soil structure combined with accurate drilling should ensure a high level of seedling emergence, which is important to obtain high yields.

The optimum pH for radish is 5.5 to 6.0 on light soils and 6.0 to 6.5 on heavier soils.

Cultivations
The grower should be aiming to produce a uniformly firm and friable seedbed, which is very level. Following primary cultivations, beds should be marked out so that secondary cultivations can use the pre-marked wheelings to avoid compaction to the growing bed area.

Nutrition
The radish crop has a low nutrient requirement especially for nitrogen. High residual salt levels can seriously impair germination and growth.

Table 49: Recommended fertilizer rates for radish (kg nutrient per hectare)

Nutrient index	Phosphate P_2O_5		Potash K_2O		Nitrogen N	
	First crop	Succeed -ing crop	First crop	Succeed -ing crop	First crop	Succeed -ing crop
0	200	NIL	250	NIL	60	40
1	125	NIL	200	NIL	25	NIL
2	60	NIL	125	NIL	NIL	NIL
3	60	NIL	60	NIL	–	–
Over 3	NIL	NIL	NIL	NIL	–	–

If soil analysis is not available use the value underlined in the table.

Sowing

Drillings commence from February and continue until September. The earliest sowings should be covered by a film cover of some type (Xiro film or Pholene) to advance maturity. It can also increase yield and improve quality.

For maximum yield and best quality, the crop should be precision drilled using graded seed to give a plant density of 450–550 plants/m² (42–51/ft²). During mid summer densities may be increased to 550–650 plants/m² (51–60/ft²) to maximize yields. A high percentage of split roots may occur where densities are too low.

Seed size has an effect on maturity date – large seed produces a marketable root earlier, the difference being most marked with early sowings. So use large seed (2.5–2.75 mm) for the earliest sowings and the smallest seed (2.25–2.5 mm) for the summer sowings. Sowing depth should be 12 mm (½ in).

Herbicides

There are no recommendations for radish. Most growers rely on the crop achieving sufficient cover to smother any weeds. Chemical soil sterilization can also be a useful aid for controlling weeds. Trials with isoproturon as a selective herbicide produced excellent results when incorporated pre-drilling at 2 kg active ingredient per hectare (1.8 lb a.i./acre). No damage was seen at double this dose. This is not an approved recommendation and can only be used at the growers' risk.

Irrigation

Irrigation should be available to give adequate water for germination as well as maintain soil moisture. The soil moisture deficit should be kept relatively low at 12–15 mm. Irrigating after a large deficit may cause a lot of splitting of roots.

Harvesting

Most crops are harvested by hand, usually with a bonus or piecework system to induce maximum efficiency from the operators. A good operator will pull 200 bunches per hour.

Harvesting machinery is available but row spacings have to be matched to the machine's working width, and machine harvested crops are usually used for the pre-pack trade rather than the fresh market.

The plants are bunched and secured with elastic bands (usually 10–12 roots/bunch). It is often necessary to spray wash the bunches prior to packing.

Trays or chip baskets may be used for packing, depending on the market to which the produce is going. The bunches are packed with roots uppermost with 20 to 50 bunches per chip or tray.

Cultivars

It is important to give adequate attention to cultivar selection. First find out which type of radish is required by your market. The round 'Cherry Belle' type is most popular in Scotland and the North, while London markets prefer the cylindrical 'French Breakfast' type. A great deal of breeding work has been centred on producing radish cultivars suitable for production during most seasons. This has resulted in modern cultivars being specific to a certain period of the year. If they are grown at the wrong time results will be very poor, eg, a high percentage of bolting. Select a cultivar suitable to the period of production.

Anticipated yield

Average yield – 64,300 bunches/ha (26,800 bunches/acre)
Good commercial yield – 85,519 bunches/ha (35,600 bunches/acre)

Pests and disease

The only pest of any importance on this crop is flea beetle, but the crop rarely warrants use of pesticides. For details of flea beetle control see Chapter 12.

Chapter Nine

Other Vegetables (Perennial Crops)

Asparagus – *Asparagus officinalis*

The asparagus crop in the UK is of minor importance. Its production is confined to the traditional growing areas of Bedfordshire and Worcestershire and new areas in East Anglia. The cost of establishing an asparagus bed (five years before a profitable return can be expected), the relatively short British growing season and competition from French imports has stopped growers putting in new plantations.

This is a perennial crop with a typical herbaceous plant cycle:

Spear production (new growths from the crown)	– mid/late April-mid June
Fern growth	– mid June-early July
Plant establishment (the photosynthetic period)	– early July-October
Dormancy period	– October to April.

The crop preferred by the British public is green asparagus, whereas white asparagus is more popular in Europe.

Site and soils

A sheltered site away from frost pockets is ideal since asparagus spears can become frosted. Like all herbaceous plants, asparagus needs deep, well drained soils so that the crown does not rot overwinter. Hence, the sandy soils of Kent and East Anglia are used to grow the crop. But much of the crop is also grown on well-structured heavy clay soils. Their fertility is the keynote to heavy yields, and here too special emphasis is made on drainage, by ridging.

Before establishing asparagus ensure that the site is free of perennial weeds, particularly bindweed, which is difficult to eradicate in the growing crop.

Obtaining asparagus stock

Seedling asparagus crowns have a wide variation in vigour. So careful selection of stocks from seedbeds has resulted in the introduction of named stocks – Connover Colossal (useful for sandy soils) and Giant Mammoth or Argenteuil (for heavy soils). Seed of these selections may be sown in seedbeds and the 'weaklings' discarded before planting at one year old. Alternatively, one-year-old crowns may be purchased from specialist growers. American stocks (MW 500W and Viking) and Dutch asparagus (Limburgia, Limbras, Limbras Early Selection, Limbras Main Crop) have also been introduced, but neither crop as heavily on British soils. New French stocks, (Diane, Larac, Minerve, Junon) may have potential.

Pre-planting cultivations

Deep ploughing the autumn before planting is essential, incorporating a heavy dressing of bulky organic manure for moisture retention. On heavy soils, or where a soil pan may be suspected, subsoiling should be carried out the August before ploughing. Cultivate down to a medium fine tilth just before planting in February/March.

Fertilizers and nutrition

The soil pH should be 6.5 or above. Application of ground limestone to bring the pH up should be carried out after ploughing and before December. For nutrition see Table 50.

Propagation and production of crowns

Most asparagus fields are planted with one year crowns, either bought in or from seedbed produced stock. Although direct seeding in the growing field has been carried out in California, it has not proved successful in this country.

Seed sown under glass in January and grown in 7 cm (3½ in) size containers can be planted in May or June, reducing the time spent producing the crowns and ensuring far higher germination of seed.

Production method

Crowns can either be grown on the flat or ridged in the rows. The latter method is by far the most popular, since better quality spears are produced. Ridging involves higher labour input but does help in keeping the crop clean.

Table 50: Recommended fertilizer rates for asparagus (kg nutrient per hectare).

Nutrient index	Phosphate P_2O_5	Potash K_2O	Magnesium Sandy soil	Magnesium Other soils	Nitrogen Base dressing	Nitrogen Top dressing	
0	175	250	60	30	150		
1	150	225	30	NIL	75		
2	125	200	NIL	NIL	50	0–75	Before Planting
3	100	150	NIL	NIL	–		
4	75	125	NIL	NIL	–		
4	NIL	NIL	NIL	NIL	–		
0	100	150					
1	100	125					
2	75	100				50–100*	Second Year
3	75	75					(along the rows)
4	50	50					
4	NIL	NIL					
1	75	125					
2	50	100					Annually after
3	50	75				50–125*	the second year
4	25	50					(broadcast)
4	NIL	NIL					

If a soil analysis is not available use the values underlined in the table.
*On sandy soils of low fertility add an extra 75 kg/ha Nitrogen to the top dressing.

Planting
The optimum depth for the crown is 100 mm (4 in). Usually trenches are ploughed out and the roots spread out in the bottom, taking care not to damage crown buds. The soil is drawn back level over the crowns. Planting takes place in February/March.

Planting densities
Two spacings are used mainly to conform to standard tractor wheel spacings so that cultivations and ridging can be carried out:
– 300 mm × 1.3 m (1 ft × 4 ft 3 in) or 25,150 plants/ha (10,180/acre) for narrow tractor wheel widths of 142 cm (52 in);
– 300 mm × 0.9 m (1 ft × 3 ft) or 36,300 plants/ha (14,600/acre) for the wider tractor wheel width of 186 cm (72 in).
The higher the density the higher the yield, but this brings a corresponding reduction in spear diameter and individual crown yield.

Ridging
Ridging is carried out on new beds the autumn after planting, initially with a small ridge. Ridges are gradually built up over the next two years.
Various tractor mounted equipment is used including ridging bodies,

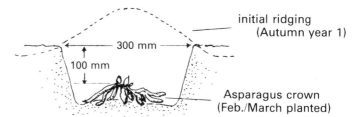

Figure 28   Planting and initial ridging

ridging boards fixed to a pedestrian controlled cultivator, and a Lillistan rolling cultivator.

Autumn winter work
The fern is cut down to 100 mm (4 in) when the tops have died and turned brown. The job can be carried out with a reciprocating knife type mower or by hand. Then light harrowing over the ridges will remove old stumps of the fern. Cultivating the valley bottoms will provide the tilth for ridging in late autumn. In February light harrowing to level off ridges is normally carried out. But beware of damaging crowns, particularly after a mild winter.

Weed control
SEEDBED STAGE   Chlorpropham/fenuron at 8.4 1/ha (6 pt/acre). Soil acting herbicide applied after seed chitted but before crop emergence.

ESTABLISHED CROP   Chlorpropham/fenuron at 22.4 1/ha (2 gal/acre) during dormancy *or* Simazine at 2.2–3.4 kg/ha (2–3 lb/acre) before spear emergence.
   Terbacil (Sinbar) applied at 3.4 kg/ha (3 lb/acre) before spear emergence. Do not use on asparagus established less than two years or on sandy soils with less than one per cent organic matter. Controls annual weeds, perennial grasses and some perennial weeds.
   Dalapon at 9.0 kg/ha (8 lb/acre) may be applied during dormancy for control of couch grass.
   MCPA at 5.6–7.0 1/ha (4–5 pt/acre) may be used as a directed spray during summer to control perennial weed build up like bindweed. Avoid spraying stems or foliage of the asparagus.

Irrigation
Irrigation may be valuable on sandy soils as the fern is developing in June, but there is little experimental evidence to show marked response to irrigation.

Harvesting

Cutting should continue for eight weeks from late April. After June 20 further cutting reduces next year's crop. Special notched asparagus knives are used to cut the asparagus by hand. The job is carried out up to four times per week. The knife is used to penetrate the ridges to cut the spear below ground level, giving a total spear length of 220–270 mm (8¾–10¾ in) with a white base to green shoot ratio of anything from 2:1 to 1:2. One man can cut 0.8 ha in an eight-hour day.

Bundling, packing/grading

See Chapter 11 on marketing.

Storage

Short term storage of trays at 1°C, covering with a thin layer of polythene, is useful to build up reasonable marketable quantities or to hold for a few days during minor periods of glut.

Life of the crop

The life of the plantation will vary from 10–20 years depending on soil drainage and the build up of perennial weeds.

Anticipated yield

Established crop – average yield 1,780 kg/ha (1,588 lb/acre).

Pests and diseases

See pest and disease charts, pages 246.

Vegetable Marrow and Courgettes – *Cucurbita pepo* (also *C. moschata*)

There are three closely related species of cucurbita grown as vegetable crops. They are commonly known as marrows, squash or pumpkins. The species most commonly grown in the UK is *Cucurbita pepo* which produces fruit commonly referred to as marrow.

The marrow is a long established crop but in recent years the demand and production of courgettes has greatly increased. The courgette is merely a very small immature marrow. The name is of French origin (French for marrow is courge, therefore courgette means small or immature marrow). It is now widely accepted in Britain. Occasionally the name Zucchini is also applied to the crop. This has the same meaning in Italian. As the nomenclature is sometimes confused, for simplicity in the text the name marrow will be used to include plants which are grown for production of marrows and courgettes.

The crop is hardier than the other members of the family (cucumbe and melons) and grows well as an outdoor crop in most parts of th country. The production of marrows has always been a minor crop i Britain, but the demand for courgettes took off in 1971 and there ha been a gradual increase in production since.

Soils

Marrows can only be grown successfully on fertile soils which must als be well drained but moisture retentive. The crop responds well to heav applications of bulky organic matter which should be applied befor ploughing. A pH level of 6.5 to 7.0 is desirable as the crop is not toleran of acidity. Where necessary, apply lime in the form of ground limeston or chalk (if magnesium levels are low use magnesium limestone) wel in advance of planting.

Cultivations

The soil should be ploughed by early spring incorporating large quan tities of bulky organic matters if available.

Secondary cultivation should give a firm and reasonably fine seec bed.

Nutrition

The main nutrient requirements are potassium and nitrogen, thougl split applications of the latter nutrient are advisable.

Table 51: Recommended fertilizer rates for marrow and courgettes (kg nutrient per hectare).

Index	Phosphate P_2O_5	Potash K_2O	Magnesium Mg Sandy soils	Other soils	Nitrogen N
0	200	250	60	60	100
1	125	200	30	NIL	75
2	60	125	NIL	NIL	50
3	60	60	–	–	–
4	NIL	NIL	–	–	–
4	NIL	NIL	–	–	–
Top Dressing					75

If a soil analysis is not available use the values underlined in the table.

A nitrogen top dressing should be applied as a single application four to five weeks after planting at 75 kg/ha, or as a top dressing applying 38 kg/ha at four to five weeks and a further 38 kg/ha at eight to ten weeks after planting.

Propagation

Where seed has a high germination capacity it can be sown direct into 75 mm (3 in) peat blocks or pots of compost. If germination is less reliable, chitting the seed in damp peat before placing in pots or blocks will avoid any waste of propagation space and compost. A minimum temperature of 20°C (68°F) is desirable for chitting, which takes approximately 48 to 72 hours. Total propagation time (from sowing to planting) is approximately four weeks. As the crop is not hardy the sowing date should be selected to give plants for transplanting after the risk of frost has passed.

In areas with a long growing season the crop can be drilled in the open ground. A vacuum drill is most suitable for this purpose.

Transplanting

This is normally four to five weeks from sowing or when the plant has four to five true leaves. Excessive delay in planting will give the crop a check which may delay harvesting. A density of 1.9 plants/m^2 (0.18/sq ft) is recommended. The actual arrangement of rows may be varied but the most common is 900 mm (3 ft) between rows and 600 mm (2 ft) between plants in the row. Where long rows are used, cross paths at approximately 65 m (70 yd) intervals are desirable.

Weed control

Only one chemical herbicide is suitable for this crop – diphenamid (Enid 50W) applied shortly after sowing or planting at 6.7–9.0 kg/ha (6–8 lb/acre). The soil must be moist and weed free before application. The effectiveness of the chemical is reduced on soils with more than 10 per cent organic matter. Use of a stale seedbed technique will reduce the weed problem before sowing or planting. Also, the use of black polythene mulch will control weeds as well as conserving moisture. When using a mulch, problems may occur with water collecting on the surface and encouraging decay of leaves on fruit. This may be overcome by slightly ridging the soil down the row before mulching to give a good run-off from the mulch. Alternatively, a perforated mulch may be used which will allow water to soak through.

Irrigation

This is very important for establishment of transplants. If soil is dry return to field capacity one to two days before planting. Once harvesting has started the crop responds to irrigation using 25 mm water at 25 mm SMD.

Harvesting

The frequency of harvest will depend on the size and type of fruit required. If fruit starts to mature and the fruit stalk starts to harden, no further fruit will set. Therefore, regular harvesting is required if continuity of production is required.

The fruit should be harvested by cutting through the fruit stalk with a sharp knife. Great care should be taken to avoid damage to the tender skin of courgettes. For courgette production, harvesting should be done at two to three day intervals when the fruits are just a few inches long (see grades below).

Grading is advisable for both courgettes and marrows. The guidelines are widely accepted by the markets.

Large marrows	Length	250–450 mm (8 in–18 in)
	Diameter	100–150 mm (4 in–6 in)
Small marrows	Length	200–250 mm (8 in–10 in)
	Diameter	75–100 mm (3 in–4 in)
Courgettes (optimum size range)		
	Length	65–180 mm (2½ in–7 in)
	Diameter	12–38 mm (½ in–1½ in)

Fruit between courgettes and small marrows may be marketed but they should be packed separately and labelled as large courgettes.

It is important that the fruit is clean and the flower abscission point is dry, otherwise botrytis rots may develop.

Packing methods vary but adequate protection from physical damage and crushing is essential. Courgettes are best packed in a cardboard box with all the fruits laid the same way across the container. Packs weighing 4–5 kg (8–10 lb) are the most popular. Alternatively, the crop may be marketed in overwrapped polystyrene trays with 500 g or 1 lb per tray.

The crop can be stored for short periods but low temperature damage can occur if over low temperatures are used, 1°C to 3.3°C (34–38°F) is recommended.

Anticipated yields

COURGETTES

Average yield	26 tonnes/ha (10.4 tons/acre)
Good yield	38 tonnes/ha (15.2 tons/acre)

MARROWS

Average yield	65 tonnes/ha (26 tons/acre)
Good yield	75 tonnes/ha (30 tons/acre)

The yield from courgettes is lower than that for marrows, but higher returns from courgettes usually compensate for the lower yield.

Cultivars

Choice of cultivar is important as very few modern cultivars are suitable for production of both marrow and courgettes. Also, different skin colours are available and should be related to the market.

Cultivars may be placed into six main groups:

OPEN POLLINATED, BUSH GREEN TYPES – These types are only suitable for production of marrows. The plants are dense with abundant foliage.

GREY ZUCCHINI TYPES   Eg, Emerald Cross, Sleeford Cross, Zephyr and Clarita – this type is only suitable for use as marrows, which are club shaped with a mottled skin of three shades of green. At the courgette stage the fruit is club shaped and covered with short hairs.

BLACK ZUCCHINI TYPES   Eg, Ambassador, Diplomat, Marco, Black Jack and Chefini – many of the cultivars in this group are F_1 hybrids and are more suitable for courgette production as the fruit is very large before it is mature. It tends to be club shaped.

STORR'S GREEN TYPES   Eg, Storr's Green, Diamant, Diamond and Early Gem. These produce a more uniform and cylindrical shaped fruit with a mottled dark green colour. The group is composed mainly of F_1 hybrids. They produce excellent courgettes and a few cultivars can be used as dual purpose cultivars eg, Prokor.

YELLOW SKINNED TYPES   These are increasing in popularity but it is important to check with your market before producing. The cultivar names usually indicate the skin colour, eg, Butter Nut and Gold Rush. The yellow cultivars are only used for courgette production.

TRAILING MARROWS   These types produce good quality marrows but the trailing habit is difficult to deal with in commerical production, therefore little used by the trade.

Pests and diseases

See pests and diseases chart Chapter 12.

Sweet Corn – *Zea mays*

The crop is grown as a fresh vegetable and also for processing. It is particularly suited to farm gate sales and could be developed as a 'Pick Your Own' line on suitable holdings. Production of the crop is limited to climatically favourable areas. The main areas are in the south and east of the country – Essex, Kent, Sussex, Hampshire and the Isle of Wight.

The crop can be grown further north but careful selection of the best early maturing cultivars is essential. Transplanting of glasshouse raised plants will be required in place of direct drilling. But they can only be grown well in a warm sheltered site.

Soils

The crop will grow well in a variety of soils, although deep, well drained medium loams are preferable. The crop is not particularly sensitive to pH but pH levels of 6.0 or above are preferable.

Cultivations

Deep cultivation (preceded by subsoiling if necessary) is desirable for this crop. Secondary cultivation should produce a level, firm and moderately fine seed bed to enable precision drilling and to get effective residual weed control.

Cultivars

Basically, sweet corn is maize which has been bred to produce sweet soft grains in the immature stage. Maize grown as a farm fodder crop does not possess this character and should NOT be grown or sold as sweet corn. Apart from contravening the Trade Description Act this is likely to suppress subsequent sales.

Because the genetic character bred into sweet corn is derived from a recessive gene, cross pollination from a fodder maize to the sweet corn crop could result in serious loss of eating quality. For this reason, it is best to keep the two crops as far apart as possible.

Some suitable cultivars are listed below with number of days from sowing to maturity. This information is invaluable in scheduling the crop.

EARLY (harvest early-late August)

Early Vee	117 days
Earliking	118 days
Kelvedon Sweetheart	120 days

MID SEASON (harvest late August to mid September)

Indian Dawn	123 days
Early Belle	128 days
Northern Belle	131 days
Commanche	134 days

LATE SEASON (harvest late September to mid October)

Jubilee	141 days
October Gold	146 days
Epic	147 days

Nutrition

Bulky organic manures are not usually used prior to this crop as its nutrient requirements are modest, but an application of a balanced fertilizer dressing is advisable based, if possible, on soil analysis.

Table 52: Recommended fertilizer rates for sweet corn (kg nutrient per hectare)

Nutrient index	Phosphate P_2O_5	Potash K_2O	Magnesium Mg Sandy soils	Other soils	Nitrogen N
0	125	125	60	60	150
1	100	100	30	NIL	100
2	60	60	NIL	NIL	75
3	30	NIL	–	–	–
Over 3	NIL	NIL	–	–	–

If soil analysis is not available use the values underlined.

Drilling (sowing)

The crop is only half hardy and therefore, easily damaged by frost. Drilling usually starts during the first or second week of May in the south and end of May in the north. Soil temperatures are important for germination so it is not advisable to drill before the soil temperature reaches 10°C (50°F).

If a succession is required either make three sowings at 14-day intervals using the same or similar cultivars, or sow a range of early, mid and late cultivars at approximately the same time selecting cultivars according to their speed of maturity. For processing crops it is desirable to limit the cultivar range. Therefore, the former method of spreading the harvest is preferable in this case.

There is little firm evidence on which to base recommendations for density. For the 'Pick-Your-Own' trade wider row spacings of 750 mm (30 in) are advisable to give easier access. For commercial crops 600 mm (24 in) is the most widely used row spacing. The optimum densities used for 600 mm spaced rows are as follows: early crops 4.4 plants/m² (0.4/ft²), which means an in row space of 380 mm (15 in); main crops 3.7 plants/m² (0.32/ft²) in row space 450 mm (18 in), late crops 3.1/m² (0.29 ft²) in row space 510 mm (20 in).

Sowing may be carried out by hand on small areas, using the tines of a cultivator to open out a furrow. Alternatively, sowing can be done with a planting machine. The seed is dropped manually into the furrow by the operator sitting in the machine. Where large areas are sown the use of a modern precision drill is essential. Maize seed is not easily handled by precision drills and careful consideration should be given to the type of metering system employed, those using the vacuum system being ideal. The seed may be group sown or equally spaced (see Chapter 2). Drilling depth should be 37–50 mm (1½–2 in); the deeper sowings help to reduce losses to rooks which will feed on the seed.

Where small areas of crop are grown it is essential to keep the area as near a square block as possible as the crop is wind pollinated and the male flowers are produced at the apex of the plant. Long, narrow areas of crop would result in the female 'silks' receiving very little pollen. This results in malformed and poor quality cobs.

Weed control

PRE-EMERGENCE HERBICIDES   Weed control is easily achieved in this crop by using pre-emergence residual herbicides. Use simazine wettable powder at 2.2–3.4 kg/ha (2–3lb/acre) or the liquid formulation at 2.2–3.4 l/ha (31–48 fl oz/acre). Simazine is dependent on soil moisture for its activity. Where soil conditions are very dry the use of atrazine up to seven days after sowing at 2.2–3.4 l/ha (31–48 fl oz/acre) will give more reliable results.

POST-EMERGENCE HERBICIDES   Atrazine at the rates given above can be used post-emergence before the weeds are 40 mm (1½ in) high.

Both herbicides persist in the soil for some time, particularly on heavy soils, and the residues may cause problems with the crop that follows.

If residues prove to be a problem for following crops cyanazine (Fortrol) may be used pre-emergence at 5.6 l/ha (4 pt/acre). Adequate soil moisture is necessary for activity and residual life is short compared with other residual treatments.

Thinning

This is usually done at the five to six true leaf stage. Any plants attacked by frit fly show as multiple stems and these should be hoed out. The remaining plants can then be singled to the appropriate density (see drilling).

Irrigation

Throughout the life of the crop use 25 mm (1 in) irrigation at a 50 mm (2 in) SMD.

Harvesting (see Figure 29)

From early sowings, harvest will usually start in mid August and the season can extend to late October or early November with late drillings or late cultivars. Cold wet spells during summer may result in very late cultivars failing in some seasons, while similar conditions at flowering can result in partly filled or very uneven cobs.

Two or three picks will be required to clear a crop and picking at the correct stage is essential. The optimum stage is usually reached four to six weeks after pollination, when the female flower (silk) at the end of the cob has started to wither. The grain inside will be a pale to dark yellow when the husk is peeled back. The best test of maturity is to press one or two grains with the thumb nail. The contents should be a thick milky coloured liquid. Once this stage has passed the grain will contain a dough-like substance and the cob will already have started to deteriorate. Experienced pickers can judge maturity with the minimum of inspection. Great care will have to be taken with self-pick enterprises to ensure husks are not picked from immature cobs and then left to waste when the person realizes the cob is not mature.

Once harvested the cobs must be marketed as fast as possible as the sugars in the grain are quickly converted to starch, greatly reducing quality. Quick removal of field heat helps considerably in increasing shelf life. To maintain high quality the crop should be transported and marketed in a cooled or refrigerated environment. For basic 'corn-on-the-cob' the husk is left on to prevent drying out of the grains. Alternatively the husk may be stripped off and the cob shrink wrapped, this makes an attractive pack with a longer shelf life.

Storage

The maximum storage period is one week at 0°C (32°F). The humidity must be 95 to 98 per cent or alternatively the cobs must be kept from drying out by placing them in polythene lined bins.

Anticipated yields

Average yield – 52,500 cobs/ha (21,260 cobs/acre)
Good commercial yield – 70,000 cobs/ha (28,350 cobs/acre)

Pests and diseases

The major problem on this crop is frit fly – for details of control see pests and diseases chart Chapter 12.

Rhubarb – *Rheum rhaponticum*

Rhubarb is a hardy herbaceous plant and the most important of the

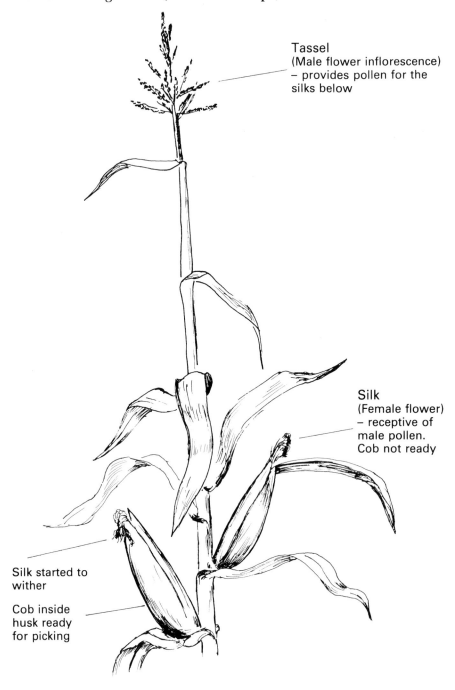

Tassel
(Male flower inflorescence)
– provides pollen for the
silks below

Silk
(Female flower)
– receptive of
male pollen.
Cob not ready

Silk started to
wither

Cob inside
husk ready
for picking

Figure 29   Pollination and harvesting stage of sweet corn

Right hand plant shows typical frit fly damage on sweet corn.
Left hand plant normal.

few perennial vegetable crops. Production tends to be concentrated in
a number of small specialist areas. The most important are the Leeds
area in Yorkshire and the Glasgow area of Scotland.

Soils

The crop will grow well on almost any soil type providing it is well
drained. Soils which lie wet in the winter result in poor establishment
of new plantings and are slow to produce a crop in the spring. The crop
produces a dense canopy early in the season resulting in a high demand
for water. Therefore, moisture retentive soils are preferable.

It is essential to start with a site free from perennial weeds as these
can build up quickly in the crop and will be difficult to eradicate. The
crop will tolerate acid soil conditions but every effort should be made
to maintain the pH between 6.5 and 7.0 on mineral soils and around
5.8 on peat soils, if maximum yield is to be achieved.

Cultivars

A range of cultivars are available and new ones are occasionally released
by the Stockbridge House Experimental Horticulture Station. Rhubarb
plants become dormant as the daylength reduces in the autumn. Before
the plant will break dormancy (resume growth) it must be exposed to
low temperatures for an appropriate length of time. The low temperature requirement for each cultivar is expressed as Accumulated Cold

Units (ACUs). A coid unit is every 1°C below 10°C, as measured at 9.00 am. GMT (standard Meteorological Office practice) at a soil depth of 100 mm (4 in). The cold units measured each day are accumulated by adding each day's cold units together.

The number of cold units required before a cultivar will break dormancy vary greatly, for example, 'Timperley Early' 130 ACUs; 'Victoria' 320 ACUs. The earliness of a cultivar can, therefore, be assessed by referring to its ACU requirement.

The position is further complicated by the release of virus-free clones of the major cultivars. Once virus free the plant has a higher ACU requirement than the same cultivar with virus. Trials with virus tested material have been inconclusive in terms of increased yield. In most cases yield increase is small and the cost of changing to virus free stock may not be covered by the yield increase.

FRESH MARKET CULTIVARS

Timperley Early   – main cultivar because of earliness.
Hawks Champagne } – Locally important cultivars but not
Prince Albert   }   as early as Timperley Early.

Stockbridge Arrow } – Newer cultivars released from Stockbridge
Cawood Delight   }   House EHS and worth consideration but may
                                    not yield so heavily.

PROCESSING CULTIVARS

Timperley Early   } – Very early and may be too early for some
Merton Formost   }   processors

Prince Albert   – Early, but lower yielding than the Sutton or
                              Victoria.
The Sutton   – The heaviest yielding cultivar.
Victoria   – Late and heavy yielding

The processing trade generally prefer green fleshed cultivars so that artificial colouring can be added during canning. But this may be changed as a result of further legislation on artificial colouring of food.

Nutrition

Incorporation of bulky organic matter well in advance of planting is desirable on most soils. Where structure is poor or the soil is very light bulky organic matter is essential and a 50–100 tonnes/ha (20–40 tons/acre) should be incorporated and worked in to the full depth of the top soil.

A base fertilizer dressing should be applied pre-planting. The rate of application will be determined by soil analysis (see table below) and the amount of farmyard manure used. If farmyard manure has been applied the base dressing may be reduced as follows:

For every 10 tonnes of farmyard manure used reduce the P_2O_5 by 20 kg/ha, K_2O by 40 kg/ha and N by 15 kg/ha.

Table 53: Recommended fertilizer rates for rhubarb (kg nutrient per hectare).

Nutrient Index	Phosphate P_2O_5	Potash K_2O	Magnesium Mg		Nitrogen N	
			Sandy soils	Other soils	Base dressing	Top dressing
Establishment (first year)						
0	175	250	60	30	175	
1	150	225	30	NIL	125	
2	125	200	NIL	NIL	75	
3	100	150	–	–	–	
4	50	125	–	–	–	
Over 4	NIL	NIL	–	–	–	
Annual Dressings						
0	100	250				250*
1	100	200				250*
2	75	150				250*
3	75	150				
4	NIL	NIL				
Over 4	NIL	NIL				

If soil analysis is not available use the values underlined in the table.
*Split application for fresh market crop; single application for processing crop.

Propagation

Propagation from seed is unsatisfactory as the resulting stocks lack uniformity. Rhubarb is traditionally propagated by dividing the crown with a spade or a half moon edging iron. A good two-year-old crown will divide into three to four pieces, and a three-year-old crown into five to six pieces. The pieces of divided crowns are known as 'sets'. Each set must have at least one bud and a reasonable portion of root. Where old crowns are used for division only the outer edge of the crown should be used as the central area lacks vigour and will only give poor plants.

Two newer techniques have been developed for rapid propagation of new cultivars, and the bulking up of virus-free stocks. These involve the use of leaf bud cuttings or the use of minisets. The latter technique may be useful for some growers as the work can be carried out indoors when weather conditions prevent outside work being done. In addition, planting of minisets can be carried out at the optimum time of year which should reduce establishment losses.

Soil preparation
This should be carried out well in advance of planting. Subsoiling during a dry period in the preceding summer is advisable followed by deep ploughing incorporating bulky organic matter if possible. Where lime is required this should be spread before breaking down the plough mould. The base dressing can also be applied prior to secondary cultivations. Cultivations are aimed at breaking the soil down to a coarse tilth. The soil should then be allowed to settle for a few weeks before planting (planting on recently worked soil results in many sets drying out). If necessary, the surface can be broken up by a light harrowing immediately prior to planting.

Planting
Early cultivars should be planted in October or early November as they start into growth soon after Christmas in mild areas. The planting of late cultivars may be delayed until the Christmas to March period, provided soil conditions permit planting at this time.

A density of 1.43 plants/m^2 (1.20 plants/yd^2) gives 14,346/ha (5,810/ acre). The most common spacing for sets is 900 mm (3 ft) approximately down the row with 760 mm ($2\frac{1}{2}$ ft) between rows. If the crowns are to be lifted for forcing, or where the soil lies very wet in the winter, it is advisable to plant into ridges. Otherwise, planting on the flat is quite satisfactory.

Much of the crop is hand planted, but ploughing out a furrow to plant into saves a great deal of time. In heavy soils, the side and base of the furrow may tend to smear. If this happens the smeared surface must be broken, as planting proceeds. Great care must be taken not to damage the buds. At this stage, a greatly reduced plant stand will result if buds are damaged.

The sets should be covered to a depth of 25 mm (1 in) which, after settling, will leave the crown buds exposed.

Herbicides
While the soil surface is still weed-free following planting, simazine should be applied as an overall herbicide treatment at 4.5 kg/ha (4 lb/ acre) on light soils and 6.7 kg/ha (6 lb/acre) on medium to heavy soils. Do not use simazine on highly organic soils. On established plantations, paraquat at 4.2 l/ha (3 pt/acre) plus simazine (rates as above) should be applied as a tank mix annually during the dormant season (late

November). This treatment should provide adequate weed control for the season.

Where simazine-resistant weeds become a problem use of chlorpropham/fenuron mixtures (Herbon Red and Herbon White) used during crown dormancy offer an alternative. For sands, very light soils and soils low in organic matter use Herbon White at 11.2 1/ha (1.0 gal/acre). For other soils use Herbon Red at 22 1/ha (2.0 gal/acre).

If perennial weeds become a problem, including couch grass, Propyzamide (Kerb 50 W) applied at 1.7 kg/ha (1.5 lb/acre) in conjunction with simazine at 2.2 kg/ha (2 lb/acre) applied between October 1 and December 31 should help to reduce the problem. Do not use the latter combination on plantations less than one-year-old.

Persistant perennial weeds and seedlings arising from the introduction of straw should be controlled by spot treating them with MCPA, 2,4–D or Aminotriazole. For grass weeds, including couch and volunteer cereals, overall application of Alloxidim-sodium is very effective.

Top dressing

For continuous pulling throughout spring apply 125 kg/ha nitrogen just after bud burst and a further 125 kg/ha immediately after the last pulling. For processing crops (where a single harvest is usual) a single annual top dressing of 250 kg/ha nitrogen should be used.

Strawing

Growers in early areas with light soils, a sheltered aspect and early cultivars can advance the first pick by covering the ground with a layer of straw at approximately 20 tonnes/ha (8 tons/acre) before the end of January. This insulation protects the young growth from frost and gives brightly coloured petioles (stalks) in addition to advancing the crop. Damage to crowns must be avoided during the strawing operation.

Harvesting

Harvesting (pulling) for the fresh market may start as early as March (stems of 150–200 mm or 6–8 in are acceptable early in the season) and continue to June or later. Pulling is done by sliding the thumb or first finger down the inside of the petiole to its base and then pressing it away from the crown. The leaf blade is trimmed just above its junction with the petiole (stalk) leaving a small fan formed by the leaf mid ribs.

Grading and marketing

Leaf stalks must be turgid, clean and fresh with no physical or insect damage. The crop is usually marketed in 3–6 kg (6.6–13 lb) units using a long narrow-lidded fibreboard or solid board boxes.

Harvesting and packing of processing crops

The processing crop is only harvested once a year (with the exception of the first year when NO crop is taken). All stalks or flower stems are pulled. Any reject stalks along with flower stems and trimmed leaf are dropped back on the field. Preference is usually for 20–30 mm (0.8–1.18 in) diameter sticks but sometimes the processor will take over-thick sticks for splitting at the factory.

The trimmed sticks are either bunched into 13 kg (28 lb) bundles using portable bunching cradles in the field or they can be packed into pallet-based bulk bins. Careful handling is essential as bruising will result in down grading of a consignment. Also, the crop must reach the processing plant quickly while it is still fresh and turgid.

Anticipated yields

This depends on cultivar and time of harvest, but the following are typical yields from a high standard of growing crops:

PROCESSING CROPS

The Sutton	80 tonnes/ha (33 tons/acre)
Victoria	65 tonnes/ha (26.8 tons/acre)
Prince Albert	55 tonnes/ha (22.6 tons/acre)

FRESH MARKET

Timperley Early and Prince Albert	50–55 tonnes/ha (20.6–22.6 tons/acre)

Pests and diseases

This crop is little troubled by pests and diseases – see Chapter 12 for details.

Figure 30   Propagation of rhubarb crowns

The crowns are divided using an edging iron or spade. Each set should contain a bud and a good portion of root.

Table 54: Cropping summary chart sowing time, seed rates, plant spacing, density and harvest times

Species	Sowing time	No. seed/gram	Average seed rate/hectare Direct seeded	Trans-planted	Final plant spacing in mm	Average plant pop./m²	Min. temp. for germ. °C	Average life (yrs.) under natural storage	Harvest time
ASPARAGUS	Sow in seedbed April Plant out crowns following Feb./March	50	–	600 g	1300 × 300 900 × 300	2.56 3.70	13	3 yrs	Late April–June
BEANS Broad	Sow November or February/March	1	250 kg	–	450 × 150	14.80	5	3	June–September
French	Sow end April (south), May/June (north)	4	120 kg	–	400 × 60	43.00	10	3	July–October
Runner	Sow end April to May pinched beans	2	50 kg	–	800 × 150	8.33	10	3	July–August
	Sow end May/June stick bean crop	2	80 kg	–	300 × 130 Double rows at 1.50 m centres	10.80	13	3	July–October
BEETROOT Early bunched	Sow end March	100	6 kg	–	380 × 50	53.80	8	4	June onwards
Ware	Sow April–July	100	5.5 kg	–	280 × 75	47.62	8	4	July onwards
Baby pickling	Sow April–July	100	26 kg	–	210/m²	210.00	8	4	through to winter
BRUSSELS SPROUTS Freezing	Sow under frames Feb. onwards or sow in open seedbed mid March–April	250	500 g	300 g	500 × 500	4.00	4	5	Mid August through to mid March
Pre-pack	Direct seeding or seeded from early April to mid May	250	400 g	250 g	500 × 600	3.34	4	5	July onwards
Fresh		250	300 g	200 g	600 × 600	2.77	4	5	July onwards

Table 54: (continued)

Species	Sowing time	No. seed/ gram	Average seed rate/hectare Direct seeded	Trans- planted	Final plant spacing in mm	Average plant pop./m²	Min. temp. for germ. °C	Average life (yrs.) under natural storage	Harvest time
CABBAGE									
Spring greens	Sow early July direct drilled	280	1.0 kg	–	380 × 150	17.50	4	5 yrs	Jan.–March
Spring hearts	Sow July–Aug.	280	–	500 g	380 × 250	10.50	4	5	Late March–May
Summer (early)	Sow early in frames or peat blocks	280	–	400 g	300 × 400	8.33	4	5	Early June–early July
Summer	Sow mid March–early May	280	700 g	300 g	400 × 400	6.26	4	5	July–Aug.
Autumn/winter	Sow seedbed or direct drilled May	280	500 g	200 g	650 × 500	3.08	4	5	Sept.–March
CALABRESE									
Main fresh crop	Direct drilled to a stand April to late June	250	1.25 kg	–	380 × 250	10.50	4	5	July onwards
High density crop	Direct drilled April to late July	250	3.25 kg	–	225 × 225	20.00	4	5	July onwards
CARROT									
Dicing/slicing	Sown direct drilled in open ground from February to	900	10 kg	–	–	540.00	4	3	Earliest Xiro grown crop June, remainer July onwards.
Freezing		900	8 kg	–	–	430.00	4	3	
Canning	June. Earliest crops sown under	900	6.6 kg	–	–	376.00	4	3	
Pre-pack	Xiro film	900	3 kg	–	–	160.00	4	3	
Ware		900	2 kg	–	–	100.00	4	3	
CAULIFLOWER									
Summer (early)	Sow in cold frames Oct. or heated glass Jan. Plant out March	350	–	150 kg	600 × 450	3.70	4	5	End May–July

Summer	Sow under cold frames March/April or direct drill	350	300 g	150 g	600 × 450	3.70	4	5 yrs	July–August
Autumn	Sow cold frames, seed-bed or direct	350	250 g	125 g	600 × 600	2.78	4	5	Sept.–Nov.
Winter heading	Sow cold frames, seedbed or direct	350	200 g	100 g	600 × 710	2.38	4	5	Nov.–early June
Spring heading	Sow cold frames, seedbed or direct	350	190 g	95 g	670 × 670	2.23	4	5	Late March–June
CELERY Self-blanching	Sow Feb–April under heated glass pricked into blocks, planted mid. Apr.	3000	–	100 g / 70 g	250 × 250 / 300 × 300	16.00 / 11	4	6	July–Oct.
Trench	planted mid. Apr. to May	3000	–	50 g	1200×125/ 150	6.66 / 5.55	4	6	August–Oct.
LEEK	Seedbed Feb. onwards, plant out June onwards. Or direct drill April	400	1.5 kg	1.5 kg	450 × 100	22.22	4	1	
LETTUCE Cabbage Cos and crisp	Sown under glass or in blocks Jan. for planting March. Direct drilled April onwards.	800 800	1 kg 750 g	200 g 150 g	300 × 250 300 × 350	13.33 9.52	7 7	5 5	Earliest June onwards. Continues until end Oct.
ONION Ware	Sow Aug./Sept. or Feb./ March direct	260	6 kg	–	96 plants/m²	96.00	4	1	July–Oct.
Pickling	Sow March–April direct	260	40 kg	–	500 plants/ m²	500.00	4	1	July
Salad autumn sown	Sow July–end Aug. direct	260	25 kg		270–350	270–350	4	1	March–May
spring sown	Sow Feb.–June direct	260	36 kg		430 plants/ m²	430	4	1	May–Aug.

Table 54: (continued)

Species	Sowing time	No. seed/ gram	Average seed rate/hectare Direct seeded	Trans- planted	Final plant spacing in mm	Average plant pop./m²	Min. temp. for germ. °C	Average life (yrs.) under natural storage	Harvest time
PARSNIP									
Pre-pack	Sow Feb.–March	180	7 kg	–	400 × 60	41.67	4	1 yr.	Oct.–Feb.
Ware	Sow Feb.–March	180	3.5 kg	–	460 × 110	20.00	4	1	July–Feb.
Processing	Sow Feb.–March	180	5.3 kg	–	460 × 70	30.00	4	1	Oct.–Nov.
PEAS									
Fresh	Sow Nov. or Feb. – June drilled to a stand	4	240 kg	–	150 × 70	95.24	4	3	May–Oct.
RADISH									
Prepack	Sow Feb.–Aug., drilled	100	85 kg	–	650 plants/ m²	650.00	4	5	May–Oct.
Ware	to a stand	100	72 kg	–	550 plants/ m²	550.00	4	5	April–Oct.
SWEET CORN	Sow late May outside	4	20 kg	–	600 × 450	3.70	13	1	July–Oct.
SWEDE	Sow mid March–May direct drilled	4		–	380 × 150	17.54	4	5	Autumn to Spring
TURNIP									
Early bunched	Sow end Jan.–Feb. under Xiro direct			–	75 × 75	177.77	4	5	end March/April
Maincrop	Sow March – Aug. direct drilled and chopped out	400	2.5 kg	–	380 × 7	35.08	4	5	May to Nov.
VEGETABLE MARROW	Sow under glass March– April in blocks or containers	10	3.5 kg	1.75 kg	900 × 600	1.85	10	5	June (Courgettes July–Oct. (Marrows)

Chapter Ten

Machinery for Vegetable Growing

The agricultural and horticultural industry has become increasingly mechanized as a means of reducing labour costs. While it is not possible to give detailed coverage of every specialist piece of machinery used in vegetable production, an outline of the main types of equipment are covered in this chapter. The equipment outlined ranges from basic cultivation equipment to vegetable washing machines. They are covered under the following headings:
(1) Primary cultivation equipment
(2) Secondary cultivation equipment
(3) Rotary cultivators
(4) Drills and drilling equipment
(5) Peat blocking machines
(6) Transplanting machinery
(7) Spraying equipment
(8) Harvesting machinery
(9) Washers and cleaners
(10) Cold stores and coolers

Primary Cultivation Equipment

During the last decade a wide range of alternatives to the mould board plough have been introduced to the agricultural industry. But for the intensive vegetable grower the mould board plough is still the main tool because of its ability to invert the soil and therefore bury the extensive crop residues left after vegetable crops.

The reversible plough, which is now widely available, should be considered a necessity not a luxury. Uniform plant stands cannot be achieved unless there is a uniform depth of cultivation. The traditional fixed furrow plough results in shallow areas at the edge of each ploughed 'land'. These are eliminated by the use of the reversible plough.

The long standing problem of the plough, ie, smearing the furrow bottom, may be overcome in a range of ways. The fitting of small subsoiling tines, designed to run 25 mm (1 in) below the furrow bottom is very effective. Alternatively, a conscious effort to plough 50–75 mm (2–3 in) deeper every few years can eliminate a developing plough pan.

Secondary Cultivation Equipment

This covers the operation required to produce a sowing or planting tilth. The range of implements available is very large but the special requirements of the vegetable grower (a fine level and firm seedbed) have caused certain implements to find special favour.

Inter-row cultivator working in a carrot crop.

NON-POWERED CULTIVATORS   The initial breaking down of the plough mould is frequently carried out by disc harrows or spring tine cultivators. The latter are frequently fitted with a levelling board on the front, and levelling combs or rotary crumblers on the rear to achieve the maximum effect.

Perhaps the most popular implement for the final preparation of the seed or transplant bed is the Dutch levelling harrow (Dutch scrubber).

An angled levelling board on the front gives a very level finish while the heavy frame crushes up any clods. A heavy crumbler roller is frequently fitted to the rear to give a fine and firm surface tilth. The roller must not be forgotten on a dry or fluffy seedbed where it can be very valuable. The Cambridge (ring) roller is most suitable as the loose rings crush clods more effectively and give better consolidation. If production is very intensive the use of a mounted roller should be considered as this allows a considerable reduction in headland width.

POWERED IMPLEMENTS   Power cultivators are becoming more common in vegetable production and can be useful in forcing a tilth quickly.

RECIPROCATING HARROW   This consists of vertical spikes set on bars (2, 3 or 4). These bars are oscillated sideways at up to *500 cycles per minute*. This equipment produces an effect similar to normal drag harrows but in a single pass. The basic reciprocating harrow tends to produce slight ridging of the soil. It is therefore important where a level seedbed is required that the machine is fitted with anti-ridging boards plus a levelling comb or rotary crumbler.

ROTARY POWER HARROW   This implement has a similar effect to the reciprocating harrow but consists of pairs of driven rotors which contra-rotate about a vertical axis at up to 300 rpm. Anti-ridging boards are again required, while a crumbler roller is usually fitted as standard.

Rotary Cultivators (Rotavators)

Unlike the power harrows, which are only suitable for secondary cultivation, the rotary cultivator can be used for primary and secondary cultivations. It is also useful for chopping up crop debris prior to ploughing.

A wide range of machines is available, from the small pedestrian models to the large tractor mounted type, but the principle remains the same. A horizontal shaft carries a series of L-shaped blades which rotate in the same direction as the tractor wheels. The tilth can be varied in three different ways: the forward speed of the tractor, the rotor speed (changed by means of the cultivator gear box) and the position of the metal shielding. The more cuts per metre the finer the tilth. Operating with the rear shield in the down position produces a finer surface tilth as the clods of soil shatter when they impact on the casing. The tilth produced by a cultivator is very fluffy and open, so rolling is required before drilling or planting, and heavy rain reduces the soil to the consistency of porridge.

Incorrect use of a rotary cultivator can do a great deal of harm to the soil. Attempts to force a tilth when conditions are not suitable causes serious damage to soil structure. Smearing of the soil can also occur with this equipment giving rise to a 'plough pan' type condition.

PEDESTRIAN OPERATED ROTAVATORS These machines are very useful for cultivation of small areas, eg, glasshouses or cold frames. Their effects on soil structure are effectively the same as those discussed for tractor mounted rotavators (see page 195). They can also be used for inter-row cultivation, though this function is now reduced by the modern herbicides.

Control of tilth with these pedestrian machines is limited to control of forward speed but use of higher forward speed is only possible where the ground conditions are reasonably good. Under very hard or difficult soil conditions the machine is unlikely to have adequate power to operate at high forward speed.

It is not within the scope of this book to discuss maintenance of these machines, but it is essential that:

(1) The on/off switch functions properly and is within easy reach of the normal working position.

(2) The 'dead mans handle' system functions where the machine has a reverse gear; (this mechanism requires the operator to hold a control lever in position during reversing, should the operator fall or let go of the machine for any reason the machine will automatically stop).

(3) That any guards supplied with the machine are kept in place. Failure to observe the above codes of practice would constitute a contravention of health and safety regulations.

Drills and Drilling Equipment

Seed drills commonly used in vegetable growing can be placed into three groups, based on their method of seed metering:

AGITATOR ASSISTED GRAVITY FEED DRILLS The Gloucester Random Seeder, commonly known as the 'Bean Seeder', is still widely used. Metering is achieved by means of a disc containing a range of holes, any one of which can be used to regulate the flow from the hopper to the coulter. Forward speed is also a critical factor in the calibration of this drill – the faster the forward speed the lower the seed rate.

METERED FEED NON-SPACING DRILLS These drills give a random distribution but the feed rate is more accurate than the agitator assisted gravity feed drill. The rate of seeding is self compensating in relation to forward speed. One of the smallest and simplest drills available belonging to this group is called the 'frame drill'. It is very valuable for the sowing of high density seed beds under protection.

Both of the groups already mentioned are suitable for drilling to a stand or drilling seed beds.

Simple semi-precision frame drill.

PRECISION OR SPACING DRILLS Where crops are drilled for singling the only suitable unit is the precision drill machine, which gives greatest financial saving in seed and singling costs. For these drills to be fully effective, the distance the seed falls from the metering unit to the ground should not exceed 50 mm (2 in). For drilling single seeds at each position, these drills require approximately spherical seed.

Where the natural seed is not spherical, pelleted seed can be used to enable accurate drilling. Natural seed should also be graded to facilitate precision.

Metering units

CELL WHEEL FEED The seed metering is achieved by alloy cell wheels which can be changed to suit the seed size and spacing. This system has the advantage of positive drive which eliminates any slip within the metering unit.

BELT FEED This system has become very popular. The seed metering is carried out by means of a rubber or plastic faced belt. In many respects this operates in a similar way to the cell wheel. The only difference is that belts may contain one, two or three lines of seed holes. There is a danger with belt feeds that seeds become trapped and cause the belt to slip. An electrical system is fitted to the drill which allows the tractor driver to monitor all the units by way of a panel of lights mounted in the cab.

CUP FEED   This old principle, used in the first seed drills, has been revived in the Swedish Nibex machine. There are ranges of caps to suit the different seed sizes. Each set is colour coded. The seed falls 175–200 mm (7–8 in) from the cap to the soil.

VACUUM DRILL   The vacuum system is a new principle which offers a number of potential advantages. The seeds are sucked on to holes in the metering disc by a partial vacuum and held there until released by a break in the vacuum. This positive filling and holding in the cells should enable higher drilling speeds and also allow the use of irregular shaped natural seed to be used for single seed sowing.

Traditionally, the drive to the seed metering unit was by means of the land wheel on each individual unit. It is preferable to take the drive by means of a set of master land wheels (with cleated rubber tyres) driving each unit by a 'V' belt from a common shaft. Though this latter sysem is more costly if offers a number of advantages. There is a more positive drive which allows slightly higher drilling speeds through less risk of drive wheel slip. A choice of seeding rates can be achieved by changing the drive ratio through variable pulley sizes or a gear box.

The speed for precision seeding is 3.2–4.8 kph (2–3 mph). For vacuum drills speed may be 10–11 kph (6–7 mph).

Peat Blocking Machines

Peat blocks can be made by simple hand moulds which are plunged into a mound of moist blocking compost and the formed blocks ejected by squeezing a lever on the handle which is linked to an ejector plate. These hand units are available for a range of block sizes.

Powered blocking machines are available in a wide range of sizes. The main difference is the width of the blocking mechanism and discharge conveyor. Choice of machine size must be based on the number of blocks/hr which are required (and the capital available). Machines with a very high output require efficient handling of materials to get blocking compost to the machine and completed blocks away from the machine. Bad handling of materials can result in the machine running below its potential output. The output of blocking machines varies according to the size of the machine. An example is the 'Tayblocker Minor' (a small blocking machine) which has a capacity of 5,000 blocks per hour (38 mm or 1½ in size). Most machines can be adjusted to give a range of block sizes. Also, the pins which make the depression in the top of the block are interchangeable from shallow holes (5 to 6 mm or ¼ in) for direct seeding to deep holes (18 mm or ¾ in) for pricking out.

SEEDING UNITS   There are two forms of seeding unit available. One is the simple mechanical seeder which is fitted as standard to most machines. This will handle pellets or graded regular seed with reasonable accuracy placing one seed in each block. The alternative is a more complex seeder usually operating on hydraulic principles and capable of sowing any set number of natural seeds per block, thus enabling the sowing of multi-plant blocks and saving on seed cost where single seed sowing is practised.

Transplanting Machinery

Where a crop is not field drilled transplanting will be required. On all but small areas a machine of some type will be used to enable maximum output from the workforce.

'Drawn' or 'peg' plants were originally used for transplanting. But there is an increasing trend towards the use of container grown vegetable plants. Such plants receive less check to growth when transplanted and if the container has several plants (as in multi-plant blocks) the speed of planting can be increased.

In selecting a planting machine consideration should be given to its flexibility of use – will it plant at the spacing required for the variety of crops grown? Will it handle bare roots and container raised plants? Where a bed system of growing is used the planter should be capable of planting the whole bed at one pass. The planters currently used in the UK are made up of units each having:
(1)   A furrow opener in the form of a 'V' shaped share adjustable for depth and width.
(2)   A plant handling mechanism to move the plant from the operator to the furrow.
(3)   A firming device, usually in the form of two steel wheels orientated in an incomplete 'V' shape. An operator is required for each unit and the person is seated above the steel press wheels to give added weight to the firming of the plants.

The principal difference between the various machines available is the plant handling unit. On very simple machines the operator has to place the plant by hand direct in the furrow. Plant spacing has to be judged, though a 'clicker' driven from a ground wheel is frequently used to give an audible signal as to when the plant should go in to the soil. Skilled operators are essential.

There are two common mechanical placement mechanisms. These still require 'feeding' by the operator but work rates are higher as the distance the operative has to move is greatly reduced. The disc system employs a pair of flexible steel or rubber discs which open at the upper tangent to allow a plant to be placed between them and then close again to carry it to the furrow. Here the discs part allowing the plant to be trapped in the soil.

Spacing is achieved by marks on the discs showing where a plant should be inserted. Interchangeable sprockets on the drive system enable the grower to use different spacing. The 'plant holder' system employs a disc with a number of plant clips around the perimeter. These clips usually open and close automatically in a similar manner to the disc system. Alteration in spacing is achieved by changing the drive ratio from the presser wheel or by altering the number of plant clips. The usual range of plant spacing by the mechanization is 100 mm (4 in) to 1600 mm (64 in).

Optional equipment is available for many machines to enable them to plant blocks. If this equipment is not available or is not working properly due to poor soil or container conditions the plant-handling mechanism can be removed and the planter treated as a simple machine.

To change spacing between rows the individual planting units can be slid along the main frame but the minimum row spacing which can be achieved is 500 mm (20 in). For closer row spacings it will be necessary to mount the units in tandem on a double main frame, the rear units planting between the rows planted by the front units. A tandem system results in a considerable rear weight on the tractor which must be counterbalanced by front end weights.

Where a large amount of transplanting is carried out, and particularly at high densities where a slow forward speed is required, the use of the NIAE self-steering system should be considered. This enables the tractor driver to work on the planter (once the first pass down the field has been made), returning only to turn at the end of the field. Apart from the obvious saving in labour this also eliminates a very tedious job.

Work rates depend more on operator skill and plant spacing than any other factor. Though high speeds are possible for short periods they cannot be sustained. Work rates (per unit) of 2,500–2,800 plants/hr for close spaced plants and 1,300–1,500/hr for wide spacings are acceptable.

Where high density planting is carried out, tractor forward speed may be as low as 0.33 kph (0.2 mph). Few tractors are capable of 'pulling' at this speed. The very low engine 'revs' required would not provide enough power to draw the planter through the soil. This can be overcome by use of a hydrostatic drive tractor or by fitting an epicyclic gear box as a sandwich between the normal gearbox and the back axle casing. This will only add about 100–125 mm (4–5 in) to the tractor's length and can be fitted in a few hours by a skilled mechanic. These units are available for a number of popular tractors.

SEMI-AUTOMATIC AND AUTOMATIC TRANSPLANTERS   These are aimed at the container raised plants. They have reached an advanced stage of development with some semi-automatic machines in commercial use. The plant handling mechanism usually consists of a group of vertical cylinders into which the container plant is dropped by the operator. Each cylinder releases the plant at an appropriate interval. A tube or shute carries the plant down to the furrow opening shore. These machines offer faster work rates per operator.

Fully automatic transplanting can only be considered where the plant production system is designed for the automatic planter. A special form of Japanese paper pot which forms an endless chain can be used to raise plants for the Lannen semi-automatic planting machine. The NIAE Bandolier consists of a chain of paper-wrapped peat blocks which can be used in conjunction with the NIAE automatic planting machine. These fully automatic systems have so far had little use under commercial conditions but appear to offer a number of advantages where a complete production system is available.

Sprayers

The sprayers used in vegetable growing differ little from the basic agricultural sprayer. In this section the various parts of a sprayer are described and any special recommendations for specific components are added.

TANKS   Three materials are commonly used for tank construction – plastic, 'fibre glass' and galvanized steel. Plastic tanks are becoming increasingly common as they are cheap and corrosion free, which means they require little maintenance. Tank sizes range from 150–450 litres (30–100 gal).

PUMPS   There is frequently a choice of pump offered with any given machine. The 'roller-vane pump' is the most commonly used sprayer pump – water displacement is on semi-positive basis and therefore is capable of reasonable pressure and output. It can also be easily serviced on the holding. Where only liquid chemicals are used this pump could be considered as it is reasonably cheap and easily serviced. Where wettable powders are used regularly they cause severe wear to pump mechanisms and the use of a diaphragm pump should be considered. The diaphragm pump achieves liquid displacement by the movement of a piston in a cylinder. But unlike the piston pump the working parts are protected from direct contact with the spray chemical by means of a synthetic rubber diaphragm.

Any other forms of pump are not generally suitable. If the grower is in doubt he should discuss the matter with his machinery dealer. But be certain to point out the chemical formulations which will be used in the sprayer.

AGITATION This is very important when suspensions or emulsions are used in the sprayer. Without adequate agitation both of these formulations will separate in the spraying tank causing very irregular application rates. Few modern sprayers are fitted with mechanical agitation (a propeller or stirrer in the tank). Instead most sprayers rely on hydraulic agitation. Hydraulic agitation relies on the pump supplying a greater volume and pressure of spray than is required by the spray boom. The pressure regulator 'bleed-off' takes this excess and returns it to the tank through a jet which produces the agitation effect. Provided the sprayer is fitted with a pump of adequate capacity, hydraulic agitation is generally adequate.

BOOMS The only choice available to the purchaser is in the width of the booms – they vary from 4.5 m (15 ft) to 21 m (70 ft). Where crops are grown on a bed system the boom length should be a multiple of the bed width so there is no problem with overlapping on the next run. Wide booms have several disadvantages: it is difficult to match up the spray bout, unless a bed system is used; large booms are prone to whip or bounce which causes uneven application, which in turn may cause direct crop damage. There are many systems employed to reduce whip in large booms but most vegetable growers should give careful thought to the matter before selecting spray booms in excess of 10 m (33 ft).

SPECIAL BOOMS Brussels sprout growers frequently use a boom fitted with 'row crop droppers'. These are flexible mounted legs which hang from the booms spaced so they hang between the rows of the crop. Each leg carries several nozzles which are set sideways so the spray is directed on to the sprout stem and buttons.

ANTI-DRIP SYSTEMS There are two main ways of avoiding dripping and consequent over dosing. *Spring loaded valves* can be used at each nozzle.

These only open when the operating pressure is reached. The *suck back control* system uses the pump to suck the spray liquid out of the booms and return it to the tank. It is essential the anti-drip system works. Any failure should be rectified before further use.

NOZZLES   This is the most important and most often neglected part of the machine since the nozzle regulates the application rate and spray pattern.

Fan nozzles are reasonably cheap and long lasting. They are constructed from brass or brass with a ceramic inset and give a spray distribution in a triangular pattern. The operating height must be set correctly. Changes in pressure have little effect on output so nozzle size must be selected according to output required. Pressure does affect droplet size and fan nozzles tend to produce a high percentage of small droplets. Therefore pressure should be regulated to minimize risk of spray drift (higher pressure equals more drift).

Cone nozzles produce a spray pattern which is rectangular or trapezoidal. Boom height is even more critical with this type of nozzle. But the risk of spray drift is reduced, even with variation in pressure. They are also more accurate in their application provided the sprayer is set and driven accurately.

SETTING THE SPRAYER   The manufacturer's instruction book should be followed faithfully for setting and calibration of the sprayer. BUT RE-MEMBER: check nozzle size and condition (they can wear quickly); check forward speed (the tractor meter may not be accurate); check boom height (spray water on dry concrete to check the uniformity of spray distribution across the swath); check pressure (most nozzles work best at one pressure).

HAND SPRAYERS   The most common type used is the knapsack sprayer which has a capacity of 10–15 l. Where these small sprayers are used for herbicides and pesticides it is common practice to keep one for herbicides only and a second for pesticides and fungicides. The herbicide sprayer will normally be fitted with a flood jet-type nozzle which gives a wide swath and a larger droplet size to minimize drift. Where inter-row spraying is carried out a hood can be fitted to contain the spray and minimize crop damage. Some makes of sprayer have a variable pressure relief valve which can be set to give three or more pressure settings. Low pressures (15 psi) reduce drift by reducing droplet size while a high pressure (45 psi) gives a finer droplet which may be required to obtain good coverage (as required when using fungicides).

CALIBRATION OF HAND SPRAYERS   Calibration of knapsack sprayers for the application of herbicides frequently causes problems. The sprayer must be calibrated by the person who is to carry out the job of spraying. A comfortable walking pace should be used during calibration and this should be adhered to when actually spraying.

Table 55: Calibration for spraying an area of 1,000 sq m

Calibration method	How the job is carried out
(1) Mark out an area of about 100 m² on a hard surface. The width of the area should be equal to the swath width of the nozzle when held at the height at which it will be used in the crop. (2) Fill the sprayer with clean water and spray the marked area. (3) Refill the sprayer measuring the amount of liquid required to refill to the previous level. (4) The volume of liquid applied per square metre can be calculated and then multiplied by the number of square metres to be sprayed.	If the operator sprays 8 litres of water on 100 m² during his/her calibration then 80 litres will be required to spray the 1000 m² area. With a 15 litre knapsack this means $5^{1}/_{3}$ fills (ie, 5 fills plus 5 litres). By dividing the total simazine for the plot (200 g) by the number of litres of water for the plot (80 1) we get the amount of simazine/litre. $$\frac{200}{80} = 2.5 \text{ g/1}$$ Therefore full knapsack requires 2.5 × 15 = 37.5 and the $^{1}/_{3}$ knapsack requires 2.5 × 5 = 12.5 g.
(5) Calculate the amount of chemical required in each sprayer full of water.	Simazine is to be applied at the rate of 2g/ha. The actual plot to be sprayed is only 1000 m² Therefore the amount of simazine required $$= \frac{2 \text{ kg} \times 1000 \text{ (g/ha)}}{10,000 \text{ (m}^2/\text{ha)}} \times \frac{1000 \text{ m}^2}{1}$$ $= 0.2 \times 1000 = 200$ g simazine required.

Note that kg/ha or l/ha can be simply reduced to g/m² or ml/m² respectively by dividing by 10.

After spraying, any surface, chemical should be discharged safely, preferably on to the sprayed area, an adjacent headland or into a special soakaway point. The sprayer should then be washed out thoroughly using a little wetting agent and the washings disposed of in a similar manner. DO NOT discharge surplus spray or spray tank washings into drains or surface water ditches. Ensure that disposal points are well away from any river or surface water drain which could be polluted by seepage.

Harvesting Machinery

The machinery used for harvesting tends to be specific to each crop and to detail every machine available is beyond the scope of this book. However, this section does give a summary outline of the main types of machinery involved with each crop.

BRUSSELS SPROUT HARVESTERS   The complete harvester for this crop is so costly that only the very largest growers or processing companies could consider its use. Semi-automatic harvesters are now widely used and they require an operator for each row of sprouts. The machine cuts off the sprout stem just above ground level and the stem is then transferred manually to a stripping head which removes the buttons from the stalk.

The operators using this machine can work under cover and are therefore protected from the worst of the weather. A simpler alternative is to mount a stripping head in a trailer or in the packing shed, the stems are then cut by hand and taken to the stripping head.

To use most Brussels sprout harvesters, the crop has to be de-leafed prior to taking off the buttons. After harvest some form of trash separation is needed to remove remaining pieces of leaf-stalk. Also, the crop will require passing over an inspection conveyor to enable the removal of any diseased or damaged sprouts before grading and weighing. De-leafing is normally carried out by hand with a de-leafing ring, a vegetable knife, or simply breaking off leaf stalks manually.

LEGUME HARVESTERS   The machinery used for harvesting legumes is very specialized and extremely expensive. Most peas and broad beans are harvested as a two-stage operation: the haulms are cut and windrowed, then a mobile viner lifts and vines the crop from the windrow. There is increasing interest in the use of pod picker viners as these reduce the throughput of haulms, therefore speeding up the vining process. They also reduce the labour input as the pod picker is a single stage operation. French beans are harvested by means of a pod picker. Recent developments have greatly improved the efficiency of these machines.

LEEK HARVESTERS   This crop is rarely lifted mechanically, though a top puller harvester can be used where row spacing is adequate. It is more usual to undercut the crop as an aid to lifting. This can be done with a simple undercutter blade, or more effectively, with a vibrating blade powered by the PTO shaft (Figure 31). The job can be carried out several days before harvesting all the crop and this enables pulling of the crop as and when required.

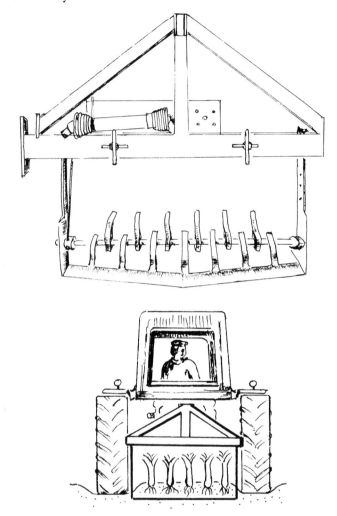

Figure 31   An undercutting blade used in leeks

ROOT HARVESTERS   There are two basic forms of machine used for root crops. The *top puller harvester* lifts the crop by the foliage, leaving soil clods and stones in the field. Row spacing must be wide enough and the row or band width must not exceed 100 mm (4 in). This machine is confined to crops which have foliage and is therefore not used for winter lifting.

The *digger elevator harvester* (hoover) scoops the crop out of the ground by means of a share running under the crop. The volume of soil lifted is very large, though a large proportion of this falls back to the field as the crop is elevated up the rod conveyor system. A trash separator takes

Simple digger elevator harvester.

Digger-elevator harvester fitted with a front mounted flail topper (in foreground) working in a carrot crop.

out some debris before the crop is loaded into trailers, but clods of soil or stones tend to remain with the crop and have to be removed at the packing shed (see washing and cleaning, page 208). The main advantage of this machine is its flexibility. The crop can be lifted at any time of year and a range of machine sizes are available so that a full bed can be lifted at one pass.

MOBILE PACKING UNIT This is useful for a wide range of crops, particularly where no washing is required before packing, eg lettuce and cauliflower. The unit is usually built around a tractor which acts as the power unit. The harvesting operatives cut the crop and place it onto wing conveyors which carry the produce to the main platform of the machine where a separate team grade and pack the produce ready for the market.

The system makes maximum use of the operators as selectors of suitable crop, leaving grading/packing to other workers. Double handling of produce is reduced but use of the machine may be limited if soil conditions become very wet.

Washers and Cleaners

These fall into two groups – those designed to handle root crops and those designed for leafy and salad vegetables.

ROOT CLEANING AND WASHING The input point consists of a dump hopper which should be capable of taking at least two loads of produce so that continuity of throughput can be maintained. A conveyor takes the produce from the hopper up to a pre-cleaner which should be set high enough to allow it to discharge straight into trailers or bins. The pre-cleaner consists of a barrel of approximately 900 mm diameter (3 ft) and the sides of which are composed of parallel rods. This barrel revolves on an almost horizontal axis with just enough slope to convey the crop through to the other end. The gap between the rods allows small roots, soil and stones to fall through. Pre-cleaning may be carried out dry, or spray lines may be fitted to provide a pre-wash action.

After the pre-cleaner, it is frequently necessary to pass the roots through a hydraulic stone separator unless the stone content is very low in which case they can be hand picked. The modern stone separator uses a fast water current into which the produce is deposited. The roots are carried along by the current and picked up by a conveyor. The stones sink to the bottom and are taken out by a separate waste conveyor. The water is re-cycled, therefore the water requirement is quite small.

The root washers vary in their design and construction. The most common being the partially immersed barrel type constructed of wire mesh or wooden slats. The barrel is usually lined with rubber, hessian or brushes. The barrel revolves slowly in a horizontal axis with the lower third immersed in water. The roots are repeatedly tumbled as they pass through the lining of the barrel, having a scrubbing action on the falling roots. As the crop emerges from the washer it is given a final rinse of clean water from overhead sprays. The spray water then passes into the main washer tank, displacing the waste water which overflows.

The water requirements for these washers are about 180–270 l/tonne (40–60 gal/ton). Some re-circulation of water may be possible but the level of suspended soils causes considerable problems.

SALAD AND LEAFY VEGETABLE SPRAY WASHERS   These vegetables are spray washed in contrast to the immersion washing of root crops. The machine usually consists of a horizontal conveyor of mesh or rod construction which carries the produce through a cabinet where it is sprayed from all angles by high pressure water jets. Most machines have an uneven spray volume across the width of the conveyor. This means that the butt end of produce can be placed on the conveyor in such a position that it obtains the highest volume of spray.

It is possible to include trimmers as part of the same conveyor line so that crops such as leeks, salad onions and celery can be laid across the conveyor and are thus trimmed at one or both ends prior to going through the washer unit. Water consumption for medium sized units is around 22,800 l/hr (5,000 gal/hr) at 2.8–3.5 kg/cm (40–50 psi).

Cold Stores and Coolers

There are three principal methods of pre-cooling vegetables.

VACUUM COOLING   This is achieved by placing the produce in a sealable chamber. The air is then evacuated by means of a vacuum pump. By creating a partial vacuum, a small proportion of the water in the produce 'boils off', thus absorbing the heat from the produce. (For a temperature drop of 10°C approximately 1.7 per cent moisture will be lost.) The process takes approximately 30 minutes per batch of produce. Where high throughput is required two chambers can be employed with a single vacuum pump serving both chambers.

In vacuum cooling the pressure is reduced (the Phase I stage) to 15 mm absolute mercury and then the pressure is maintained (the Phase II stage). There are several techniques employed for producing the vacuum and for handling the large amount of low pressure water vapour generated in the chamber during Phase II.

This cooling system is most suited to vegetables with a large surface area and a high water content, eg, lettuce, Brussels sprouts and celery.

It can also be used for cauliflower, sweet corn and cabbage. The major advantage is that cooling is uniform and can be carried out after the material has been packed, provided the package or box is not hermetically sealed.

Vacuum coolers are expensive but can be constructed as mobile units driven by internal combustion engine. They can also achieve a fast temperature drop in produce already packed and ready for despatch.

ICE BANK COOLING   The ice bank system for cooling vegetables is a relatively new innovation, though it has been used for cooling many other commodities. The cooler consists of a cold store type storage chamber which may be used as a cooler and a cold store. This is cooled by an ice bank system and not by direct refrigeration. The refrigeration equipment is used to build up a large ice bank at times of low cooling demand in the storage chamber. This ice bank is then used as a large reserve of chilling capacity to meet the short periods of peak demand when the store is loaded. Cooling of the storage chamber is achieved by circulating the air from the storage chamber through a heat exchanger. While air from the store passes up through the heat exchanger, cold water from the ice bank is sprayed in at the top. Water as the heat transfer agent keeps relative humidity of the store very high, which prevents any desiccation of produce. The large reserve of iced water gives a much faster cooling capacity than the conventional refrigeration units fitted to cold stores.

COLD STORES   The cold store may be of a direct refrigeration type with the cooling coils in the store, or it may be cooled by an ice bank system or jacket store where the refrigerated air is circulated in a cavity wall between the storage chamber and the outside wall.

Specialist advice should be sought on cold store design.

Chapter Eleven

Marketing Your Product

In large scale industry, firms employ highly paid specialist marketing managers to develop two important aspects of marketing: evolving an attractive sales package; and developing the sales outlets most suitable for the product.

It is unfortunate that few horticulturists have the skill to develop these to a satisfactory level. It is in this area that growers have the most to learn. Successful businesses are all about good marketing.

Evolving an Attractive Saleable Product

The horticulturist needs to consider two basic factors – firstly the quality produced and secondly the way it is packed, and this is carried out as follows:

STRICT GRADING STANDARDS The grower must maintain quality standards. All too often consistency of pack is undermined by one item in the pack being too small. Those that maintain high standards soon obtain a name associated with quality – a bit like obtaining a brand name. This in turn brings regular buyers requesting their produce so that market salesman like handling their crops.

Co-operative marketing schemes help small growers, who might not have facilities or sufficient crop, to grade to a consistent standard. Table 56 shows a brief summary of the grading package standards required for vegetables.

PACKING TO HIGH STANDARDS An odd assortment of containers, old and new, are used to market vegetables. There can be little doubt that the retail buyer in the wholesale market is more likely to buy the better packed goods. Sample labelling packs are illustrated in Figure 33 and show the sort of standards required.

Packaging has improved markedly in recent years and new, more attractive ways of packing vegetables are being produced every week by the many packaging companies in the business. Standard size containers for each of the vegetables are named in Table 56. The better the quality and the earlier the crop is produced, the smaller the pack size that is used.

The irony of this is that while quality packaging and grading sells in the wholesale market, few people shopping see the pack in the retail situation, since most greengrocers carry out their own heaped window displays.

Table 56: Wholesale market, packing and grading requirements for fresh vegetables

Crop	Pack type	Count/ weight	Quality	Size
ASPARAGUS	Non-returnable cartons/ trays	500 gm, 1 kg, 2 kg, bundles.	*Asparagus must be labelled as green, white or violet.	Shoots divided by length/diameter.
		Only one size to a tray.	*All asparagus* must be fresh, whole and p & d free, clean, free of dirt, cut cleanly at base, shoot must not be hollow or split.	*Length* Long 17–22 cm Long green 17–27 cm Short 12–17 cm Tips Less than 12 cm
			Class Extra Straight shoots, compact tips free of rust and woodiness.	*Size* min. 10 mm and 12 mm for *Extra* size diam.
			Class I Shoots slightly curved, compact tips, slight rust allowed.	
			Class II Shoots more curved, less compact, traces of rust allowed.	
			Class III Shoots curved, tips slightly open, traces of rust allowed.	
BROAD BEANS	Green nets	At present (1981) 20 lb – will change to 10 kilo	No standard EEC grading requirement. Pods picked direct into nets, only swollen pods harvested. Beans must be fresh clean and whole.	No size requirement – all pods should contain beans.

Table 56: (continued)

Crop	Pack type	Count/ weight	Quality	Size
BEANS FRENCH / RUNNER	Chip baskets (early crop only) Waxed board or solid board trays (maincrop)	4–6 kg (8–12lb) 6–9 kg (12–20 lb)	*Beans must be whole, fresh, clean and of sufficient size. Class I straight or nearly straight, young, tender, stringless, free from blemish. Class II marketable, reasonably tender, wind damage and stringiness allowed, some blemish.	No size requirements
BEETROOT	Red nets	At present (1981) 28 lb – converts to 12–13 kg	No standard EEC grading requirement. Growers merely remove bolted roots, small, damaged and diseased roots. Leaves trimmed.	No specific size grading required for fresh market. The public prefer roots of about 100 mm diameter.
BRUSSELS SPROUTS	Green Nets Non-returnable cartons of trays	At present (1981) 20lb will change to 10 kilo 4 kilo loose.	*Sprouts must be whole fresh, free from P & D, clean, if untrimmed the fracture should be clean; if trimmed cut just below the inter leaves. Class I Firm, tight top quality, free from frost. Class II Slightly less firm, but not open may show slight frost damage. Class III As above, but colour defects, bruising, traces of earth allowed.	Trimmed 10 mm min. Untrimmed 20 mm min. Class I uniform sprout size Maximum variation 20 mm Class II variations optional Class III no size requirements.
CABBAGE (Round-headed)	Green nets or non-returnable wood veneer or composite crates (for high value crop only).	20–30 lb or 10–14 kilo as required by the market.	*Cabbages must be whole, fresh, not burst clean of earth pests, etc. Class I hearts compact, leaves firmly attached, properly trimmed, slight bruising and crack or tears in outer leaves Class II of marketable quality, more outer leaves removed, greater bruising allowed.	Summer Cabbage – 350 gm min Other cabbage – 500 gm min. Uniformity – No cabbage must be more than twice weight of lightest

*EEC statutory grading standards

Table 56: (*continued*)

Crop	Pack type	Count/ weight	Quality	Size
CARROTS	Orange nets	At present (1981) 28 lb – converts to 12–13 kg	*Roots must be sound, clean, firm, not woody, adequately drained if washed. *Class Extra* Top quality, smooth, free from cracks, well shaped, good colour. *Class I* Good quality but slight defects in colour, slight washing cracks allowed.	Early or bunched carrots min 10 mm (8 gms) max 40 mm (150 gms) Main crop min 20 mm (50 gms)
	Cartons or trys for bunched crop	20 bunches	*Class II* Roots meet minimum requirements, healed cracks allowed	
CAULIFLOWERS	Collapsible crates	12, 18, 24 or 30/crate	*Curds must be fresh, whole sound, clean. *Class Extra* Top quality, deep curd, compact, uniformly white, free of blemishes *Class I* Curds firm, close, defects allowed – slight discolouration, wooliness. *Class II* Defects allowed – curd misshapes, slightly loose, woolly, bruised.	*Curd* – Min. diam. 11 cm Variation in curd size must not exceed 4 cm.
CELERY	Solid board trays or composite board boxes. Celery may be sleeved in polythene bags.	9–30 packed upright.	*Celery must be described as trenched, self-blanched, green, pink, etc. All celery must be white, sound, free from cavities and pest and disease. *Class I* top quality, regular shape, perfect colour, no stalks broken, split or stringy – blanched celery must be white for half length.	*Weight min. only* Large over 800 mm Med 500–800mm Small 150–500 gms

Table 56: (continued)

Crop	Pack type	Count/weight	Quality	Size
			Class II marketable quality, slight traces of bruising and slight splitting allowed. Blanched celery must be white third length.	
LETTUCE	Cardboard trays. Lettuce may be sleeved in polythene bags	9,12,15, or 18 per tray packed butt upward, usually in one layer. Cos are packed 9–15/deep box upright	*Sound, fresh, cleanly trimmed, soil-free, turgid lettuce of uniform size (10% variation). Class I – lettuce well formed solid hearts. Class II – lettuce reasonably formed hearts. Class III – as for class II. Lettuce also graded on weight (see next column)	Size graded by weight per 100 lettuce. Class I – minweight 15kg/ 100 lettuce (150kg each). Class II – min. weight per 100 lettuce 80 kg.
LEEKS	Solid board trays	loose 4–8 kg/tray (9–18 lb)	*Minimum EEC requirement – leek must be whole, fresh, withered leaves removed, leaves cleanly cut, adequately dried (if washed) Class I – good quality with only minor defects. White part ²/₃ total length or ½ sheathed size.	Size – minimum diameter at neck must be 10 mm. In class I the largest leek diameter in the bundle must be no larger than twice the diameter of the smallest leek.
	Trays or crates (Scotland)	1 kg bundles packed 4–8 kg/tray (9–18 lb)	Class II–quality to minimum standards. White part ³/₄ length or ¹/₃ sheathed length. Class III–slight bruising, colour faults & flowers stems, traces of rust & dirt allowed.	
MARROWS	Cardboard crates	4–5 kg (8–10 lb)	Fruits of similar size are laid the same way across the container. The only quality grading is to eliminate diseased, highly bent or badly marked fruits.	No statutory EEC requirement but marrows are normally size graded:
	Polystyrene trays (courgettes)	500 kg(1 lb)		Large–250–450 mm×100–150 mm Small–200–250 mm×75–100 mm Courgettes–65– 180 mm×12–38 mm

*EEC statutory grading requirements

Table 56: (*continued*)

Crop	Pack type	Count/ weight	Quality	Size
ONIONS	Red nets	56 lb will become 25 kg	*Onions must be whole, sound, dry, typical in shape, no growth showing from and compact. *Class I* Top quality, good shape, free of root tufts, some small skin cracks allowed *Class II* As above but traces of rubbing cracking, bruising and misshape allowed *Class III* Firm, root tufts, bruising and slight regrowth allowed.	*Grade to named sizes* Max. and min. diams. quoted 5 mm variation any size between 10–20 mm. 15 mm variation on any size between 20–40 mm. 20 mm variation above 40 mm Other sizes – 40– 60 mm. 60–80 mm, 80–100 mm, 100 mm+
PEAS (fresh)	Dutch trays (early crop) Green nets (main crop)	5 kg (12 lb) 9 kg (20 lb)	*Pods must be intact, sound, clean, fresh, and of normal size. *Class I* Peas of good quality fully grown, stalks attached, fresh, tender, suitably coloured for variety – pods must contain at least 5 peas. *Class II* – Peas more mature and harder, slight discolouration allowed, pods must contain at least 3 peas.	No size requirements.
PARSNIPS	White nets	28 lb – converts to 12–13 kg	Parsnips are trimmed to remove leaves. No EEC grading standards exist. Class 1 parsnips must be shaped true to type, be clean, washed and free from pest and disease. Class II parnisps allow for blemishing (some canker), and slight discolouration. Fanged parsnips are not sold under these classes.	No size requirements However, 40–180 mm diameter roots normally marketed.

Table 56: (continued)

Crop	Pack type	Count/ weight	Quality	Size
RADISH	Chip baskets	20–50 bunches roots upwards	No EEC grading standard. Grading carried out by picker, similar sized radish being placed in the bunch. Diseased, blemished, very small or misshapen fruits are discarded.	No size requirements. Optimum size 12–15 mm.
RHUBARB	Long narrow fibreboard or solid board boxes	3–6 kg units (6½–13 lb)	No EEC grading standards exist. Only clean, fresh, turgid, unblemished, straight leaf stalks should be marketed. Stems of about the same length are placed in the box. Good colour is essential on early crops.	Minimum length for early crop is 150–200 mm Main crop 200 mm and above
SWEDES	Red nets	28 lb – convets to 12–13kg	No EEC grading requirement. Wash and trim roots, discarding insect eaten or diseased swedes. Roots should weigh between 200–700 gms	No size requirement. Optimum size 130–150 mm
TURNIPS	Dutch trays (early bunched) White nets	5 kg (12 lb) bunched 8 lb (12–13 kg)	No EEC grading requirement. Wash and trim roots, discarding insect damaged or diseased roots. Early crop may be bunched in 3, 6 or 8's	No size requirement Optimum size about 75–100 mm

*EEC statutory grading standards

USING COLD STORAGE ensures that your vegetables arrive at the market in good condition. Most large vegetable growers install some form of cold storage. The ideal is an ice bank cooler. This enables extensive storage of a wide range of vegetables (see Table 57 for storage requirements of vegetables). Not that long term storage is often necessary or desirable – it is the short term use that has greatest advantage for the grower. It enables mature crops to be harvested on Friday and held over the weekend in cold store when the wholesale markets are shut. Some crops become wasted if they are not picked at correct maturity. Cold storage also allows the shrewd grower to hold crops in store a few days until the market prices improve. Here again, market intelligence information is vital to success.

KEY.
- 🌑 Vegetable growing areas.
- ⊙ Major markets.
- • Other markets.
- ✕ Auctions.

Aberdeen.

Edinburgh.

Glasgow

Gateshead.

Blackburn.

Bradford.   Leeds.

Huddersfield.

Preston.   Halifax

Wigan

Liverpool.   Hull.

Doncaster.

Wisbech and District

Sheffield.

Derby.   Nottingham

Manchester.

Birmingham   Leicester   Ipswich and Distr

Wolverhampton.

Coventry.

Worcester ✕
Pershore. ✕✕ Evesham.

Newport.
Cardiff.

LONDON.
Borough Market

Swansea.

Greenwich.

Bristol.

New Covent Garde

Spitalfields.

Newquay

Western Interna

Brighton.   Stratford.

Southampton.

Portsmouth.

Plymouth.

Figure 32 Map of the major wholesale vegetable markets in the UK

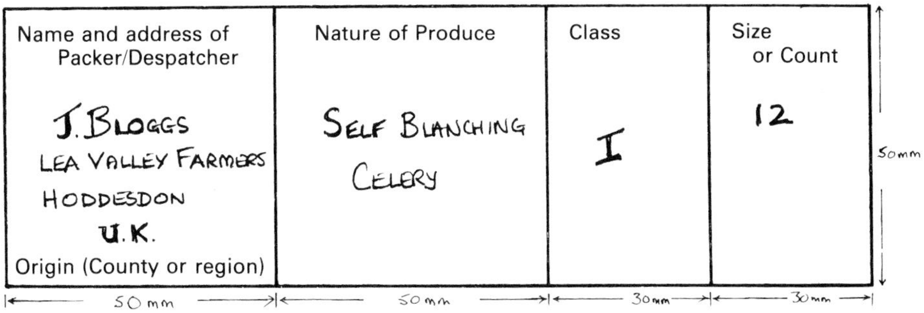

Name and address of Packer/Despatcher	Nature of Produce	Class	Size or Count
J.Bloggs Lea Valley Farmers Hoddesdon U.K. Origin (County or region)	Self Blanching Celery	I	12

| ← 50 mm → | ← 50 mm → | ← 30 mm → | ← 30 mm → |

Figure 33 Labelling packs – standard label for wholesale pack

Developing a Market

It is always stated that before growing you should establish that a market exists for your product. This is where the indecisiveness of our marketing system for vegetables falls down. So many factors can affect both supply and demand, not least is the weather. The grower has to foresee when the market most needs his product and at the same time avoid periods of glut. The various ways of marketing include the traditional wholesale systems right through to self-pick. Special emphasis has been made of this latter technique since it offers so much scope for the futuristic vegetable grower. Many growers also try to develop a brand name to encourage buyers to recognize and buy their product. This particularly applies at wholesale markets.

WHOLESALE   Figure 32 shows major wholesale markets. It is interesting to note that these have developed near the traditional vegetable producing areas. Goods are transported to these centralized markets where brokers sell the goods to retailers. Many of the larger growers act as brokers in the market in their own right. The markets operate from Monday to Friday only and they take the bulk of our vegetable production. For their service the brokers take 10 per cent commission from the total sale price. Many growers use more than one broker to spread risk of poor prices at a particular broker. But prices between the various commissioned agents vary little and any variation is a result of quality differences. The details of average weekly prices are shown in the 'Grower' magazine but the good grower should keep in daily contact with brokers in the market.

Market intelligence is another aspect which we as an industry have to learn. Keeping a chart of week by week returns for each vegetable should, over a number of years, enable you to establish a pattern of peak price periods. Figures 34 to 36 illustrate this. In times of glut the wholesale market can give depressingly low returns – since brokers attempt to sell everything rather than stock pile in the market. On the other hand, in periods of shortage, returns can be excellent.

AUCTION MARKETS (Wholesale)   Auction marketing is carried out at places like Evesham and Pershore but returns by this system seem to make little difference in the overall price received by growers. Dutch auctioning, where bidding occurs on a falling price clock, started at Cheltenham several years back but was a complete disaster.

RETAIL OUTLETS (Wholesale)   selling direct to local outlets (shops and hotels) can be very profitable, but growers must be able to offer a regular supply of a variety of vegetables delivered to the door. With experience, this sort of market can be established over a period of time but it is unlikely to be large enough to take up the entire production of a successful vegetable unit. On the credit side, salesman's commission is avoided, packaging may not need to be so elaborate and buyers may be willing to collect, saving transport costs.

DIRECT RETAIL SELLING UNITS   More and more growers are looking to this style of selling – it brings excellent returns but needs a back-up of produce to increase either the range of produce or year round sales. Traditionally, direct selling was carried out through an in-town green-grocers shop supplied from the producing area. But such a shop has to offer a wide range of fruit and vegetables, so the grower has to involve himself in buying the produce he cannot grow. Also, growers need to familiarize themselves with retail techniques and trading laws. More recently farm shops have developed on the producing sites. Here too the trading laws still apply. It is farm shops and, more recently, self-pick that has encouraged householders to motor out to the grower on the basis that fresh produce is worth travelling for. Farm shops have the added advantage that the grower does not necessarily have to provide the entire range of produce that is found in a greengrocers shop.

Pick-Your-Own

The 'Pick-Your-Own market' has expanded rapidly in England. Recent estimates suggest that over half the strawberry and raspberry crops are marketed in this manner. Vegetables are not too reliant on this market, but self-pick units of the future are those which can provide a wide range of crops including soft fruit, vegetables and even flowers. The whole concept is to produce an 'outdoor hypermarket', designed at the outset to encourage the public to self-pick. The versatile vegetable grower may well have to diversify to succeed in this market. A few details on the self-pick market are worthy of expansion.

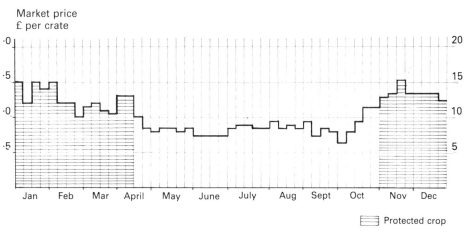

Figure 34 Average wholesale market prices for Lettuce 1980

Average returns for lettuce shown in bar chart form on a week by week basis. Prices drop markedly as soon as outside crops become available. Peaks in summer prices coincide with better weather.

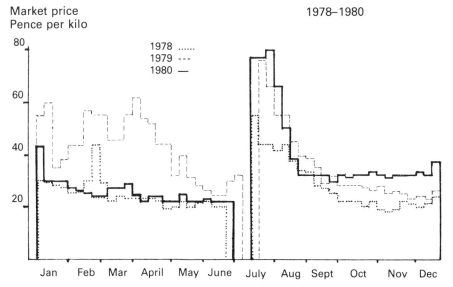

Figure 35 Average wholesale market prices for leeks

Average wholesale market prices for two crops compiled over three years on a week by week basis. Although prices vary very markedly from year to year the pattern of major peaks and hollows is seasonally the same almost every year.

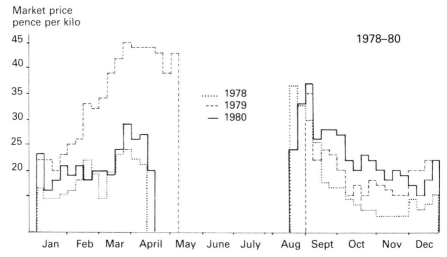

Figure 36   Average wholesale market prices for Brussels sprouts

Table 57: Recommended storage temperatures, humidity and storage life of vegetables (The most suitable condition for storage is provided by an icebank cooler)

Crop	Storage temperature °C	Relative humidity	Storage life	Symptoms of freezing injury in storage and susceptibility of crops to damage (s = susceptible, m = medium, r = resistant	
Asparagus	1 (34°F)	95%	2 weeks	(s)	Tip of spear becomes limp remainder is watersoaked
Beans broad	0 (32°F)	95%	2–3 weeks	(m)	Pitting and russetting of bean pods
Beans French	4.4 (40°F)	90–95%	7 days	(s)	Pitting and russetting of bean pods
Beans runner	4.4 (40°F)	90–95%	7 days	(s)	Pitting and russetting of bean pods
Beetroot (bunched)					Root takes on a watersoaked appearance. Leaves blacken quickly
Beetroot (topped)	3 (37°F)	95–98%	6–8 months	(r)	Root takes on a watersoaked appearance
Broccoli	0–2 (32–36°F)	98%	3 weeks	(m)	Young florets at centre turn brown & smell when thawed
Brussels sprouts	0 (32°F)	95–98%	3–4 weeks	(r)	Leaves become watersoaked, brown & smell when thawed

Table 57: *(continued)*

Crop	Storage temperature °C	Relative humidity	Storage life	Symptoms of freezing injury in storage and susceptibility of crops to damage (s = susceptible, m = medium, r = resistant
Cabbage (Winter white)	0 (32°F)	95%	8 months	(r) Leaves become watersoaked, translucent, limp when thawed
Carrots	0–1 (32–34°F)	95–98%	6–7 months	(m) Blistering, cracking of skin, watersoaked when thawed
Cauliflower	1 (34°F)	95–98%	3 weeks	(m) Curds turn brown, strong odour when thawed
Celery	½–1 (33–34°F)	95%	3 months	(s) Leaves and sticks wilt, watersoaked appearance
Leeks	0–2 (32–36°F)	95%	3 weeks	(m) Leek scales become yellow soft & watersoaked when thawed
Lettuce	½–1 (33–34°F)	95%	1 week	(s) Blistered dead cells on outer leaves – leaves become tan colour
Onions	0 (32°F)	70–80%	8 months	(m) Bulb scales become, yellow soft & watersoaked when thawed
Parsnip	0–1 (32–34°F)	95–98%	6 months	(r) Damage very minor–some cracking of skin.
Peas	0 (32°F)	90–95%	1–2 weeks	(s) Pitting and russetting of pods, peas blacken
Radish	1–3 (34–37°F)	95–98%	7–10 days	(m) Thawed tissue translucent, roots soften & shrivel
Salad onions	0 (32°F)	95–98%	2 weeks	(m) Thawed onions soften and yellow
Sweet corn	0 (32°F)	95–98%	7 days	(m) Protective scales brown, corn turns very starchy
Turnip	0 (32°F)	90–95%	4 months	(r) Small pitted watersoaked spots on root surface – offensive odour
Swede	0 (32°F)	90–95%	5 months	

Choice of site for pick-your-own

The basics for self-pick are fairly obvious – nearness to a large centre of population (50,000 plus) is a must. People will travel as far as 48 km for fresh produce but the majority will only come from within 24 km. Nearness to a major road with a large volume of passing traffic, good access by road to the picking fields and adequate car park space are also important. Contact with local planning authority and the police before setting out on the venture will avoid many problems.

Experts now say that established and traditional growing areas are not the place to start self-pick. Too many growers are flooding into the self-pick market. Better to look to new areas – particularly in the west, where there are larger centres of population and the higher rainfall supports better scheduling of crops without the cost of irrigation.

How much can you put down to self-pick

No hard and fast rules can be made. But look to earning about £2,500 gross per hectare (£1,000 per acre). With a total local population of 50,000 the maximum you can expect to visit over a season, even with good publicity, is some 8,000 to 10,000 people. With 8 hectares (20 acres) of land down to self-pick your 10,000 public would need to spend £2 each over the season to make the enterprise viable. This would seem reasonable for public expenditure at the start of a venture in an area where self-pick was just beginning.

Crops that can be grown

There can be little doubt that soft fruit has been the entré to self-pick and vegetable growers should consider putting an area down to these crops as an inducement to draw the public. Remember, the criteria for the public wishing to buy self-pick are, firstly freshness and flavour, and secondly the ability of the crop to freeze well. The latter is important if quantity sales are to be made. From the growers point of view, those crops where harvesting makes up a high percentage of the crop costs are the most advantageous to sell, since this offers him the biggest cost savings.

Those which offer most advantages for sale are:

Peas	Sweet corn	Brussels sprouts (early crop)
Broad beans	*Potatoes	Calabrese
Runner beans	Cauliflowers	Courgettes
French beans	*Carrots	

*crops which need lifting are more difficult.

To maintain an interested consuming public where repeat visits become habit-forming quality has to be good, the range of crops wide and a continuity of supply maintained throughout the summer.

Basic rules of the self-pick game

CROP FACTS   Row spacings need to be wider than normal – 20 per cent extra is suggested to allow for easy movement among crops (see French beans and sweet corn). Selection of varieties is critical to success – they must be specifically selected for flavour, long holding qualities and long picking season. Successional drillings/plantings are a must to give a steady supply of crops, particularly with peas and cauliflowers. Aim for quality production – the public will always pay for good quality even in glut periods.

ORGANIZATION AND ADMINISTRATIVE FACTS Self-pick needs good and carefully worded *advertising* to tell the public what is available and where. Local papers are good, provided the wording is right. Roadside signs are vitally important but should be simple with large easily read-able letters. House to house leaflet distribution can be very effective in nearby towns. Local radio can also be useful. Never neglect advertising and expect to pay 2 to 3 per cent of your gross income on this aspect of the business.

Staffing needs to be good and well organized. It is a seven-day-week job, so overtime will have to be paid. Two staff in the picking field can cope with up to 300 people provided the area to be picked is clearly marked off with ropes! A further person will be required to man the car park.

Good car parking facilities are essential if a large range of crops are to be grown. Cars require 28 sq m (300 sq ft) per vehicle to park and understanding of layouts is essential if a maximum number of cars are to be parked. Parking in headlands merely causes trouble, since most of your people will come at weekends you must cater for this. If you anticipate 500 cars per week for self-pick, over 300 will come at a weekend. Maximum required space at any one time would be for approximately 75 cars would be a total area of 2,100 m^2 (2,520 sq yd).

Toilet facilities are another essential element – near to car park.

Adequate *cash tills* and *weighing machines* are vital for success. The bigger operators have two or three machines at the edge of the field. As a safeguard a receipt should be given with each sale and this is then shown to the car park attendant as a means of leaving the holding through a narrow exit.

You may need a back-up *casual picking force* to harvest the crop in situations where excess production or weather have stopped self-pickers from coming to the unit.

OTHER USEFUL HINTS Customers need containers in which to pick. Nowadays most units sell punnets, chip baskets or cheap card trays (with known weights) for the public to use for picking. Polythene carrier bags are also useful. Many people come out as a family unit for a day's entertainment and growers should not forget this. Play areas and crèches for children are a great aid to encourage family visits. Teas, ice cream and buns can also be sold. These attractions should be mentioned as a major plus in the advertising campaign. Also, people like to visit smart clean places. Clean culture, good parking space, even a small amount of landscaping at the farm entrance all go a long way to encouraging visitors. Above all, provide a picnic area, clearly defined between the parking and the picking area. Litter bins are also vital for keeping the area tidy.

Pricing your crop

Various methods of pricing the crop have been adopted by the many growers in the self-pick business. Obviously, a costing exercise could be carried out to calculate exactly how much the crop has cost you to grow – but this is probably too complicated a manoeuvre to carry out at the particular time you have to decide the price to charge the self-pickers. A simple yet effective way is to work from the current wholesale market price and you know you will be charging a competitive price.

A PRICE BASED ON THE CURRENT WHOLESALE MARKET PRICE   This involves working with the current wholesale price and taking away the harvesting cost, which will be saved by self-pick, and adding the costs of supervision required in the fields and the extra costs of providing facilities. Then add the mark-up which should be a minimum of 35 per cent to give a good return. This gives a realistic price based on market price, which means the customer obtains a fair deal, since the self-pick price will probably be a little less than current retail price.

Example: *Cauliflower crop* (summer 1981)

Average wholesale price per cauliflower	15.4p
LESS harvesting costs – picking 1.9p	
– cost of crate 1.9p	
– salesman commission 1.6p	
– carriage 0.5p	−5.9p
	9.5p
PLUS costs of facilities/supervision/advertising etc. at £1,700/ha and a yield of 1,440 crates = £1.2/crate or per cauliflower	8.0p
PLUS MARK-UP (35%)	6.75p
	24.25p

So charge 25p   (wholesale price: 15p)
                              (retail price on the day: 34p)

On studying prices for self-pick the author has noted a direct correlation between them and the wholesale and retail prices over a wide range of crops. Usually, the retail price is about 1¾–2¼ times the wholesale price and the self-pick price fits mid way between these.

This particular system of pricing may fall down in periods of glut when prices fall to rock bottom in the wholesale market. It is therefore always wise to have an idea of the sort of price which would break even on the costs spent in producing the crop. It may still be possible to sell at a relatively high price compared with local retailers on the basis of the freshness and quality. Your advertising campaign will have to reflect this.

Conclusion

The businesslike grower does not put 'all the eggs in one basket'. To rely entirely on one type of market outlet may not be the best approach. Wise growers diversify into a number of markets, providing this does not interfere too greatly with the cultural activities of growing crops. Use of the wholesale market may well be the mainstay of the grower's policy, but by looking towards other outlets, like self-pick or farm sales, there could be good returns. Outside of this, a new business interest brings a special challenge to the enterprise, which may also be welcomed by working staff. Growers should, however, beware of 'jumping on the band wagon' of highly priced specualtive crops. Inevitably prices crash the following season as so many growers fall into the trap of producing this crop.

Chapter Twelve

Control of Weeds, Pests and Diseases

It is commonly assumed by many young horticulturists that the answer to all problems associated with weeds, pests and diseases is to use chemicals. The use of modern chemicals is a vital part of modern vegetable growing but the grower should never forget that many problems can be avoided by good cultural practice. Chemicals are no substitute for this. Our predecessors managed quite well without any chemicals. The ensuing chapter is only a brief survey of the various ways in which weeds, pests and diseases can be controlled.

Weed Control

Unless starting with virgin land, most weeds in vegetable crops are annuals which seed at a tremendous rate, mainly throughout the growing season. They compete for light, water and nutrients, often harbour pests and diseases, make cultural operations difficult and hamper the harvesting process. And the grower with clean, weed-free crops is usually admired by his fellows. To be able to carry this out means a thorough understanding of the following:

WEED RECOGNITION IS ESSENTIAL   It is amazing how particular weed seedlings grow on the same area of land each year. Recognition of weeds present, particularly at seedling size, is vital for their control. Regular use of the same chemicals encourages build up of resistant weeds. Figure 37 shows 18 common annual weed seedlings and the soils on which they are likely to grow.

KNOW YOUR SOIL   Soil type and soil moisture content determine not

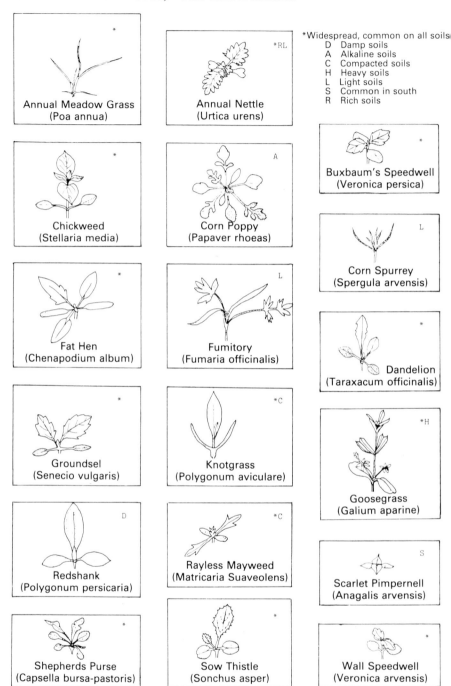

Annual Meadow Grass
(Poa annua)

Annual Nettle
(Urtica urens)

Chickweed
(Stellaria media)

Corn Poppy
(Papaver rhoeas)

Buxbaum's Speedwell
(Veronica persica)

Corn Spurrey
(Spergula arvensis)

Fat Hen
(Chenapodium album)

Fumitory
(Fumaria officinalis)

Dandelion
(Taraxacum officinalis)

Groundsel
(Senecio vulgaris)

Knotgrass
(Polygonum aviculare)

Goosegrass
(Galium aparine)

Redshank
(Polygonum persicaria)

Rayless Mayweed
(Matricaria Suaveolens)

Scarlet Pimpernell
(Anagalis arvensis)

Shepherds Purse
(Capsella bursa-pastoris)

Sow Thistle
(Sonchus asper)

Wall Speedwell
(Veronica arvensis)

Figure 37   Eighteen common crop weeds

only the weed species that grow, but the capacity of herbicides to work well – consequently the rate of application varies according to soil type. Light sandy soils leach easily and dosage rates for the soil acting herbicides are usually lower. Sandy soils also dry out quickly which makes absorption of soil acting herbicides less effective. Loams are much easier while highly organic soils like peats tend to absorb residual chemicals to such a degree that they are ineffective. Many soil acting herbicides are not recommended for use on soils containing more than 10 per cent organic content.

TIMING OF CONTROL   Even in basic hoeing everybody knows that timing of control is important. Young weed seedlings are easy – large plants like groundsel in flower are problematical. Hoe out the flowering groundsel and it seeds itself within 24 hours. Obviously, the job has to be carried out in dry weather, otherwise hoed weeds merely root back into the soil again. Timing is even more important with chemical control – a day can be the difference between weed control and crop damage. Correct use of herbicides in relation to weather conditions is vital, spraying should not be carried out when rain is expected within six hours. Heavy rain can cause leaching of soil applied herbicides and contact weedkillers can be washed off weed foliage. High temperatures may increase the risk of crop damage eg. Dinoseb used on legumes. Never spray when frost is expected.

STAGE OF CROP GROWTH   Most herbicides are applied at the stage at which crop plants tolerate the particular chemical used without being damaged. For example, no foliage acting herbicide should be applied to alliums between emergence and crook stage.

Weed Control Without Chemicals

CULTURAL CONTROL   Deep autumn ploughing will turn in weeds and contribute to a sound start to the season. Use of well rotted manure ensures weed seeds are not carried in by this means. Fallowing – leaving soil uncropped for the summer and repeatedly cultivating – is still an admirable way of clearing land of perennial weeds like dock and couch grass.

HOEING/HAND WEEDING   Although outmoded, there is still a place for this in intensive growing situations or on steep slopes where machinery cannot reach. The planet hoe is still widely used to speed up the process. Hand weeding, too, has a place alongside modern chemical technology. No soil acting chemical is 100 per cent effective. The resistant weeds species will inevitably grow – maybe only a few, but if allowed to flourish they will flower and seed, thus building up the population of that weed. Far better to go through the crop hand pulling out large weeds so as not to perpetuate or even accelerate the problem in the future.

Chemical Weed Control

Chemical weed control is fast becoming a complex subject so a brief description of the many aspects of herbicides is necessary. There are basically three types of chemicals:

SOIL ACTING (residual)   The material when applied to soil is absorbed into the top 5–10 mm of soil. These herbicides kill emerging annual weed seedlings, but not established weeds. They rely on the soil being fine, moist and weed free at application time, eg, chlorpropham, propham, linuron, lenacil. The majority of vegetable herbicides come into this category.

FOLIAGE ACTING (contact)   These chemicals when applied to weed foliage kill on contact. Some contact herbicides are non-selective and should only be applied to weeds, eg, paraquat (this chemical also has some translocated properties). Other contact chemicals are selective because of the physical or physiological characteristics of the crop, eg, use of ioxynil on onions.

FOLIAGE ACTING (translocated)   These materials when applied to foliage of existing weeds are absorbed into the plant's sap stream, causing various reactions on their growth which leads to death – usually in two to three weeks. Because they are translocated to all plant parts the roots are killed as well as foliage. Temperature markedly affects their use and they are generally used during periods of active growth. They are particularly effective on perennial weeds. However, translocated herbicides are rarely used during vegetable cropping. They are extensively used to clear land of perennial weeds prior to vegetable cropping and the planting of crops like asparagus and rhubarb. Glyphosate is an example of a translocated herbicide commonly used to control couch grass and other perennial weeds.

SOIL AND FOLIAGE ACTING   Many vegetable herbicides have dual action, eg, linuron. Also, chemical companies formulate mixtures of chemicals to obtain both soil and foliage acting properties, eg, Alicep which contains chloridazon (soil acting) and chlorbufam (foliage acting).

Timing

Timing of chemical spraying has been mentioned already, but Figure 38 shows when and how herbicides are used in the context of vegetable growing.

The terminology of spraying

Since timing is so important, phrases like *pre-emergence* and *post-emergence* are very important. These are terms applied to the crop sprayed. For instance, a typical pre-emergent residual herbicide application is the use of simazine on broad beans, which is applied immediately after sowing. Ioxynil, on the other hand, is used as a post-emergent contact spray to onions once they have grown to three erect leaf stage (see Figure 21). Both of the above treatments are used as overall sprays.

Not all spraying needs to be as an overall treatment. *Band spraying* is the use of a band treatment (180 mm or 7 in wide) sprayed over the seed drill line. This saves chemical and the job can be carried out at the same time as drilling in one operation.

Inter-row spraying may be used to control weed growth between the rows. This is usually carried out with a directed contact spray, like paraquat. Inter-row contact sprays are often used where residual herbicides have been ineffective or where resistant weeds have appeared.

Chemical weed control in specific crops

Although detailed weed control is covered under the cultivation of each crop, Table 58 may be useful to the grower. It enables the reader to check not only the various alternative materials for a particular crop, but also the range of crops on which each material can be used. Of course, read the instructions for use of a chemical before it is applied to any crop to ensure that safe application occurs.

Susceptibility of weeds to herbicides

Selection of herbicide depends not only on the tolerance of the crop to the herbicide, but to the susceptibility of the weeds present. Table 59 shows the susceptibility of a number of common weeds to most of the important herbicides used in vegetable growing. So, for example, where chlorpropham is used to control weeds in lettuce you can expect a build up of weeds like groundsel and mayweed.

HERBICIDE USAGE

The timing of spraying is very closely related to the type of herbicide used. The diagrams below show how herbicides of different types can be used with success.

FOLIAGE ACTING

RESIDUAL

STALE SEEDBED HERBICIDE TREATMENT
– *Presowing or preplanting with a contact herbicide.*
Prepare seedbed 2–3 weeks (depending on time of year) in advance of sowing or planting. Weedkill germinated weeds two days before sowing with contact herbicide e.g. Paraquat.

SEEDBED INCORPORATED HERBICIDE
– *Presowing or preplanting with a residual herbicide.*
Prepare seedbed 1 week in advance of sowing or planting. Incorporate residual herbicide into top surface layer (100–150 mm, 4–6 ins) by rotovating or harrowing. Then roll surface to create herbicide skin. Drill or plant into herbicide layer, e.g. Trifluralin before sowing.

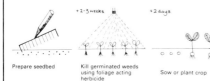

Prepare seedbed   Kill germinated weeds using foliage acting herbicide   Sow or plant crop

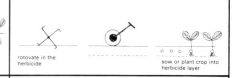

rotovate in the herbicide   sow or plant crop into herbicide layer

AFTER DRILLING AND JUST BEFORE CROP EMERGENCE
–*Pre-emergent foliage acting herbicide* – applied when weeds come up but before crop comes through. Kills all weed foliage it touches. Ideal for slow germinating crops, e.g. leeks or parsnips.

AFTER DRILLING VEGETABLE CROPS
– *Pre-emergent residual herbicide* Applied as soon after sowing as possible before weeds germinate. Material kills germinating annual weed seeds. Soil must be moist, e.g. Chlorthal-dimethyl and propachor on leeks.

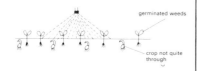

germinated weeds

crop not quite through

soil moist   her herbicide in top 5 mm

weed seeds

crop seeds

USE OF HERBICIDES AT SPECIAL STAGES OF GROWTH TO OBTAIN SELECTIVITY BETWEEN CROP AND WEED – Post emergent foliage acting herbicides may be used at special stages of crop growth when because of the leaf shape, thickness of the wax cuticle, or physiological resistance they are able to withstand herbicide treatment whereas weeds are killed, e.g. use of loxynil (Ester Form) on onions at 3 erect leaf stage – herbicide merely runs off on to weeds below.

AFTER CROP HAS EMERGED OR BEEN PLANTED
– *Post emergent residual herbicide.* Applied to clean soil – herbicide absorbed into top 5–8 mm of soil to kill most germinating annual weeds. Crop roots deeper than herbicide or plants naturally resistant to chemical.

crop such as onions

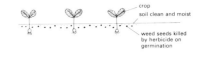

crop

soil clean and moist

weed seeds killed by herbicide on germination

Figure 38   Herbicide usage

Pest and Disease Control

Vegetables succumb quickly to pests and diseases. That is why it is so important to deal with them at the first signs of attack. With some important pests which are a regular and persistant problem, protective treatment before the pest appears is sound practice. The grower must decide which approach to take – preventative/protective measures or application as and when attack occurs (supervisory pest control).

Control methods

Basic control starts with a hygienic approach to growing. Right from the propagation stage use clean boxes, disinfect frames and pre-sterilize seed beds. Never plant out weak or diseased plants – you are only asking for trouble. Plough in crop residues deep. If disease is present remove infected plants and burn rather than risk carry over. Keep headlands tidy and neat. Avoid growing shelter belts which can be an alternative pest host to crops – carrot willow aphid is an example.

CULTURAL CONTROL   starts with winter preparation. Autumn ploughing turns over the soil and exposes pests and diseases to winter frost. Sowing and planting at the correct time for the area is important. The commonest error is to try to plant or sow too early. Occasionally it may work, but remember that frost damaged plants are prone to disease. Irrigate at the correct time – plants subject to water stress are much more easily infected by disease, particularly diseases like fusarium on peas. Feed plants the correct and balanced diet. High potash tends to harden plants against pest and disease attack. Feeding ratios of higher than 3:1 nitrogen to potash may create problems with over-fleshy growth.

CHEMICAL CONTROL   Chemicals are the growers standby when other methods fail. That does not mean waiting until the problem is a major disaster before starting to spray. The grower with understanding should select and use the best chemical available for the job and carry the job out before the problem becomes endemic. But there are certain pests and diseases where, if the grower were to wait until he saw evidence of the problem, it would be far too late. So routine preventative treatment is essential before attack occurs. This applies to the following more common pests and diseases – cabbage rootfly, carrot fly, club root 'damping off' of seedlings, downy mildew, frit fly, slugs on new transplants and white rot on salad onions.

Insecticides are basically of three types – contact, systemic and stomach poisons. *Contact* materials, such as Permethrin, immediately kill the pests which are hit or come into contact with the spray or spray deposit. Picking of edible crops can safely be carried out within a few

Crop / Chemical name	Alloxidim sodium	Atrazine	Aziprotryne	Bentazone	Carbetamide	Chlorbromuron	Chloridazon + Chlorbufam	Chlorpropham	Chlorpropham mixtures	Chlorthal-dimethyl + methazole	Dalapon	Desmetryne	Dinitramine	Dinoseb acetate *	Diphenamid	Ethofumesate	Ioxynil	Lenacil	Linuron	Methazole	Metoxuron
Type of herbicide	C	S	S	C	FS	CS	S	S	S	S	T	C	S	C	S	TS	C	S	CS	TS	TS
Asparagus	√								√ w		√										
Beans, Broad									√ d					√ po							
Beans French			√						√ d					√ pe	√						
Beans, Runner			√						√ d				√	√ pe	√						
Beetroot									√ d									√		√	
Brassicas (direct drilled)		√										√									
Brussels and cabbage (direct drilled)		√										√									
Brassicas (all) (transplanted)										√											
Brussels and cabbage (transplanted)		√		√						√		√									
Carrots						√			√ (pe, po)			√ s							√ d,s		√
Celery																		√ s			
Leeks (transplanted)		√				√	√ s	√ s	√								√ t		√		
Lettuce								√ d													
Onion sets		√				√			√ s	√				√ s			√ t				
Onions & leeks (direct drilled)		√				√	√ d,s		√ d	√				√ po			√ s			√	
Parsnips						√		√ d	√ (po, d)										√ d,s		
Peas		√ (po, pe)							√ d	√ pe				√ po							
Rhubarb	√								√ w			√									
Spinach									√ d												
Swede and turnip						√								√							
Sweet Corn		√																			
Vegetable marrows															√						
Stage of growth when chemical normally used.	d	pe, po	s	s	s	pe, s, po	pe, s, po	various	various	d or t	w	s, po	e	pe, po	d	d, po	various	d, e	various	s	s, po

Table 58: Chemical weed control in vegetable crops

TS	C	CS	C	S	TS	S	S	S	S	C	S	S	S	S	S
Nitrofen	Pentanochlor	Pentanochlor mixtures	Phenmedipham	Propham/propham mixtures	Prometryne	Propachlor	Propachlor mixtures	Propyzamide	Simazine	Sodium monochloroacetate	TCA	Terbutryne/terbuthylazine	Tri-allate	Trifluralin	Terbacil
								√ pe							√
								√ d			√	√	√		
												√	√		
												√	√		
			√	√								√			
√ pe						√	√					√	√		
√ pe						√	√		√ s		√	√	√		
						√ t	√ t					√	√		
						√ t	√ t	√ (w/s)			√ t	√	√		
	√ po	pe √ po		√								√	√		
	√ po	√ po		√											
				√		√ t	√ t								
			√ d				pe √ po		√						
						√ t	√ t								
										po √ Onions only		√			
	√ po	√ po												√	√
			√ e	√ pe									√	√	
						√ w	√ w				√ w				
√ po											√				
							√ pe								
d, po	s, po	pe, s, po	po	pe, d, po	s	d, t	d, t	s	various	various	e	d	e	e	pe

*Denotes poisonous chemical
– full protective clothing must be used

Type of herbicide code:
C Contact herbicide
F Foliar acting herbicide
S Soil acting herbicide
T Translocated herbicide

CODE:
pe pre-crop emergence
d   after drilling
po post emergence
s   specific stage of growth
w   winter dormant period
e   incorporated into soil before drilling
f   after transplanting

Table 59: Susceptibility of weeds to herbicides used in vegetable cr

Crop \ Chemical name	Alloxidim sodium	Aziprotryne (pre-emergence weeds)	Aziprotryne (post emergence weeds)	Barban	Bentazone	Bentazone + MCPB	Carbetamide (pre-emergence weeds)	Carbetamide (post emergence weeds)	Chlorbromuron (pre-weed emergence)	Chlorbromuron (post-weed emergence)	Chloridazon + Chlorbufam	Chlorpropham	Chlorpropham + Diuron	Chlorpropham + Fenuron	Chlorpropham/Propham/Fenuron	Chlorthal-dimethyl + Methazole	Cynazine	Cycloate + Lenacil	Dalapon	Desmetryne	Dinitramine	Dinoseb acetate	Diphenamid	Diuron	Ethofumesate (pre-emergence mixtures)	Ethofumesate (post emergence mixtures)	Ioxynil
Annual Meadow Grass	R	S	S	–	R	R	S	S	S	MR	MS	S	S	S	S	R	S	–	R	S	R	S	MS	S	S	R	
Annual Nettle	–	S	S	–	S	S	S	MR	S	S	S	S	S	S	S	S	S	MS	–	S	MS	S	S	S	MS	S	MS
Black Bindweed	–	MS	S	–	MS	S	S	–	MS	MR	S	S	S	S	S	S	S	MS	–	MS	S	S	R	MS	S	S	
Black Nightshade	–	S	S	–	S	S	–	–	R	R	–	R	MS	MS	S	S	S	S	–	S	MS	S	–	–	MS	MS	S
Charlock	–	MR	S	–	S	S	R	R	S	S	S	MS	MS	MS	MS	MS	S	MS	–	MS	R	S	–	MS	S	S	S
Chickweed	–	S	S	–	S	S	S	MS	S	S	S	S	S	S	S	S	S	S	–	S	S	S	S	S	S	S	
Common Hemp-nettle	–	–	S	–	R	MR	–	–	–	S	R	S	S	MS	MS	–	S	S	–	S	S	S	–	–	MS	S	MS
Corn Poppy	–	–	MS	–	MS	MS	–	–	–	–	S	S	S	S	S	S	S	–	MS	S	S	–	S	MS	S	–	
Couch Grass	S	R	R	–	R	R	MR	MS	R	R	R	R	R	R	R	R	R	R	S	R	R	R	–	MS	MR	R	R
Dead Nettle	–	–	S	–	R	R	R	R	S	S	S	R	MR	MR	MR	S	S	S	–	MR	–	–	–	MR	MS	S	MS
Fat Hen	–	S	S	–	MS	S	S	MS	S	S	MS	S	MS	MS	S	MS	S	–	S	S	S	MS	S	S	S		
Field Pansy	–	S	S	–	–	MS	S	MS	S	R	–	R	R	R	R	S	S	MS	–	S	S	–	–	–	–	S	MS
Field Penny-cress	–	R	MR	–	S	S	–	–	S	R	S	S	S	S	S	R	–	MS	–	MS	–	S	S	S	MS	S	S
Fumitory	–	MS	MS	–	S	S	R	R	R	R	MS	MS	S	MS	MS	MR	MS	S	–	S	MS	S	R	R	S	MS	
Goosegrass	–	R	R	–	S	S	MS	MR	MS	MS	S	R	MR	MR	MR	S	R	MR	–	R	MS	MS	–	–	S	MS	MS
Groundsel	–	S	S	–	MS	S	R	R	S	R	S	R	MS	MS	MR	MS	MS	–	MS	MR	S	S	MR	MS	S		
Knotgrass	–	MS	S	–	R	S	MS	MR	S	MS	S	S	S	S	S	MS	MS	–	MR	S	MS	MS	MR	S	R		
Mayweed	–	S	S	–	S	S	R	R	S	MS	S	R	MS	MS	MS	S	MS	S	–	R	MS	MS	MS	S	S	MS	S
Redshank	–	S	S	–	S	S	S	–	S	S	S	S	S	S	S	MR	S	MS	–	S	MR	S	MS	MR	S	MS	
Scarlet Pimpernel	–	S	S	–	S	S	–	–	S	S	MS	R	MS	MS	MS	–	S	S	–	S	–	S	–	S	S	S	–
Shepherd's Purse	–	S	S	–	S	S	MS	MS	S	S	MS	S	S	S	S	S	–	MR	MR	S	S	S	S	S	S		
Sow Thistle	–	MS	MS	–	MS	MS	R	R	MS	MS	S	R	R	R	S	–	–	S	–	S	MS	S	–	MS	S	–	MS
Speedwells	–	MS	S	–	R	R	S	MS	MS	MS	S	MS	MS	MS	MS	S	S	S	–	S	S	S	–	R	S	S	MS
Spurrey (Corn)	–	–	MS	–	S	S	R	R	–	S	–	S	S	S	S	–	S	S	–	S	MS	S	S	S	MS	MR	
Volunteer Cereals	S	–	–	–	R	R	MS	S	–	–	–	R	R	R	R	–	R	–	–	–	S	R	–	–	MS	MS	R
Wild-oat	S	–	MR	S	R	R	MS	S	R	R	MS	R	R	R	S	R	R	R	S	S	R	MS	R	S	–	MS	MS	R

S = Susceptible
MS = Moderately susceptible
MR = Moderately resistant
R = Resistant

e 59: (continued)

Crop	Linuron (pre-weed emergence)	Linuron (post weed emergence)	Linuron + Metoxuron	Methazole	Metoxuron	Monolinuron	Nitrofen	Nitrofen (post emergence)	Pentanochlor	Pentanochlor + Chlorpropham	Pentanochlor/Chlorpropham/Metoxuron	Phenmedipham	Propham	Propham + Diuron	Prometryne (pre-weed emergence)	Prometryne (post weed emergence)	Propachlor	Propachlor + Chlorpropham	Propachlor + Chlorthal-dimethyl	Propyzamide (pre-emergence weeds)	Propyzamide (post emergence weeds)	Simazine	Sodium monochloroacetate	TCA	Terbutryne/Terbuthylazine	Triallate	Trietazine/Simazine	Trifluralin	Terbacil
low Grass	MS	MR	S	S	S	S	S	R	MS	S	S	R	S	S	S	R	S	S	S	S	S	S	R	S	S	S	MS	S	S
Nettle	S	S	S	S	S	S	S	S	S	S	S	S	S	S	S	S	S	S	S	S	S	S	S	–	S	–	S	MS	S
indweed	S	S	S	S	S	S	S	MS	S	S	S	S	S	S	S	–	R	S	MS	S	S	MS	S	–	S	–	MS	S	S
ightshade	S	S	S	S	MS	S	S	S	R	R	MS	MR	R	R	S	S	MS	MS	S	S	S	S	S	S	S	–	MS	R	S
:k	S	S	S	S	S	S	R	S	S	S	S	R	MR	S	MS	S	R	MR	R	R	R	S	S	–	S	–	S	R	S
eed	S	S	S	S	S	S	R	S	R	S	S	S	S	S	MS	S	S	S	S	S	S	S	S	–	S	–	S	S	S
on p-nettle	S	S	MS	S	MS	S	S	S	S	S	S	S	MS	S	S	S	S	S	S	–	–	S	S	–	–	–	MS	S	S
oppy	S	S	S	S	S	–	MS	MS	–	–	S	S	S	S	S	S	–	S	S	R	R	–	R	–	S	–	S	MS	–
Grass	R	R	R	R	R	R	R	R	R	R	R	R	R	R	R	R	R	R	R	R	MS	MR	R	R	S	R	R	R	S
ettle	S	MS	S	S	S	S	MS	MS	S	S	S	S	MR	MR	–	–	S	S	S	R	R	S	S	–	S	–	S	MS	S
	S	S	S	S	S	S	S	S	S	S	S	S	R	MS	S	S	MS	MS	S	S	S	S	R	S	–	S	–	S	S
ansy	S	S	S	S	S	S	S	S	S	S	S	S	R	R	–	S	R	S	S	R	S	–	–	MS	S	–	S	R	–
enny-cress	S	S	MS	–	–	S	–	–	S	S	S	MS	R	S	S	R	MS	R	S	S	S	–	–	MS	S	S	–	S	R
ry	R	R	MS	MR	MS	R	MS	MS	S	S	S	S	R	S	S	S	R	MS	R	MS	MS	MS	R	–	S	–	MS	MS	S
grass	MS	MR	MS	S	MS	S	–	–	S	S	S	MR	R	R	R	R	S	S	S	MS	MR	R	MS	–	R	–	R	R	MS
sel	S	MS	MS	S	MS	S	R	R	MR	MS	MS	S	R	MS	S	MS	S	S	S	R	R	S	S	MS	–	S	–	R	MS
ass	MS	MS	S	S	MS	S	S	S	S	S	S	S	S	S	S	R	S	S	S	MS	R	R	–	S	–	S	S	S	S
ed	S	MR	S	MS	S	S	R	R	MS	MS	S	MR	R	MS	S	S	S	S	S	R	S	S	R	–	S	–	S	R	–
nk	S	S	S	S	S	S	S	S	S	S	S	S	S	MS	S	S	R	S	MS	S	S	S	S	–	S	–	S	S	S
Pimpernel	S	S	MS	S	–	S	MS	MS	S	S	S	MS	R	S	S	S	S	S	S	R	S	S	–	–	S	S	–	S	S
rd's Purse	S	S	S	S	S	S	R	S	R	S	S	S	MS	S	S	S	S	MS	MS	S	S	S	–	S	–	S	S	R	S
istle	S	S	S	S	S	S	–	R	S	S	S	R	S	R	S	–	MS	MS	MS	R	R	S	R	–	–	–	S	S	S
vells	MS	MS	S	R	MS	S	S	S	S	S	S	MS	S	S	S	MS	S	S	S	MS	MS	S	S	–	S	–	S	S	S
(Corn)	S	S	S	–	S	S	MS	MS	S	S	S	S	S	S	S	S	S	S	S	–	–	MS	S	–	S	–	S	MS	–
er als	–	–	–	–	R	–	–	R	R	R	R	–	–	–	R	R	R	R	R	S	S	–	–	S	R	R	S	S	S
at	R	–	–	R	MS	R	MS	R	R	–	MS	R	S	–	R	R	R	R	R	S	S	–	–	MS	R	S	R	MS	S

S = Susceptible
MS = Moderately susceptible
MR = Moderately resistant
R = Resistant

days of spraying (but read the label). *Systemic* chemicals are absorbed into the sap stream and remain there for some time, killing mainly those insects which have sucking mouth parts, eg, aphids, whitefly and red spider. The interval between spraying and harvesting for systemic materials tends to be much longer but there is not quite the necessity to be so thorough with the spraying technique. *Stomach poisons* are used to kill caterpillars or other insects with biting mouthparts, eg, methiocarb pellets (Draza) used on slugs and leatherjackets. Many chemicals have both contact and stomach poison properties, notably HCH, trichlorphon and chlorfenvinphos.

With fungicides, the choice is between disease protectant and eradicant chemicals. Protectant materials, like zineb and dichlofluanid, should be applied before disease appears as routine. Eradicant chemicals, such as benomyl, have a curative effect as well as a protective action. These eradicant fungicides are partially systemic which gives a curative effect on existing disease infection. These have become popular in recent years but build up of disease resistant to systemics is commonplace. Hence many growers use a combination of protectant and systemic chemicals to overcome possible resistance. To avoid resistance build up, choose fungicides from different chemical groups on an annual basis.

Approach to pest or disease problems

A systematic approach to control is required when tackling plant problems – tracking down the trouble may be an important part of the job so define the symptoms carefully before taking action. If necessary call in the help of your local advisory officer. Secondly, decide whether the problem is a pest, a disease, or a deficiency. This can be ascertained from the symptoms or, for deficiencies, by tissue analysis. Finally, take IMMEDIATE action and note down the problem, its timing and treatment. With many diseases regular annual protective treatment may be necessary – particularly if there is a known history of that disease.

Chemical formulation

The type of chemical chosen depends on situation but for vegetable growing, chemicals which can be diluted in water are the most convenient. Water sprays penetrate plant growth well and ensure reasonable control. Dusts are more difficult to apply evenly and are very subject to drift. Granules, too, are particularly valuable and easy to apply, especially for dealing with soil pests, eg, cabbage root fly.

Spray coverage

When spraying for pests and diseases good coverage of leaves and plant tissue is important. It is normal to apply the materials to 'run-off'.

Crops with waxy leaves, like brassicas, when sprayed need the addition of wetting agents to ensure the materials stick to the leaf surface.

A quick guide to chemical control of major pests and diseases is shown in the Summary Chart on page 251.

Safety and the Use of Chemicals

Much emphasis has been placed on safety and the use of chemicals . . . and rightly so. The 1974 Health and Safety at Work Act places an obligation on both employers, self-employed and employees to ensure reasonable care of their own health and safety at work. Certain chemicals are detailed where special care has to be taken in their use and these are called *scheduled* substances. These are classified in three grades – Part 1, 2 and 3 scheduled substances, the most dangerous being Part 1 and the least dangerous Part 3. The special requirements for these chemicals are given in the Ministry of Agriculture Leaflet, 'Safe Use of Poisonous Chemicals on the Farm'. Basically, they make specific reference to the use of protective equipment in the following ways.

Part 1 substances – These require special protective measures to be taken. These operations are often carried out by contractors, eg, chloropicrin application.

Part 2 substances – Full protective clothing – rubber gloves, boots, face shield or mask depending on substance, rubber coat, hood/souwester at all operations, eg, dinoseb, mevinphos. When the granular formulations are used certain relaxation in protective clothing requirements is allowed.

Part 3 substances – Rubber gloves and face shield when handling the concentrate.

However, as a general guide it is always wise to wear protective clothing. The regulations provide for minimum requirement only. The wearing of rubber gloves and face shield when handling chemicals is always good practice. The wearing of rubber coats, rubber boots and waterproof clothing when applying chemicals prevents ordinary clothing from becoming chemically contaminated.

Storage of chemicals

Many agricultural chemicals currently used are subject to the Poisons Act. The regulations include general and specific provisions for labelling and storage. It is a legal requirement that chemicals are locked in a dry, well ventilated store. Scheduled poisons must be booked against the operator and the hours of use recorded. It is a worthwhile procedure to book all chemical use as routine practice.

Information on the use of chemicals, the use of protective clothing and first aid requirements should be prominently displayed in, or near, the poisons store. Instructions for use of specific chemicals should be carefully maintained. Where leaflets come loose with the chemical, file them in a binder, when they appear on a can or bottle, ensure that you make out a copy for the file in case they become stained and unreadable by chemical spillage.

Disposal of containers used for chemicals is always a difficult problem. Some local authorities will collect and dispose of these containers. For detailed information on the subject see 'Guidelines for the Disposal of Unwanted Pesticides and Containers on Farms and Holdings' available from the Ministry of Agriculture, Fisheries and Food, or the Health and Safety Executive.

Avoiding spraydrift

This aspect should not be underestimated – particularly if you are in an exposed site, because the number of days in which spraying can be carried out may be few. Many chemicals have to be sprayed at a specific stage in the crop growth. A very good reason for choosing a sheltered spot for growing crops.

The pointers are (a), use a large droplet size as this will reduce drift, (b) use a low pressure spray (no more than 2 bars pressure), and (c) use a boom height as low as possible over the crop to obtain the correct coverage.

As a guide to wind speeds the following table as to when to spray or not spray may help.

Table 61: A guide to wind speeds

Wind speed	Description	Rough guide	
0 mph	Calm	Smoke from fire rises vertically	
1–2 mph	Light air	Smoke drifts away from fire	SPRAY
3–5 mph	Light breeze	Leaves on tree rustle, wind just felt on face	
6–10 mph	Gentle breeze	Leaves and twigs in constant motion	DON'T
11–15 mph	Moderate breeze	Paper and leaves on ground blown about	SPRAY

Table 60: Twelve practical pointers in the safe use of chemicals

BEFORE SPRAYING	(1)	Read the label before using a chemical and adhere to the precautions.
	(2)	Use the product as recommended on the label – not on unspecified crops as this might cause damage.
	(3)	When mixing water based chemicals add concentrate to water and not the reverse way round.
	(4)	Don't put in 'a little extra concentrate for luck' – this will only cause problems. Close all concentrate containers tightly and store safely away from children.
	(5)	Don't mix 'cocktails', they rarely work unless specified by the manufacturers
DURING SPRAYING	(6)	Avoid drift of chemicals so only spray on windless days. Early morning or evening is best since this is usually the calmest part of day. Translocated herbicides are the worst – even relatively small quantities (as low as 1 ppm) can cause damage to tomato plants. So beware of these chemicals near glasshouse crops.
	(7)	Avoid spraying in hot sunshine – a water droplet can act like a magnifying glass and scorch leaves.
	(8)	Use a methodical approach to spraying and avoid overlapping or missing strips.
AFTER SPRAYING	(9)	Wash out the sprayer thoroughly and clean with detergent. It is particularly important to ensure lances are internally cleaned by washing through detergent and water.
	(10)	Wash hands and exposed skin thoroughly after using any chemicals and particularly before eating, drinking or smoking.
	(11)	Clean protective clothing thoroughly after use.
	(12)	Never transfer pesticides to other storage containers, especially beer, lemonade or soft drink bottles.
NOTE		Ideally, separate sprayers should be used for pesticides, fungicides and herbicides. It makes for greater safety.

Training in the use of chemicals

Spraying and use of chemicals for the novice should not be undertaken lightly. The need for training is a must for which the Agricultural Training Board offers suitable courses. Manufacturers of spray equipment and the chemical companies also offer invaluable guidance. The uninitiated grower should start in a small way and gain experience before embarking on large scale spraying operations. It may take time, but it will be worthwhile in the end. Some failures will be inevitable but that is all part of learning the skill.

Selecting a suitable chemical

The Ministry suggests that the best way of selecting chemicals is to ask yourself five safety questions:

(1)   *Operator safety* – is this the least toxic chemical available for this purpose?

(2)   *Consumer safety* – can the chemical be applied in time to leave the necessary harvesting interval?

(3)   *Environmental safety* – is this chemical least likely to affect wild life and bees if used?

(4)   *Safety to crops* – is the variety of crop suitable and are the time and conditions for application correct?

(5)   *Safety of neighbouring crops* – is the chosen chemical the one least likely to damage or drift on to neighbouring fields or land?

If the answer is 'yes' to all these questions then the best chemical has been selected for the job.

Selecting the correct nozzle and nozzle height for the job

Selection of nozzle type is important for good results. There are two basic nozzles for commercial sprayers – fan and cone nozzles. Some general rules on use are:

(a)   Low pressure cone or fan nozzles are used for residual herbicide sprays to avoid drift.

(b)   Cone nozzles are used when spray coverage of crops is important – for fungicides and many pesticides.

(c)   Fan nozzles must be used when penetration of spray is required in upright crops, eg, sweet corn.

Also check the height of the nozzles above the target to obtain as even a spray pattern as possible. Spray booms should be adjusted so that the bar is parallel to the ground. The spray fans/cones should overlap where they meet the target (see Figure 39). When spraying with a hand knapsack sprayer, judgement (and the use of manufacturers' recommendations) will be required to assess the distance from the target. The position needed is where good coverage by the spray is achieved without excessive drift. Remember when spraying insecticides and fungicides over the crop that the target is the crop, not the soil.

Before spraying test your sprayer, using water, on a clear piece of concrete or tarmac – to check the working of the nozzles. Nozzles will need replacing at regular intervals.

A methodical approach should be taken in spraying any area – Figure

40 shows a methodical approach to tractor spraying in an irregular shaped field.

Figure 39 Boom height for spraying

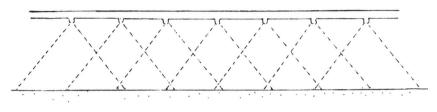

TARGET – THE SOIL

For boom spraying, the height is critical – this overlapping pattern should be produced. Test on concrete before commencing to spray.

Figure 40 A systematic approach to spraying

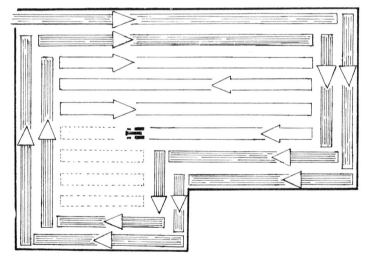

(i)   Work round headlands first.
(ii)   Then in strips up and down the centre of the field.
(iii)   Note that the sprayer is turned off at corners so that turning can be carried out. Start respraying when positioned correctly for the next run and beginning to move.

Types of sprayers

For details see Chapter 10.

Useful publications (*Publications of particular value.)
A number of valuable Ministry of Agriculture publications are available from H.M. Stationery Office.

Health and Safety (Agriculture) (Poisonous substances) Regulations 1975.
*Poisonous Chemicals on the Farm (HS(G)2).
Guidelines for Disposal of Unwanted Pesticides and Containers on Farms and Holdings.
*Approved Products for Farmers and Growers.
Crop Spraying.
Guidelines for Applying Crop Protection Chemicals.
Storage of Pesticides on Farms.
Poisoning by Pesticides (MS(B)7).

Also, two invaluable publications are:

The Weed Control Handbook, edited by J. Fryer and R. Makepeace (publisher: Blackwell)
*The Pesticide and Fungicide Handbook, edited by Hubert Martin and Charles R. Worthing (publisher: Blackwell)

Table 62: Pest Summary Chart

Crop/Pest	Damage caused, symptoms of attack – Most likely times of occurrence	Control treatment	Timing/method of treatment
PESTS ATTACKING A WIDE RANGE OF CROPS			
Cutworms (Noctuidae)	Large fat khaki coloured, legless soil caterpillars, which curl in a 'C', mainly found in soil overwinter/spring. *Chew seedlings* at ground level so they keel over and die, particularly on beetroot and lettuce. Common.	Chlorpyrifos Triazophos HCH baits	Apply in late spring when cutworms small, and young, before excessive damage occurs.
Leatherjackets (Tipula spp.)	Grey coloured legless larva of the daddy-longlegs. Eggs laid in late summer, hatch over winter. Damage worst in spring. Young seedlings *roots and stems eaten.* Common	Methiocarb baits HCH (not potaoes)	Dust mixed with bait or ready made pellets. Sprays less effective.
*Slugs (Agriolimax and Arion spp.)	Slug damage occurs mainly in *wet weather* – eats leaves and stem of plants near or at ground level – slimy trail usually obvious, even if slug is not. Very common.	Metaldehyde baits Methiocarb baits IMPROVED DRAINAGE	Apply pellets or mini-pellets after planting.

Table 62: *(continued)*

Crop/Pest	Damage caused, symptoms of attack – Most likely times of occurrence	Control treatment	Timing/method of treatment
Stem Eelworm (Ditylenchus spp. and Heteradera spp.)	Various races of eelworm attack a wide range of host vegetables. Onion base becomes swollen, malformed and twisted; parsnips become dry mealy and split (difficult to discern), beans distort and become twisted and stems may collapse; in rhubarb it causes crown rot. Difficult to discern eelworm without expert advice. Worst on heavy soils.	Hygiene is the only real treatment – remove ALL DEBRIS. Do not grow crop again on land infested with eelworm since they survive several years in the soil. On onion sets hot water treatment valuable. Chemical soil treatment (Aldicarb or Oxamyl) valuable for onions. Use long rotations.	
Wireworms (Agriotese spp.)	Orange/brown fast moving larva about 1″ long. Live up to four years in the soil. Prevalent on *newly turned in grassland,* or land previously cropped with grain. Beware particularly on potatoes and sweet corn where larva feed on roots rarely killing plant, merely reducing the root system, thus lessening yield. Common.	HCH Dust. (except on potatoes use Aldrin)	Apply to soil just prior to planting or sowing. *OR* Seed Dressing.
ASPARAGUS Asparagus beetle (Crioceris asparagai)	Adult beetle feeds on new shoots causing distortion. Fronds later skeletonized.	Malathion.	Apply at first sight, and following year as shoots appear.
BEETROOT/ SPINACH Beet Leaf Miner (Pegomya betae)	The larva feed and cause blistering of leaves of beetroot and spinach. Most damaging on young plants, especially on spinach where leaves are the saleable part.	Top Dress with high nitrogen feed *and* use Trichlorphon.	Apply when damage first seen.
Black Bean Aphid (Aphis fabae)	Carrier of virus, causes stunting and malformation of leaves – see details under Peas/Beans.	Control as for peas and beans.	
BRASSICAS Cabbage Aphid (Brevicoryne brassicae)	White fluffy aphid seen on undersurface of leaves. Causes twisting of leaves – carries cauliflower mosaic.	Disulfoton, Demephion, Pirimicarb, Formothion, Dimethoate, Phorate.	Sprays most effective-choice may depend on harvest interval after spraying.

Table 62: (*continued*)

Crop/Pest	Damage caused, symptoms of attack – Most likely times of occurrence	Control treatment	Timing/method of treatment
Cabbage caterpillars (Cabbage white-Pieris spp. Cabbage moth – Mamestra brassicae)	Caterpillars of both species eat and *skeletonize leaves*. Cabbage white are green grubs with black spot working mainly July to September, Cabbage moth are green caterpillars damaging plants from June to October. Common.	Mevinphos, Triazophos, Pirimiphos-methyl, Permethrin, Trichlorphon, Chlorpyrifos. BIOLOGICAL CONTROL.	When spraying add a wetter to the pesticide since brassica leaves are difficult to wet. Apply when damage first seen.
*Cabbage rootfly (Erioischia brassicae)	Minute fly lays eggs on soil around brassica plant stems from April to August. *Small white larval grub eats into* the roots and works into the stem. Plants turn *blueish colour, wilt and die*, particularly on cauliflowers. Major problem on all brassicas.	Chlorfenvinphos, Carbofuran, Diazinon, Fonofos, Disulfoton.	Apply granules or sprays around base of plants after transplanting. Direct drilled or seedbed apply after 2 true leaves formed.
Cabbage stem weevil (Cautorhynchus quadridens)	Grub of the *weevil mines up stem* and through leaf petiole on spring sown brassicas. Major time of attack April to July. Uncommon.	Carbofuran	Granular application to seedbed.
Flea Beetle (Phyllotetra spp.)	Young beetles do major damage to seedlings during warm sunny days from April-June. *Seed leaves initially look pin pricked* and later these develop into small holes as leaves expand. Common.	HCH Seed Dressing – Prior to sowing HCH Crop Spray – When damage first seen Carbuforan granules – applied to soil.	
Turnip gall weevil (Ceutorphynchus pleurostigma)	Causes *swelling and galling of roots* – not unlike club root. The difference can be seen by cutting roots to reveal a maggot inside causing the swelling.	HCH	Applied as dust, band application along rows. OR in May when first seen.
CARROTS *Carrot fly (Psila rosae)	Minute fly lays eggs around carrot roots in May/June and again in August. The small white larva hatch, eat and tunnel into the carrot causing rusty marks. Heavy infestation cause carrot *foliage to turn bronzy-red*. Flys attracted by smell of carrot foliage. Common.	Carbofuran, Diazinon, Disulfoton, Phorate, Chlorfenvinphos.	Granules broadcast – worked in to the soil before seeding. Ideally granules can be drilled beneath the seed in bands. Also kills aphid.

Table 62: (*continued*)

Crop/Pest	Damage caused, symptoms of attack – Most likely times of occurrence	Control treatment	Timing/method of treatment
Willow-carrot aphid (Cavariella aegopodii)	Aphid attacks foliage causes *mottling and stunting of foliage* on carrots resulting in heavy loss of yield. Aphid carries mottley dwarf virus.	Dimethoate, Demephion, Demeton-S-methyl, Formothion, Malathion.	Spray when aphids first seen. Granules as for carrot fly.
CELERY Carrot fly (Psila rosae)	As above – young larva eats into celery roots – plants stunted – yellow and wilting – not usually as heavily attacked as carrots. Uncommon.	Disulfoton, Diazinon.	Granular application to the soil during or just after planting.
Celery fly (Philophylla heraclei)	Small fly lays its eggs from May to October in leaves. The minute *larva burrow* between the outer tissue of the leaf – Maggot detectable inside.	Malathion, Dimethoate, Trichlorphon.	Apply spray early May to catch initial attack.
LETTUCE Lettuce root aphid (Pemphigus bursarius)	The primary host for the aphid is poplar, but the aphid transfers to lettuce in July. They attack the root collars of lettuce causing sudden wilting. Worst in August. *Aphids have a woolly appearance.*	Diazinon	Granular application to soil or spray crop late June.
Other aphids	Lettuce are host to at least five other species of aphid, which transmit virus and suck at sap distorting lettuce leaves.	Diazinon, Dimethoate, Pirimicarb, Malathion	Apply spray when first seen.
MARROWS Peach potato aphid (Myzus persica)	Aphid sucks at sap from young leaves and growing points causing leaf distortion and reduced growth. Common.	Heptenophos, Dimethoate.	Apply spray when aphids first seen.
ONIONS/LEEKS Onion fly (Delia antiqua)	Flies rather like small house flies, run over onion beds in spring laying eggs on the soil around onion necks *White legless maggots eat their way into the bulb*. Worst in spring during dry weather – flies attracted by fresh organic matter.	Avoid using dung before crop. Pirimiphos-ethyl, HCH.	– seed dressing – Dust soil before sowing.
Onion thrip (Thrips tabaci)	Thrips by sucking at leaf cells causes spotting or bleaching of areas on Onion/leek leaves. Injury rarely sufficiently great to worry about.	Malathion	Apply spray when damage first seen.

Table 62: (*continued*)

Crop/Pest	Damage caused, symptoms of attack – Most likely times of occurrence	Control treatment	Timing/method of treatment
PARSNIPS Carrot & celery fly	Damage as on carrots, but far less common.	Control as for carrots	
PEAS/BEANS *Black bean aphid (Aphis fabae)	The aphid overwinters on Euonymus bushes – In spring and summer the adults migrate to beans/rhubarb and the heavy infestation of 'blackfly' occurs particularly on broad beans. Sap sucking by aphids reduces the vigour of plants markedly. Common.	Formothion, Malathion, Heptenophos, Mevinphos, Dichlorvos, Dimethoate, Pirimcarb.	Avoid spraying when crop in flower. Spray June to catch first infestation.
Pea midge (Contarinia pisi)	White jumping larva feed on flowers in June and on growing points. Pods become malformed. The Advisory Service giving warnings on first appearance of adult midges.	Azinphos-methyl mixtures (1), Fenitrothion, Carbaryl.	All of these pests on peas can be controlled by the same set of sprays in end May early June just before flowering and a second spray about ten days later – provided chemicals (1) or (2) are used.
*Pea & bean weevil (Sitona spp)	Adult weevils feed on foliage causing *notching of leaves*, grubs in spring feed on roots. Neither is completely damaging more a nuisance/crop reducer. Common.	Azinphos-methyl mixtures (1), Fenitrothion (2).	
*Pea moth (Cydia laspeyresia)	Moth lays eggs in June on the flowers on partly developed pea pods. Hatching larva bore through the pod and *grubs feed on the peas inside*. Early sowings avoid moth trouble. Common.	Azinphos-methyl mixtures, (1) Fenitrothion (2) Permethrin, triazophos.	
*Pea thrips (Kakothrips robustus)	Thrips in May/June lay eggs on flowers and pods of peas. The young orange nymphs feed on pods and leaves. Pods distort and become unsaleable – leaves show *silvering*. Common.	Azinphos-methyl mixtures (1), Fenitrothion, Dimethoate.	
RHUBARB Black bean aphid	See section on pea/bean pests. Vector of virus.	Control as for Peas/Beans above.	
SWEET CORN Bean seed fly (Delia platura)	Flies lay eggs in soil and larva burrow into germinating seeds and tunnel up young stems, killing the seedlings.	Chlofenvinphos	Seed treatment.

Table 62: (*continued*)

Crop/Pest	Damage caused, symptoms of attack – Most likely times of occurrence	Control treatment	Timing/method of treatment
*Frit fly (Oscinella frit)	Fly lays eggs from May onwards and larva feed at the base of the centre shoot causing plants to turn yellow. Small plants die, older plants produce side shoot. Common.	Chlorfenvinphos, Phorate, Fenitrothion.	– granules along rows – granules in seed drill – spray when less than 2 leaves.

*Those which need regular preventative treatment because they are so damaging
+ Other important pests

Table 63: Disease Summary Chart

Crop/Disease	Damage caused, symptoms of attack, times of occurrence	Control Methods
ASPARAGUS Asparagus rust (Puccinia asparagi)	Rust brown markings on stem in summer followed by black streaks on stems and leaves in autumn.	Collect up all top growths and burn in winter.
BEETROOT Blackleg (Pleospora betae)	*Stems of seedling beet turn black* and shrivelled so that plants die. Seed-borne disease.	Soak seed in Thiram suspension for 24 hours.
BRASSICAS Canker (Phoma lingam)	Seed may be infected – first signs are light brown or purplish cankers on stem base. Leaf spots also develop with ashen grey centres, roots blacken, rot and the plant wilts. Worst in northern Britain.	Treat seed with thiabendazole as a dry powder or in a slurry by wetting the seed.
Cauliflower mosaic	First signs on young plants is a pronounced clearing of the veins at the base of young leaves. Later veins stand out and *paler chlorotic interveinal areas* show up – chlorotic blotches and spots appear. In winter outer leaves fall off giving a palm tree effect.	Transmitted by cabbage aphid so control aphid attack. Important to isolate seedbeds away from growing areas. Destroy old brassica stumps immediately after crop finished.
*Club root (Plasmodiophora brassicae)	Soil-borne disease infects roots, causing *gall like growths* all over them. Swollen roots rot away. Plants stunted eventually wilt. Worst on acid, heavy, badly drained soils. Very common.	Lime soils, bring pH above 6.5. Encourage good drainage. Sterilize soil with Dazomet. Dip brassica roots in mercurous chloride or Thiophanate-methyl before planting.

Table 63: (*continued*)

Crop/Disease	Damage caused, symptoms of attack, times of occurrence	Control Methods
*Downy Mildew (Peronospora parasitica)	Shows as white mealy patches on the *undersurface of brassica leaves*, particularly on seedbed brassicas where plants crowded especially in poly tunnels. Warm days and cold nights favour disease. Very common.	Avoid overcrowding in seedbed, keep foliage dry overnight. Spray dichlofluanid or zineb. Avoid humid conditions in polythene tunnels when raising seedlings.
Brown Heart of Swedes (a physiological disorder)	Usually leaves look normal: but when roots cut open the centre shows a clear defined zone greyish brown and very woody. Diseased roots are bitter and tough.	Caused by a boron shortage. Apply Borax at 22 kg/ha (20 lb/acre) pre-sowing or use (Solubor post emergence at 11 kg/ha (10 lb/acre).
Powdery mildew (Erisiphe cruciferarum)	White *powdery coating appears on upper surface* of brassica leaves. Mainly occurs on swedes and turnips, usually late in summer after dry weather. Worst on lighter soils on swedes and turnips. Common.	Fluotrimazole systemic fungicide sprayed over foliage high volume, when disease first appears. Dinocyl is also used.
Ring-spot (Mycosphaerella brassicicola)	Occurs during wet weather in winter. Shows as circular brown spots about ½ in diameter on the outer foliage and sometimes stems. Centre of spots show black dots set in concentric rings. Worst in the south-west Britain. Occurs after heavy manuring.	Isolate seedbed. Rotate crops. Avoid manuring before this crop. Burn diseased plant material. Use resistant varieties.
Whiptail of cauliflowers (a physiological disorder)	Symptoms are caused by severe molybdenum deficiency. *Leaves become strap-like* with much reduced irregular leaf blades. Growing points become stunted or blind. Curds fail to develop. Most common on acid soils accentuated by dry weather.	Keep pH above 6.5. Irrigate in dry weather. Spray on a solution of Sodium Molybdate. Alternatively use a seed dressing of sodium molibdate.
Wirestem (Rhizoctonia solani)	The fungus causes damping-off, where stems of young *seedlings suddenly collapse at ground level.* With older plants the stems brown, shrink and affected plants die with the constriction. Encouraged by warm days and cold nights, overwatering and poor light after germination. Common.	Rake in Quintozene dust to the soil before sowing the seed. Cultural control vital – ventilate seedlings under protection; care with watering especially during cold nights.
CARROTS Sclerotinia rot (Sclerotinia sclerotiorum)	A disease of stored or clamped carrots. Infection occurs from soil into carrot wounds. Carrots become covered in white fungal threads which later become covered in black resting bodies.	Ventilate store or clamp well. Never store damaged or diseased carrots. Infected material should be burnt.

Table 63: (*continued*)

Crop/Disease	Damage caused, symptoms of attack, times of occurrence	Control Methods
CELERY		
*Celery leaf spot (Septoria apiicola)	Fungus causes *rusty brown spots on leaves* and stems. Worst in cool damp weather. Disease can be carried on seed.	Soak seed in Thiram suspension. Spray when fungus first seen with Benomyl or Zineb.
Root rot (Phoma apiicola)	Roots rot, particularly in nursery seedbeds, completely killing seedlings. Soil borne and seed infected.	Sterilize seedbed soil with Dazomet Soak seed in Thiram suspension.
LETTUCE		
'Damping off' (Pithium)	See brassica wire stem symptoms the same at seedling stage.	Use Quintozene fungicide.
Downy mildew (Bremia lactucae)	Worst in wet cool weather in autumn. Shows as large pale areas between leaf veins of lower leaves. White *fungus produced on undersurface.* Secondary invasion of bacterial soft rot may occur – outer leaves become brown and slimy.	Spray Zineb and repeat every 3–4 weeks. Metalaxyl + Mancozeb is a possible treatment applied as a foliar spray.
*Grey mould (Botrytis cineria)	Particularly common in late winter, early spring crops. Worst following frost and wet weather. Soil-borne disease which *enters stem through wounds.* Stem reddens – later the rot may take over so that the lettuce wilts and then the grey fluffy mould appears.	Avoid too deep planting, careless handling of lettuce stems at planting. Improve drainage. Apply Benomyl or Thiram 3 times at fortnightly intervals. Protectant dust treatments to soil better – use Quintozene.
Lettuce mosaic (virus)	Due to virus transmitted by several different aphids. Affected plants are dwarfed, *leaves pale, mottle and crinkle.* In warm conditions small dead spots appear on edges of leaves. The virus may be carried in seed.	Control aphid attack. Rotate crops regularly. Use mosaic tested seed.
Ringspot (Marssoninia panattoniana)	Sometimes called rust. Small circular sunken brown spots on outer leaves. Sometimes the spots fall out giving a shot-hole effect. Pink fungus appears on spot edge in wet weather. Worst in cold weather late winter. Lettuces dwarfed and unmarketable.	Spray Captan or Thiram at seedling stage onwards at 2 weekly intervals.

Table 63: (*continued*)

Crop/Disease	Damage caused, symptoms of attack, times of occurrence	Control Methods
MARROWS Mosaic Virus	Caused by cucumber mosaic – distinct yellow mottling of younger leaves and puckering. Diseased fruits mottled and covered with wart like areas. Virus carried by aphids. The same virus also infects many other plants – cucumbers, spinach, celery, asters, dephinium. Seed carried virus.	Buy seed, do not save your own seed. Control aphids as these insects spread virus.
*Powdery mildew (Erisyphe spp.)	Similar symptoms to all powdery mildews (see brassicas). Common.	Spray Benomyl or Carbendazim at first signs and at 14–21 day intervals.†
*Grey mould (Botrytis cineria)	Attacks flower and the rot spreads into fruits. Grey mould starts at the end of the fruit and works backwards. Worst in wet weather where poor air circulation.	Spray Benomyl or Carbendazim when mould first seen.†
ONIONS/LEEKS Downy mildew (Peronospora destructor)	Most severe attacks in wet weather, on low lying badly drained areas, especially in cold seasons. *Leaves die from tip downwards* and become covered in a downy growth. Bulbs may fail to develop. Disease carried in soil or sets. Common.	Apply Zineb plus wetter when disease first appears and 14-day intervals. Grow alliums only on well drained soils where air circulation is good. Avoid growing onions on highly contaminated land.
*Rust (Puccinia porri)	Common on leeks during warm weather. Shows as *bright orange spots on leek leaves*. Severe attack may kill leaves.	Some varieties more resistant than others. Chemicals not very effective. Triadimephon is a promising new material.
Neck Rot (Botrytis allii)	The seed borne disease attacks the neck of the bulb during storage producing a soft brown rot in the scales. Fungus shows later a greyish felt of spores with black bodies.	Avoid damage to bulbs, particularly during harvesting otherwise this encourages disease in store. Benomyl/Thiram treated seed minimize infection to crop.
Smut (Urocystis cepulae)	A serious soil-borne disease on onions. At first leaf the seedling onion is attacked below ground level. Dark lead coloured stripes appear on the leaves and bulb scales which burst to reveal black powdery spores. Seedlings are eventually killed. Sales of infected plants are strictly prohibited.	Do not use soil for growing any allium crops. The disease can be reduced by applying formaldehyde sol. down the drill after sowing but before covering the drill. Some control by pelleting seed in Thiram.

Table 63: (*continued*)

Crop/Disease	Damage caused, symptoms of attack, times of occurrence	Control Methods
*White rot (Sclerotium cepivorum)	Affects onions and leeks. Leaves turn yellow and die back. When plants pulled up roots are found to be rotten with a white grey fungus growth. Later black fruiting bodies develop.	Iprodione seed treatment gives good control on salad onions only. Sclerotia persist in soil for years – keep alliums off infected land.
PARSNIPS *Canker	Common disease of broad shouldered parsnips. Soil-borne pathogen enter root through natural cracks in the crown or wounds. Causes red rust like marks from shoulder downwards. Worst in heavy soils when wet follows a dry spell in autumn on high nitrogen soils.	Use resistant varieties eg, Avon-resister. Grow parsnips on well drained, lighter soils. Sow late to produce small roots.
PEAS/BEANS Anthracnose (Colletotrichum lindemuthianum)	Affects mainly French beans in wet, warm summers. Shows on stems as elongated sunken brown canker. Upper leaves wither, pods show sunken black–brown spots, which become slimy in rain. Beans are infected inside the pod.	Grow in drier areas. Dust seed with Benomyl. Application of a Benomyl spray at flowering time also useful. Use resistant cultivars.
*Chocolate spot (Botrytis fabae)	Found on Broad Beans mainly early spring and summer. Chocolate coloured spots up to ¼ in (6 mm) diameter on leaves. Stems becomes streaked, flowers become infected and rot. Worst in poor drained soils.	Avoid overdense sowings to improve air drainage. Apply Benomyl or copper fungicides at flowering and 2 weeks later.
Downy mildew (Peronospera viciae)	Greyish fungus on undersurface of leaves similar to brassicas. Worst in wet weather – mainly on peas. Diseased pods are seedless.	Spray with Zineb at 14–day intervals from when disease first seen. Avoid growing on low land.
Foot rot (Fusarium app.)	Attacks peas, and dwarf beans. The disease is soil borne. Occurs as peas or beans are forming pods. Lower leaves suddenly wither and die, and this continues upwards. Stems become red brown streaked and marked at base. Worst on soils where peas and beans are continually grown.	Rotate away from legumes. Difficult to control on a field scale. Remove infected plants and burn. Effects minimized where strong root system is encouraged by good drainage and manuring.

Table 63: (*continued*)

Crop/Disease	Damage caused, symptoms of attack, times of occurrence	Control Methods
Halo blight (Pseudomonas phaseolicola)	This bacterial disease causes water-soaked spots of about 10 mm diameter to form on leaves of dwarf and runner beans. 'A yellow halo' surrounds each spot. It infects pods and causes blistering on the seeds inside.	Use copper oxychloride sprays from emergence to flowering at 14-day intervals. Do not irrigate infected crop. Do not soak seed in water.
Leaf and pod spot (Aschcochyta spp. and Mycosphaerella pinodes)	Asochyta tend to be pale brown spots of ¼ in (6 mm) with a dark margin whereas Mycosphaerella are purplish irregular spots which may coalesce. Leaves and pods are affected in peas. Disease prevalent in wet years.	Use seed dressings of Thiram/Benomyl to protect plants against infection.†
Marsh spot of peas (Deffeciency)	Occurs because of manganese deficiency on marshy and other soils. Affects seeds which have a well defined brown spot in the centre when cut across. The mature plants may look quite healthy.	Apply Manganese sulphate to plants at flowering time. Avoid liming soils on which Marsh Spot appears.
Powdery mildew (Ensyphe polygoni)	This fungus covers leaves and pods with white powdery patches. Prevalent in dry weather when a considerable difference between day and night temperatures.	Spray Benomyl or Carbendazim at first signs of attack and at 14–21 day intervals.
Rust of broad bean (Uramyces fabae)	Found every year as the rust like marks on leaves, but appears too late to cause any damage. Worst on soils low in potassium.	Ensure high potassium used in base dressing. Remove old bean haulms which causes carry-over disease.
Pre-emergent Damping-off (Pythium spp.)	Name given to rotting seeds particularly peas, which takes place before they emerge.	Seed dressing with Thiram before sowing. Use high vigour seed for early sowings.
RHUBARB Crown rot (Bacterium rhaponticum)	Common in rhubarb growing areas (eg, Yorkshire). Terminal bud rots. Pith becomes soft and a cavity may form in the crown. Encourages side shoot formation. In Summer leaves turn purple brown.	No real control. Remedial measures should concentrate on eradicating the disease. Burn infected plants and never use these crowns for forcing.

Most of the seed treatments mentioned in the text are carried out as a routine operation by the weed merchants at a small extra charge. Onion seeds are now available with a hard chemical coat which reduces drilling problems.
*Important diseases which are likely to appear annually.
†Benomyl and carbendazim break down to the same chemical when used – if disease resistance to these chemicals shows up, use an entirely different chemical.

Chapter Thirteen

Aid and Advice to the Grower

Vegetable growing is becoming such a technical subject that to keep pace with new innovations, techniques, chemicals and machinery would be impossible without the many sources of advice now available to growers. But what is more important is that these services are used mainly by progressive growers who, therefore, obtain the greatest rewards.

It is not a failing or an admission of defeat to have to call in advice, but common sense. The experts should be able to help to find sources of back-up information to give the answers. Their value is that they can often provide detailed information which the ordinary grower cannot keep or store, either in the head or in a bookcase, workshop or laboratory. A quick survey of all the various sources of advice and information may draw to light some new ideas. In most instances, it is not necessarily knowing the answer to a problem, but knowing where to find the relevant information.

Government Help and Advice

The Ministry of Agriculture Fisheries and Food have hundreds of qualified men working in all aspects of horticulture and related sciences in the following agencies.

AGRICULTURAL ADVISORY AND DEVELOPMENT SERVICES (ADAS) This is the most obvious source of advice for growers in England and Wales. The local area office has its advisory officer. Regional Offices (shown on Figure 41) provide more detailed technical back-up including soil analysis services, management advisory units and specialist advisors in crops and crop protection. Most major growing areas are served by a nearby ADAS office.

THE SCOTTISH COLLEGES   In Scotland the same services are covered by the three Scottish Colleges – the North, East and West Colleges (shown on Figure 41). Regional advisers work all areas from local offices, but specialist services of soil analysis, management etc are carried out from the colleges themselves.

EXPERIMENTAL HORTICULTURE STATIONS (EHS)   dealing with vegetable crops are again linked to major vegetable growing areas: Stockbridge House in Yorkshire, Kirton for Lincolnshire growers, Luddington for the Vale of Evesham and Rosewarne for the SW growers. These stations carry out experiments to develop any crops that are locally important and new ideas coming from the research stations. For instance, ice bank cooling, which is the technique for cooling and storing vegetables in a humid atmosphere to keep them fresh, was researched and developed at Kirton EHS. Growers should make regular trips on the EHS open days to keep up-to-date with local experimental data which might have relevance to their crops. The EHS annual reports also summarize their work and are readily available.

GOVERNMENT RESEARCH   is carried out under the auspices of the Agricultural Research Council – who fund the National Vegetable Research Station at Wellesbourne. This is basic research before it is developed at a local level at the EHS's. Progressive growers must keep abreast of current research work to be competitive and the Wellesbourne annual report should be part of any grower's limited library. Other research institutes who carry out work of interest are The Weed Research Organization, Oxfordshire and the National Institute of Agricultural Engineering, Silsoe, Bedfordshire. Growers can subscribe to these research stations to be kept up-to-date with information, open days and annual reports.

GOVERNMENT MARKETING ADVICE   Specialist information on marketing is offered by ADAS, Ministry Marketing Offices and The Central Council for Agricultural and Horticultural Co-operation. They try to make growers aware of new markets and identify changes in market requirements with regard to quality, grading standards, quantity and continuity of supplies.

GOVERNMENT PUBLICATIONS   Ministry reference bulletins, advisory leaflets and booklets are produced by Ministry experts for growers to use. They are an invaluable source of information on almost every crop and problems associated with them. A list of the more important ones are given in Appendix 4.

KEY TO COLLEGES AND UNIVERSITIES

1. Aberdeen Technical College
2. Kingsway Technical College
3. Elmwood College, Cupar
4. Strathclyde University
5. Woodburn House
6. Oatridge College
7. West of Scotland Agricultural College
8. Askham Bryan College
9. Lancashire College (Myerscough Hall)
10. Welsh College (Northop)
11. Cheshire College (Reaseheath)
12. Nottingham University

13. Isle of Ely College
14. Norfolk College
15. Warwickshire College (Moreton Hall)
16. Pershore College
17. Writtle College
18. Oaklands College
19. Berkshire College
20. Somerset College (Cannington)
21. Bath University
22. Hort. Correspondence College
23. University of Reading
24. Hampshire College (Sparsholt)
25. Merrist Wood College
26. Hadlow College
27. West Sussex College
28. London University (Wye College)
29. Bicton College
30. Plumpton College

X ADAS. Regional Offices.
• Experimental Horticulture Station.
⊕ Experimental Husbandry Farms.
  (dealing with vegetable crops)
⊙ Other research organisations.
+ Universities and colleges.

Figure 41 Map showing the centres of horticultural learning, research, experimentation and advice.

Private and Commercial Sources of Advice

PRIVATE RESEARCH ORGANIZATIONS   A number of research organizations funded by means other than the government offer interesting information to vegetable growers. The Processors and Growers Research Organization at Peterborough gives advice specifically on peas and other processed crops.

COMMERCIAL RESEARCH AND TECHNICAL ADVICE   Many of the large chemical companies like Fisons, ICI, May and Baker and Shell have their own research stations or trial grounds where new chemicals and projects are developed. Technical representatives are also on call from all the commercially interested firms and will offer free help and advice to growers. Their help is invaluable since they are constantly carrying out on-site visits. But the information they give may well be routed to help sell their own products.

Horticultural Publications (Other than Government)

Growers may say they don't have time to read but this is a false economy of time. New ideas, tips and hints can be obtained by these means. The easy-to-read 'Grower', is a weekly periodical and is a must for growers and students. It offers week-by-week articles as well as up-to-date market prices. Information on 'where to buy what' is also available. 'Horticultural Industry', a monthly publication, is another useful magazine.

A more recent addition to the periodicals available to growers is 'Farm Fresh News', published and run by the Farm Shop and Pick-Your-Own Association, Hunger Lane, Muggington, Derbyshire.

On the more serious technical front, publications like 'Journal of Horticultural Science', 'Scientific Horticulture' and 'Experimental Horticulture' keep scientists, students and the technically minded up-to-date with the latest scientific data. These are normally only available in colleges and special agricultural libraries. The sources of information are normally indexed in 'Horticultural Abstracts'.

Education and Training

Horticultural education has developed rapidly both at university and college level. Some 30 educational establishments are shown on Figure 41. They offer excellent horticultural courses at varying levels – from day release level right up to degree courses. For the growers they are valuable. Formal educational training in some form, whether for growers' sons or employees is now more than ever essential. Too many growers complain of their inability to find skilled labour. They should be trying to encourage youngsters to undergo formal horticultural education. The colleges also employ specialists on almost all horticultural and scientifically related subjects, so can offer advice on a local scale. Visits to the local college can be valuable to see crop growing techniques used.

THE AGRICULTURAL TRAINING BOARD   offers courses of one or two days' duration to develop specific skills such as fencing. They are usually carried out on farms or holdings in the local area. Your local agricultural training board officer will advise you of courses available.

Horticultural Societies and Growers' Meetings

Local horticultural societies are the meeting point for growers and amateurs. Topics are various but in the interests of our industry, encouragement of horticulture in any guise will do nothing but good. Amateurs look towards professionals to lead and local societies should be supported by the professional growers.

Growers' meetings are perhaps more valuable and most major vegetable areas have their own growers' societies. Your local ADAS or college office (in Scotland) will inform you of the nearest society. It is by growers talking one to another and visiting other holdings that common problems can be solved.

Horticultural Co-operatives

More and more smaller growers are forming co-operatives to obtain the advantages of size with the independence of an ownership business. Co-operatives may offer bulk buying of raw materials, marketing expertise (a pack name, as well as market intelligence information), transport, grading, packing facilities, storage space and even common propagation facilities. Perhaps the best known example of this is the Land Settlement Association, a co-operative set up to administer estates owned by the Ministry of Agriculture. Here their occupants are compelled to market and use the many facilities of the association.

The Marketing Policy Committee of The Central Council of Agricultural and Horticultural Co-operation was established under the 1976 Agricultural Act to specifically look into the improvement of vegetable marketing. From their study they established that there was a need for co-operatives and that these organizations could provide a better service to both individual growers and their customers.

Fortunately co-operative marketing in the UK is expanding rapidly as the figures below show:—

	1977	1979 (March)
Co-operatives in field vegetables	56	59
Co-operatives in peas and beans	63	77
Co-operatives in glasshouse vegetables	14	22

There is every reason to expect this expansion to continue.

Political Aid

Despite the fact that co-operatives are being set up, many growers like to maintain their independence. Growers, on the whole, are too small enterprises to carry any political muscle and it is important that the government looks after the interests of growers (and their workers) in such matters as grants, importation of foreign vegetables, workers wages, minimum working hours and so on. The formation of the National Farmers Union (NFU) ensures that growers can have a say at top political level on any agricultural matters.

Financial Aid

Although not within the scope of this book, finance is of major importance in running a business enterprise – both in developing new projects and in maintaining cash flow. So, as a reminder, it is always worth contacting the local ADAS office or Scottish College Advisory service to see what grants are available to growers, particularly if you are starting new projects and requiring capital assistance. Both the advisory services mentioned have economic and management experts to help growers with advice on how to obtain grants and finance and how to run enterprises efficiently. Local banks, and merchants' credit are other ways of obtaining short term financial aid.

Summary

The summary sheet opposite shows the many facets of aid available to growers from both private and government sectors. No other industry in the UK can boast such a well run advisory set-up administered from central government funds. It has been the linchpin of agriculture's success.

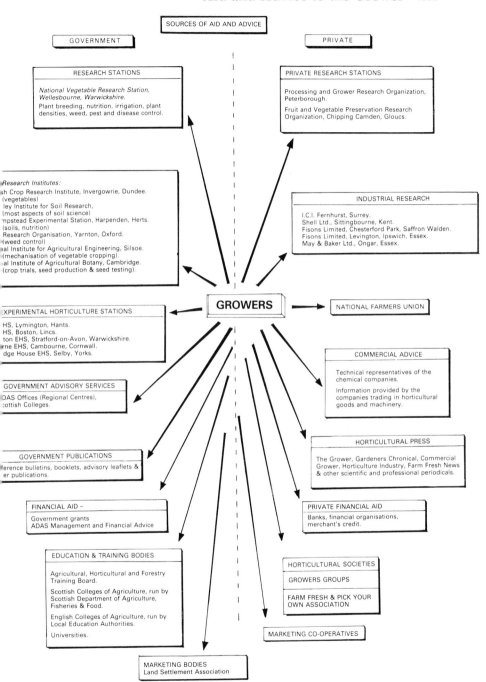

Figure 42 Sources of aid and advice

Chapter Fourteen

The Future of Vegetable Growing in the UK

The agricultural industry has over the last 30 years maintained a steady increase in output (yields) of some 4 per cent a year, which is a remarkable record of achievement. The reasons for this continued increase in output are numerous but on the vegetable side there has been almost a 'revolution' from what was a 'market garden' industry to a farm scale enterprise.

The *use of mechanization* at all stages of growth right from sowing to harvesting has meant that crops like peas are almost 'factory' produced and, apart from filling the seed drill at the start, they are never handled until they reach the processing factory. Obviously, mechanization has made what was a labour intensive industry into a mechanically intensive industry. While labour has decreased the area of land under vegetables has increased. There are still a number of labour intensive crops, like lettuce, which traditional small growers can grow competitively, but these are in a minority.

The *extensive use of herbicides* is of relatively recent origin. It was only a few years back (1950s) when sulphuric acid was recommended for killing weeds in onions. Now there are selective weedkillers for almost every weed you like to mention. All are far safer than those early ones. Not only has the range become very large but the combinations and uses of each are being extended every day.

The *work of scientists* at our research stations has helped us understand vegetable crops better. They have determined the correct nutrient status for each crop; they have determined optimum plant densities for almost every crop; and they have helped develop innovatory ideas like fluid drilling which could well revolutionize the seeding of vegetables.

Above all, the research stations and the seed companies have bred new cultivars with the very qualities that are required by the grower for a specific crop and market outlet. Nowadays we can produce the 18 mm (¾ in) diameter by 90 mm (3½ in) cylindrical carrot – bred to fit the size of a processor's can. But this can only be produced with knowledge of correct plant densities – knowledge we have gained from the researchers.

Enough of the history, what of the future? Maintaining growth of output is not easy. Obviously, mechanization will continue to increase. The elimination of the personal touch will never be complete because at the end the human factor determines when any job has to be carried out.

It is innovations like fluid drilling which will play a major part in growing. The time will come when scheduling, in days, from sowing to harvesting will be feasible for every crop, once we have the cultivars and the know how to carry it out. In the meantime the successful grower MUST keep pace with the many pesticides and ideas which are being developed by both industry and research.

And herbicides are going to become even more important in vegetable growing. With the tendency towards close row spacing it is not now possible to use that old standby, the steerage hoe, if herbicides fail. Alongside this we should be well aware of the need to maintain our environment. The safe use of chemicals is a MUST for all growers and their employees. The subject of safety and chemicals is an evocative one. Environmentalists will continue to remind us of our responsibility in this sphere.

At the same time growers have to become better businessmen. Firstly, as salesmen, for it is not enough just to grow the crop, or even grow it well. Now we are part of the EEC, European competition is becoming stronger. Our packs have to be better, our produce graded well and our standards improved if we are to compete.

Secondly, as financiers, for the use of our capital (the land) and what we grow on it has to be put to best use. Computers will become part of our lives and it may be that 'growers' will have to take second place to accountants and the computer technologists. Computers are already being used to work out viable cropping programmes, to determine when to market and when to store crops and to be used as 'inventories' of total crop capacity.

Many growers will also look for new markets to obtain a high return on capital. For the returns on vegetables are not increasing at the rate that costs (or inflation) are soaring. Since growers cannot fix the price in the wholesale market they must find other ways of selling which bring in a better return. So growers are looking towards the food processing industry for the security of contracts for their produce. This may mean a decline of the wholesale market. Figures show that an increasing quantity of crop is going direct to the food manufacturing industry. It now purchases about 50 per cent of the output of the whole of British agriculture compared with 22 per cent in 1963. The implications to horticulture are an increased demand for large quantities of quality produce grown to stringent specifications.

Self-pick is another lucrative alternative to selling through the wholesale market. This will expand rapidly. Another opportunity for the grower is to grow for large-scale multiple retail outlets such as the supermarkets. Their grading and quality standards are often far higher than the wholesale market and the grower has to be prepared to upgrade his quality control procedures – but the rewards can be good.

Dealing with multiple chain stores is not feasible for the small producing unit unless co-operatives of growers are formed. The expansion of co-operative marketing bodies will continue, particularly if growers wish to have any bargaining power over the price they receive for their crops.

The challenge to the grower is to produce the appropriate quantities, quality and form of produce required by the market they serve. The stringency of standards is something growers must come to grips with. For those that satisfy these demands the future is bright.

Glossary of Vegetable Terms

ABSTRACTION (of water) – drawing away water from an aquafer, reservoir or water source.

ACUs – accumulated cold units of temperatures (every degree below 10°C is recorded for rhubarb).

ADAS – Agricultural Development and Advisory Service.

AGGREGATE (of soils) – joining together of a mass of soil particles.

AHUs – accumulated heat units.

ALGINATE – seaweed extract used as a carrier gel for chitted seed.

ALLIUMS – members of the onion family.

ANNUAL CROPS – crops which seed, (flower/fruit and die) within one season.

AQUAFERS – water bearing stratas.

AVAILABLE WATER CAPACITY (AWC) – water that is available for plants to take up through roots.

BANDOLIER MACHINE – complete blocking and fully automatic transplanting system, under development by NIAE.

BAND SPRAYING – a band of chemical spray about 180 mm wide encompassing the seed drill area.

BAYONET (parsnip) – long thin tapering-shaped parsnip.

BDH TEST KIT – British Drug House's soil pH testing equipment.

BEAN SEEDER – a non-precision type of drill using a disc containing holes for metering the seed.

BIENNIAL – plant that grows in its first year, flowers/fruits only in its second year.

BLOCKING MACHINE – a machine which makes a peat block.

BLOCK RAISED PLANTS – plants grown in blocks, usually under protection.

BLOCKS (for sowing) – an approximately square block of compressed growing media, usually peat, containing nutrients for growth.

'BLOWING' – a condition where the Brussels sprout button begins to open up and develop into a shoot.

'BOLTING' – where a biennial crop like beetroot or carrot runs to seed before harvesting, making roots coarse and unsaleable.

BOW WAVE – a technique of incorporating pesticide granules during the drilling process.

BROADCAST (sowing) – application of seed by scattering over the general surface.

BUTTERHEAD (lettuce) – a cabbage shaped lettuce.

'BUTTONING' (cauliflowers) – a condition where the cauliflower produces only a small curd of 'button' size (about 25–50mm).

CAMBRIDGE ROLLER – a ring roller.

CAP OR CAPPING (of soil) – a situation where surface soil particles run together creating a semi-impermeable skin of soil. It may stop seedling emergence.

CFM – cubic feet per minute.

CHITTED SEED – where radicle emergence from seed has just occurred.

CHLOROPHYLL – the green matter in leaves and stems of plants.

CHLOROSIS (of leaf) – leaf yellowing normally associated with mineral deficiency.

CHUMPS (Parsnips) – 'fanged' or divided roots sold in the market during periods of short supply.

CLAMP – an outside store for root vegetables – consists of layers of straw and soil over a heap of roots to protect them from frost.

COMPOUND (fertilizers) – mixed fertilizer composed of several different nutrients.

CONE NOZZLE – a spray nozzle which produces a cone shaped spray pattern.

CONTACT HERBICIDES – a herbicide which kills every portion of leaf tissue it touches.

COS – a type of lettuce with an upright cylindrical habit of growth.

COULTER (drill) – a metal share in front of the seed drill which opens a furrow for the seed to fall into.

CRISP (lettuce) – a crinkled, wavy edge type lettuce, which is crisp to eat.

CROOK STAGE – a stage of growth of allium seedlings where the cotyledon leaf takes on the shape of a crook just before it straightens up.

CRUMB STRUCTURE – applied to surface soil in good condition – soil in small particles.

CURD – the flowering head of a cauliflower.

DESTRUCTIVE HARVESTING – complete once over harvesting.
DIBBER – a pointed peg for making the hole for planting brassicas/leeks.
DIGGER ELEVATOR – a harvester for lifting root crops.
DIRECT DRILLING – when used in relation to agricultural crops this implies drilling without prior cultivation. This technique is not currently applicable to horticultural crops.
DIRECT SEEDING – synonymous with field drilled.
DRILLED TO A STAND – seeded in final position so that the final plant density is achieved.
DUTCH SCRUBBER – a Dutch harrow for final levelling and preparation of a seedbed.

EHS – Experimental Horticulture Station.
EVAPO–TRANSPIRATION TABLES – figures provided by the Ministry of Agriculture to give estimated combined evaporation/transpiration losses from a crop covering entire ground space.

F_1 (F_1H) – first cross hybrid plant.
FALLOWING – leaving land uncropped for a period of time to enable weeds to be controlled, normally by regular cultivation.
FAN NOZZLE – a spray nozzle which produces a fan shaped spray pattern.
FERNHURST BED SYSTEM – a system of cropping in beds (see Appendix 2).
FIELD CAPACITY (FC) – the point where the soil particles hold a maximum amount of water against gravity.
FIELD DRILLED – crop seeded by drill direct in final harvesting position rather than drilling in a seedbed and transplanting to final site.
FIELD FACTOR (Ff) – a scale from 1.0–0.1 used to allow for the difference between lab germination and field germination. Value is estimated by the grower based on seedbed conditions.
FLUID DRILLING – sowing chitted seed in a gel-like fluid through a space drill.
FOLIAR SPRAY – spraying chemicals/fertilizers over the foliage of crops.
FOLIAGE ACTING HERBICIDES – herbicides which act on weed foliage when applied to the leaves.
FRAME DRILL – A small precision or semi-precision drill designed for drilling at very narrow row space and high density, usually used for seedbeds under protective structure.

FYM – farmyard manure.

GMT – Greenwich Mean Time.
GRADED SEED – seed that has been graded into size groups, which helps with precision seeding.
GREEN BUD STAGE – the point when the flower of a crop has developed green buds but no petals are showing (beans).
GREEN MANURE CROP – crop grown specifically to be turned in for addition of organic matter, once mature.

HAULM – the stem and leaf growth of legumes.
'HOOVER' – A digger elevator type harvester.
'HOPALONG' IRRIGATION SYSTEM – a system of irrigation where irrigation risers and their heads are moved along the irrigation line.
HUMIC – high in humus or decomposed organic matter.

ICE BANK COOLER – a cold store/precooler where indirect refrigeration is employed. Store air is cooled by chilled water, therefore relative humidity levels are very high and a reserve chill capacity can be stored in the water tank.
IMPERMEABLE BARRIERS – barriers which are solid or near solid and do not allow passage of air through them.

JAPANESE PAPERPOTS – a honeycomb of paperpots which are used for propagation of crop transplants.
JAPANESE (CHAIN) PAPERPOTS – as above but honeycomb separate to form a long chain for fully automatic transplanting.

K_2O – Potash nutrient in the form absorbed by the plant.
KAOLIN – china clay material often used for pelleting seed.

LEACHING (of nutrients) – draining away of nutrients by percolation through soil.
LEGUMES – members of pea and bean family.
LIMA BEANS – a bean akin to the French bean.
LOCKED-UP (nutrients) – where nutrients occur in soil but are made unavailable to plants by a change in chemical composition or because of soil pH.
LODGING – refers to crop flattening by weather.
LOOP-STAGE – a stage of growth when allium seedlings take on a loop shape during and immediately after emergence.

MAFF – Ministry of Agriculture, Fisheries and Food.

MATRIX (Soil) – the array of soil particles and the way they are formed together.

Mg – Magnesium nutrient.

MINI-PELLETS (seeds) – small seeds coated with kaolin to make a small pellet to enable precision/semi-precision seeding.

MONOGERM SEED – a seed cluster which only germinates as one seedling (eg beet).

MULTI-DIBBER MACHINE – a series of PTO driven dibbers on a frame for making holes for seeds or plants.

MULTI-PLANT BLOCK – peat block into which three to ten plants are grown to transplanting stage.

NATURAL SEED – seed which has not been graded – of varying sizes in its natural form.

NIAE – National Institute of Agricultural Engineering.

NVRS – National Vegetable Research Station.

OPEN POLLINATED – seed produced by free crossing within a single parent line.

OSCILLATION – the swing to and fro like a pendulum (a term used to apply to irrigation equipment which oscillates).

P_2O_5 – Phosphate nutrients in the form absorbed by the plant.

PAN (soil) – a hard layer in or under the soil (usually of iron salts).

PEG-PLANTS – bare root plants for transplanting.

PERENNIAL – a plant that lives more than two years.

PERMANENT WILTING POINT – the point at which soil holds moisture so strongly by moisture tension that plants cannot take up moisture from the soil.

PETIOLE – leaf stalk.

'PHOLENE' – type of polythene film with small round holes – used for covering early crops – radish, carrots etc.

PLANET HOE – a type of hoe on wheel/s which is hand pushed between rows.

PINCHED BEANS – runner beans which are pinched after first true leaf stage to induce earlier cropping.

PLATEY STRUCTURES (soil) – horizontal structured layers of soil caused by excessive compaction.

PORE SPACE – a minute passage or area among soil particles.

POST CROOK STAGE – a stage of growth in alliums when the cotyledon leaf of the seedling has straightened up.

POTENTIAL TRANSPIRATION – the estimated water loss from a crop under given climatic conditions.

PRIMARY CULTIVATIONS – cultivation by ploughing and subsoiling.

PTO – power take off from tractor.

PULLING (harvesting) – crops/plants that are harvested by pulling out of the ground, rather than digging – irrigation may be needed to aid pulling.

RAIN GUN – a tubular device for spraying/propelling out water at great force for irrigation.

RADICLE – a little root, part of the seed that becomes the root.

RESIDUAL HERBICIDE – herbicide remaining in top 12–15 mm of soil for a period of time up to a year – kills germinating weed seedlings.

RICEY CURDS (cauliflower) – a physiological disorder induced by high temperature causing curd to have a woolly or ricey appearance.

RING ROLLER (Cambridge roller) – metal roller made of a series of rings which instead of being flat on the perimeter are 'V' shaped.

ROGUEING – removing unwanted plants – eg, sibs or plants not true to type in Brassicas.

ROTARY SPRINKLERS – irrigation sprinklers with impact heads which rotate at about one circuit a minute.

ROTATION (crop) – the sequence of crops.

ROW CROP DROPPER – a special drop arm sprayer boom for spraying the stem of tall crops eg, Brussels sprouts.

RUBBED SEEDS – irregular shaped seeds which are rubbed to smooth them and make them more suitable for precision drilling.

SCATTER BANDS – where seed is drilled in scattered bands rather than placed in a single line.

SELF-TRAVELLING SPRINKLER – an irrigation system where the irrigation unit is moved or dragged through the crop at a very slow pace.

SIBS – self inbred lines. Applies to F_1 brassica plants where the seed has not been crossed with the other parent line producing a rogue plant.

SILK – the female flower of the sweet corn.

SINGLING – thinning seedling crop plants to a single plant at regular spacing along the row.

SMD – soil moisture deficit.

SPEAR – the growth shoot of asparagus as it emerges from the ground.

'SPEEDLINGS' – a transplanting system for containerized vegetable plants.

SPLIT PILL – a pelleted seed which splits when sown to allow moisture into the seed.

STALE SEEDBED – ground prepared for seedbed three weeks in advance of sowing so that weed seedlings germinate. They are then killed by herbicide just before sowing.

STICK BEANS – runner beans grown up a support system.

'STRAIGHTS' (fertilizers) – fertilizers containing one nutrient.

SUB-IRRIGATION – irrigation set below ground level.

SYSTEMIC (insecticide/fungicide) – material when applied to plants is absorbed into the sap stream.

TANK MIX – where different chemicals are mixed in the spray tank (not proprietary pre-manufactured mix).

TASSEL – the male flower of a sweet corn plant.

TENDEROMETER READINGS – degree of tenderness of peas measured by a tenderometer (pressure required to cut peas).

TEXTURE (soil) – describes size of soil particles, as a soil type, eg sand or clay.

TILTH – the surface finish produced after cultivating land.

TOP PULLER (lifting) – harvester which lifts root crops by gripping foliage and pulling out.

TRANSLOCATED HERBICIDE – material absorbed into sapstream of weed, killing it.

TRANSPLANT – a crop plant for transplanting either bare root or containerized.

TRENCH CELERY – traditional celery, which needs earthing up to blanch the crop.

TRIFOLIATE – three leaves.

TRUE LEAF STAGE – leaves which are typical of plant – not the first seed leaves which are often entirely different.

TURGID – firm and fresh, not wilted (applied to plant foliage).

UNDERCUTTING BLADE – A 'U' shaped blade which cuts below crop roots to enable ease of lifting.

VACUUM COOLING – a form of fast pre-cooling for leafy crops.

VACUUM DRILL – a seed metering system which holds and carries seed from the hopper to the coulter tube by vacuum.

WARE CROP – crop sold to the fresh market, rather than for processing, canning or freezing.

WATER BALANCE – balancing between precipitation and irrigation on the one hand and water loss from the crop on the other.

WETTER – additive to 'pesticides' to help stick spray to waxy leaves.

WHEELINGS – the marks of compaction left behind by the wheels of a heavy machine like a tractor.

WHIPTAIL – a condition on cauliflower leaves created by molybdenum deficiency.

XIRO FILM – perforated polythene film used for covering early salad crops.

Appendix 1

Field Assessment of Soil Texture

Take a sample of soil in the palm of the hand and wet it to its maximum water holding capacity. Work the soil with the fingers to ensure all soil crumbs are broken down. Then examine the sample by rubbing it between finger and thumb. Attempt to roll out a thin 'worm' of soil on the palm.

	BASIC SOIL TYPE
Gravel	Obvious
Coarse Sand	Sharp, rasping, gritty. Individual grains easily distinguished.
Fine Sand	The same, but much finer. Individual grains only just visible to unaided eye. Rasping sound when soil paste worked between fingers and thumb close to the ear, when the grains can also be felt.
Silt	Dry pellets will crush between finger and thumb, yielding a floury dust with a smooth, silky feel. When moistened and rubbed between finger and thumb silkiness persists, the paste is somewhat plastic (sticky). Individual particles quite invisible to the eye.
Clay	Dry pellets feel very hard and harsh, difficult or impossible to crush between finger and thumb. When moistened adheres strongly to the fingers (plastic).
Loams	Sandy loam, silt loam or clay loam combine the above characteristics, so that the gritty, silky or sticky properties are less easily distinguishable.

Tracking soil down to detailed type

A1	Soil gritty.	B
A2	Soil not gritty.	G
B1	Soil will not form a cohesive ball.	C
B2	Soil will form a cohesive ball.	D
C1	Soil does not stain hands.	*Sand*
C2	Soil will stain hands.	*Loamy Sand*
D1	Sand fraction obvious, does not readily stick to fingers.	*Sandy Loam*
D2	Sand not quite as obvious, sticks slightly or strongly to fingers.	E
E1	Sticks slightly to fingers moderately plastic.	*Loam*
E2	Sticks strongly to fingers very plastic.	F
F1	Sand fraction readily detectable but very sticky.	*Sandy Clay*
F2	Sand fraction only just detectable, very sticky.	*Clay Loam*
G1	A smooth soapy or silky feel dominant. 'Worms' will not form a circle.	*Silt*
G2	Soil slightly to very sticky. 'Worms' may or may not form a circle.	H
H1	Soil mainly with a silky feel but very slightly to moderately sticky. 'Worms' will not readily form a circle.	*Silt Loam*
H2	Soil moderately to very sticky. 'Worms' will form a circle.	I
I1	Soil very sticky and plastic and will glaze when rubbed between finger and thumb.	*Clay*
I2	Soil not quite as sticky and will not readily glaze.	*Silty Clay*

Appendix 2

Fernhurst Bed System

Details of row groupings for 1830 mm wheel tracks:

Beans (Broad)	4 rows per bed	300 mm × 150 mm	plants per field ha.	142 786
Beans (French)	3–8 rows per bed	450–150 as drilled	plants per field ha.	430 000
Beans (Runner Pinched)	2 rows per bed	900 mm × 150 mm	plants per field ha.	71 393
Beet (ware)	6 rows per bed	250 mm as drilled	plants per field ha.	476 200
Brussels sprouts	3 rows per bed	600 mm × 500 mm	plants per field ha.	39 130
Cabbage (summer)	3 rows per bed	450 mm × 250 mm	plants per field ha.	64 033
Cabbage (winter)	3 rows per bed	600 mm × 450 mm	plants per field ha.	35 574
Cabbage (Sp. greens)	5 rows per bed	250 mm × 150 mm	plants per field ha.	177 870
Carrots (ware)	6–12 rows per bed	as drilled	plants per field ha.	1000 000
Cauliflower (summer)	3 rows per bed	530 mm × 530 mm	plants per field ha.	37 352
Cauliflower (winter heading)	2 rows per bed	900 mm × 450 mm	plants per field ha.	23 716
Leeks	6 rows per bed	200 mm × 150 mm	plants per field ha.	213 444
Lettuce (cabb.)	6 rows per bed	200 mm × 300 mm	plants per field ha.	106 722
Lettuce (cos/crisp)	5 rows per bed	250 mm × 350 mm	plants per field ha.	88 935
Marrows	2 rows per bed	900 mm × 530 mm	plants per field ha.	18 914
Onions	6 rows per bed	200 mm as drilled	plants per field ha.	96 000
Peas	6 rows per bed	200 mm as drilled	plants per field ha.	1100 000
Rhubarb	2 rows per bed	900 mm × 600 mm	plants per field ha.	14 112
Swede	3 rows per bed	600 mm × 150 mm	plants per field ha.	177 870
Sweet Corn	3 rows per bed	600 mm × 450 mm	plants per field ha.	35 574
Turnip	4 rows per bed	300 mm as drilled	plants per field ha.	350 080

Equipment required to carry out all operations on the bed system:–

Plough – two or three furrows reversible.
Cultivating equipment – normal tractor mounted cultivators, discs and harrows.
Rollers – tractor mounted ring rollers.
Fertilizer distributor – tractor mounted, broadcast type.
Seed drills – precision seeder mounted on standard toolbar.

Planters – capable of planting drawn and block raised plants.
Steerage hoe – independently spurs blades.
Sprayer – high/low volume; 450 litre tank tractor mounted.
Trailers for harvesting – wheel track must fit bed system.
Crop carrier cages – tractor mounted on buck-rake principle 'cages' as tillages.

Appendix 3

Soil nutrient status and fertilizer recommendations

Use of index numbers from soil analysis recommendations.

The recommendations assume satisfactory soil conditions for the crop in question. The nitrogen status is based on the previous cropping history of the soil while the phosphorus and potassium status is assessed by soil analysis.

The ADAS have devised an index system which spans the whole range of soils from extensive agriculture to intensive glasshouse culture, using the figures 0 to 9 for phosphorus and potassium and 0 to 4 for nitrogen.

Nitrogen index

The nitrogen index is related to the holding system and the previous cropping. Index 0 = Very Low; 1 = Low; 2 = Medium; 3 = High; 4 = Very High.

For field vegetable growing, phosphorus and potassium index numbers range from 0 to 4 plus, nitrogen index numbers from 0 to 2.

Phosphorus and potassium index

The phosphorus and potassium status of a soil is easily obtained by soil analysis. The index numbers follow a similar pattern to those for nitrogen. If no soil analysis is available use the values underlined in the 'Tables of recommended fertilizer rates' for each crop.

Nitrogen index based on last crop grown/past cropping

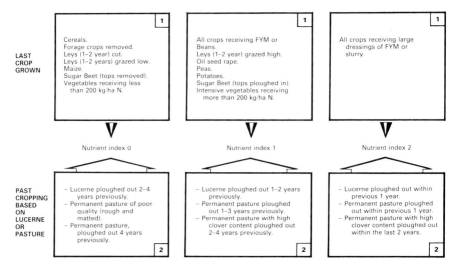

LAST CROP GROWN

	1
Cereals. Forage crops removed. Leys (1–2 year) cut. Leys (1–2 years) grazed low. Maize. Sugar Beet (tops removed). Vegetables receiving less than 200 kg/ha N.	

	1
All crops receiving FYM or Beans. Leys (1–2 year) grazed high. Oil seed rape. Peas. Potatoes. Sugar Beet (tops ploughed in). Intensive vegetables receiving more than 200 kg/ha N.	

	1
All crops receiving large dressings of FYM or slurry.	

Nutrient index 0   Nutrient index 1   Nutrient index 2

PAST CROPPING BASED ON LUCERNE OR PASTURE

– Lucerne ploughed out 2–4 years previously. – Permanent pasture of poor quality (rough and matted). – Permanent pasture, ploughed out 4 years previously.	**2**

– Lucerne ploughed out 1–2 years previously. – Permanent pasture ploughed out 1–3 years previously. – Permanent pasture with high clover content ploughed out 2–4 years previously.	**2**

– Lucerne ploughed out within previous 1 year. – Permanent pasture ploughed out within previous 1 year. – Permanent pasture with high clover content ploughed out within the last 2 years.	**2**

HOW TO USE THE TABLES

(1)   If Lucerne, long leys or permanent pasture have *not* featured in the last 5 years USE TABLES 1 ONLY.

(2)   If the last crop grown were lucerne, long ley or pasture, USE TABLES 2 ONLY.

(3)   If past cropping from the tables indicates different nutrient index values, then USE THE HIGHEST OF THE 2 VALUES.

Appendix 4

Government publications of use to the vegetable grower

Reference bulletins

(Substantial works, which are priced)
GENERAL
RB 35 Lime and Liming
RB138 Irrigation
RB202 Water for Irrigation
RB209 Fertilizer Recommendations
RB210 Organic Manures
RB420 Residual Value of Applied Nutrients
RB429 Soil Physical Conditions & Crop Production

CROP GROWING
RB323 Brussels Sprouts
RB344 Propagating and Transplanting Vegetables

PESTS & DISEASES
RB509 Pesticide Usage Survey – Vegetables

Short Term Leaflets

STL119 Brussels Sprouts: Harvest and Packhouse Systems
STL137 Vegetables Growing and Harvesting on the Bed System

284 **Appendix**

Booklets

Leaflets (Single topics of a few pages)

PESTS AND DISEASE

L18	Cabbage Root Fly
AL54	Black Bean Aphid
L61	Pea, Bean & Clover Weevils
AL62	White Rot of Onions
L68	Carrot Fly
L69	Cabbage Caterpillars
L85	Onion Downy Mildew
L87	Celery Fly
L91	Beet Leaf Miner
L109	Flea Beetles
L115	Slugs and Snails
L126	Pea & Bean Beetles
L150	Millepedes & Centipedes
L163	Onion Fly
L170	Thrips on Peas
L179	Leather Jackets
L196	Turnip Gall Weevil
L199	Wireworms
L225	Cutworms
L233	Beet Cyst Eelworm
AL241	Celery Leaf Spot
L261	Onion & Leek Smut
L265	Scleortinia Disease
L269	Cabbage Aphid
L276	Club Root

L334	Pea Moth
L346	Violet Root Rot
L370	Cauliflower Mosaic
L392	Lettuce Aphids
Al440	Stem Eelworm on Vegetables
L462	Pea Cyst Eelworm
AL559	Botrytis of Lettuce
AL576	Insect Pests of Brassica Seed Crops
AL577	Lettuce Downy Mildew
L594	Pea Midge
L747	Hot Water Treatment of Celery and Broccoli Seed
L603	Willow-Carrot Aphid
L756	Bolting in Brassica Crops, Buttoning of Cauliflowers

GENERAL

L257	Green Manuring
L320	Poultry Manure
L435	Making the Most of Farmyard Manure
L441	Nitrogen Fertilizers
L442	Posphatic Fertilizers
L443	Potassium Fertilizers
L444	Magnesium Lime and Magnesium Limestone
L542	Lime in Agriculture
L587	Liquid Fertilizers
L596	Magnesium Fertilizers
L646	Guide to Current Fertilizer Recommendations
L655	Sampling Soil for Analysis
L751	Ammonia as a Fertilizer
L721–741	Various Aspects of Field Drainage

CROPS

L189	Turnips and Swedes
L297	Sweet Corn
L419	Spinach
L621	Asparagus
L622	Outdoor Rhubarb

Appendix 5

Metrication in horticulture

Useful conversion factors

To convert from:	To:		Multiply by:	
acres	ha		0.4	(0.405)
/acre	/ha		2.5	(2.471)
btu/h	W		0.3	(0.294
bushels	l		36	(36.0514)
bushels	m^3		0.4	(0.361)
cu ft	m^3		0.03	(0.0283)
cu yd	m^3		0.8	(0.765)
cwt	kg		50	(50.803)
cwt/acre	kg/ha		125	(125.440)
degrees F	°C	−32	$^5/_9$	(0.556)
fl oz	ml		28	(28.413)
fl oz/acre	ml/ha		70	(70.156)
fl oz/gal	ml/l		6.3	(6.250)
ft	m		0.3	(0.305)
/ft	/m		3.3	(3.281)
gal	litre		4.5	(4.546)
gal/acre	l/ha		11	(11.225)
gal/sq yd	l/m^2		5.4	(5.437)
guage (polythene)	μm		0.25	
hp	kw		0.75	(0.746)
in	mm		25.4	(25.381)
lb	kg		0.45	(0.454)
lb/acre	kg/ha		1.1	(1.121)
lb/gal	g/l		100	(99.868)
lb/cu yd	kg/m^3		0.6	(0.593)
miles	km		1.6	(1.609)

oz	g	28	(28.350)
/oz	/g	0.03	(0.0353)
oz/bushel	kg/m^3	0.8	(0.785)
oz./bushel	g/l	0.8	(0.785)
oz/gal	g/l	6.25	(6.236)
oz/lb	g/kg	62.5	(62.445)
oz/sq yd	g/m^2	34	(33.907)
oz/yd	g/m	31	(31.004)
pt	litres	0.57	(0.568)
pt/acre	litres/ha	1.4	(1.402)
psi	KN/m^2 (K Pa)	6.9	(6.895)
psi	M Bars	69.0	(68.95)
sq ft	m^2	0.1	(0.0929)
/sq ft	/m^2	11	(10.764)
sq yd	m^2	0.84	(0.836)
/sq yd	/m^2	1.2	(1.196)
Tons	Tonnes	1.0	(0.984)
Tons/acre	Tonnes/ha	2.4	(2.430)
units	kg	0.5	(0.508)
units/acre	kg/ha	1.25	(1.254)
yd	m	0.9	(0.914)

If it is necessary to convert back to imperial units, dividing by the conversion value will achieve this.

Index